FROM TREE TO SEA

To the layman: Twigs
                 Boughs and branches
                Trunk

To the shipwright: Boat knees and bends
                   Bole
                   Wrongs
                   Top hamper

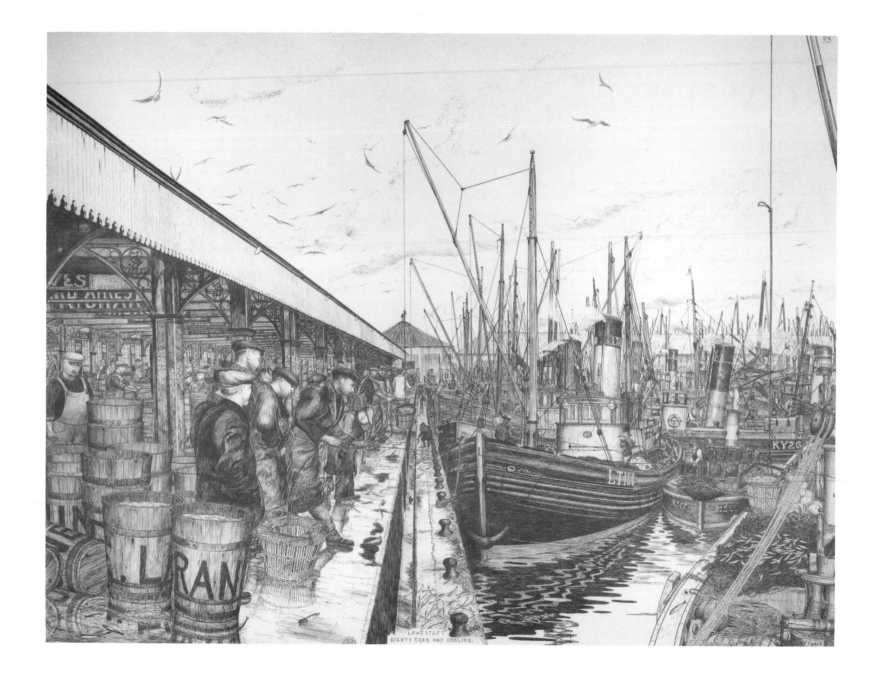

LOWESTOFT
EIGHTY CRAN AND COALING.

FROM TREE TO SEA

The building of a wooden steam drifter

TED FROST

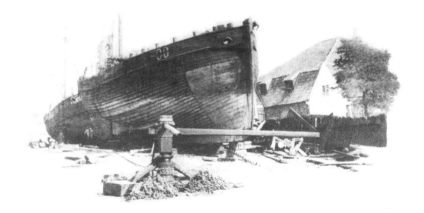

TERENCE DALTON LIMITED, LAVENHAM, SUFFOLK 1985

Published by
TERENCE DALTON LIMITED

ISBN 0 86138 033 9

Text photoset in 9/10 pt Baskerville

Printed in Great Britain at
The Lavenham Press Limited, Lavenham, Suffolk

Contents

For Esme

Preface

TED FROST grew up at a time when Lowestoft and Yarmouth were enjoying a boom and the herring industry was reaching the peak of its prosperity. Lowestoft alone had very nearly six hundred first class fishing vessels, many of them steam drifters of the kind featuring so largely in *From Tree to Sea*. It was a marvellous period for any boy with a love of ships and the sea to be living in Lowestoft, and "Boy Ted" revelled in his surroundings.

I lived in Bevan Street, about four or five minutes' walk from the fish market, and had already become a market ranger, he recalls. Right at the height of the 1913 Home Fishing I had to stay away from school for three weeks on doctor's orders; what sights I saw, what sounds I heard!

How wonderful it all was among all those boats, all the fishermen, the market workers, the Scots girls, the fish workers, the horses, the carters, the terrific hustle and bustle, all the many people working day and night. Shipwrights and fitters were working on board many of the vessels repairing damage, possibly sustained through collision, in order to get them to sea again as quickly as possible.

Time was indeed money as the shoals of herring slowly but surely worked their way south past Lowestoft and Yarmouth. The herring would have come and gone in about ten weeks, the peak period for catching them being round about the middle of October to the end of November, especially around the full moon when it occurred during that period.

How lucky I was to be growing up at that time!

I had wanted to be an apprentice shipwright as soon as I left school, but just at that time war broke out and the uncertain state of affairs led to a cessation of shipbuilding in the local yards. After a time, of course, it was realised that quite a number of small vessels would be required and work restarted, giving lads like myself the chance to get on the yards. How fortunate I was!

The hours were long, the work was hard and the pay was small, but in spite of that we enjoyed ourselves. And how we enjoyed ourselves! I remember the time we found a six-inch shell among the ballast that had been taken out of a yacht laid up for the winter in Bullens Shop. Of course, the shell was rusted and in a very dilapidated condition after several years of lying around on the yard.

During those years it had always been an object of interest. At last the day arrived when it was decided we could no longer go on just wondering if it were live. During the dinner hour three or four of the boys lifted it on to the shoulder of the strongest apprentice on the yard, who staggered with it to the ground in front of the shop, facing the river.

The shell was given a few light taps with a hammer, but nothing happened, so a cold chisel was sent for and we tried to start the thread of the fuse cap. No good. More forceful methods were needed, so a withe punch and maul was employed. Very soon a crack appeared where the cap fitted the shell, and after that it was easy; the fuse was soon unscrewed.

An auger was used to bore out some of the material from the inside. Was it explosive? The material was placed in the bottom of a wheelbarrow, a lighted match applied to it, and to everybody's delight it went up in a great flame. There was only one thing to be done, and that was try to blow the shell up. The shell was aimed directly at Colby's yard on the other side of the river, with whose apprentices we were in a constant state of rivalry. A trail of oakum was laid from inside the shop out to the shell, and everybody retired to the shop and took cover under the keel blocks. The oakum was lit, and away went the smouldering flame towards the shell.

Nothing happened. We found the flame had gone out about two feet six inches from the shell, so one of the more daring lads went on his hands and knees to blow the flame up again. No sooner had he dashed back into the shop than the thing went off with a shattering explosion. We all thought the world had come to an end as the roof lights fell in and earth and stones rained down on the corrugated iron roof of the shop.

Nobody was badly hurt, though one chap was hit by a stone. Everybody concerned was called up to the office early that afternoon and severely rebuked; but I have always thought that everybody, including the management, was secretly relieved that the shell had been exploded and the uncertainty was ended.

The rivalry with Colby's and the other yards found expression in other ways, too. For instance, during the dinner hour the yard boats would set out carrying ammunition in the shape of bolts, nuts, washers, plate punchings and so on; and we had fairly hefty oars with which to give our opponents a crack on the skull if possible.

Often the boats would meet in mid-river with boats from a rival yard and the bottom boards would be raised in order to ward off the barrage of nuts and washers. There was plenty of abuse and threats of what would happen if our rivals could only get us, but I do not remember anybody being seriously hurt.

It was all good fun and helped to make my life what it has been, a life full of happy memories of relations, friends, workmates and shipmates. What more could one wish for?

Acknowledgements

I N ORDER to compile a book of this sort when so many years have elapsed since the events took place, I felt that I should not try to write it entirely alone, without consulting some of the people who actually had something to do with the various works that I am describing. Over the last twelve years or so I have contacted quite a number of my former workmates and other people with a knowledge of shipbuilding, and of the fishing industry, in order to discuss with them not only the way that we did certain things but why we did them that way.

There are others who have very little knowledge of the subject but who have been kind enough to help me by reading the work in progress, and have helped me to judge the layman's point of view from their observations.

To all these very kind people I would like to offer my grateful thanks, especially to the following former shipwrights:– my uncle, Mr Fred Rouse, Mr Percy "Preel" Jillings, Mr Stuart Jackson, Mr Jack Paine, Mr Llew Greengrass, Mr Charles Breach, Mr George Herring, Mr Arthur Brown, Mr Frank Castleton, Mr Bob Snelling, Mr David Bucknole and Mr Fred Woolnough. To former shipsmiths Mr Bert Green and Mr Billy Bloom, and to former blacksmith Mr David Penman; to my fisherman friends Mr William P. Soloman, Mr Vernil Tuck, Mr Allen Delf, Mr Russell Gower, Mr Ernest Pye, Mr Ernest Crowfoot, rigger Mr Walter Killet and Mr Joe Boyce; to my daughter Valerie; to my friend, journalist and author Mr Robert Malster, and Mrs Brenda Malster, whose help has been invaluable to me; Mr David Butcher, Mr Charles Lewis, M.A., curator of the Maritime Museum of East Anglia, and also to Mrs Ivy G. Smith, Mrs Brenda Keaveny, Mrs Blanche Hornsey and Mr Frano Jackson; and Mr Jack Mitchley of the Port of Lowestoft Research Society and members of the Lowestoft and East Suffolk Maritime Society.

The illustrations used in the book I have drawn myself and are original, except for the plan of the yard on sheet No. 1, which I developed from an Ordnance Survey map.

Loading the drug.

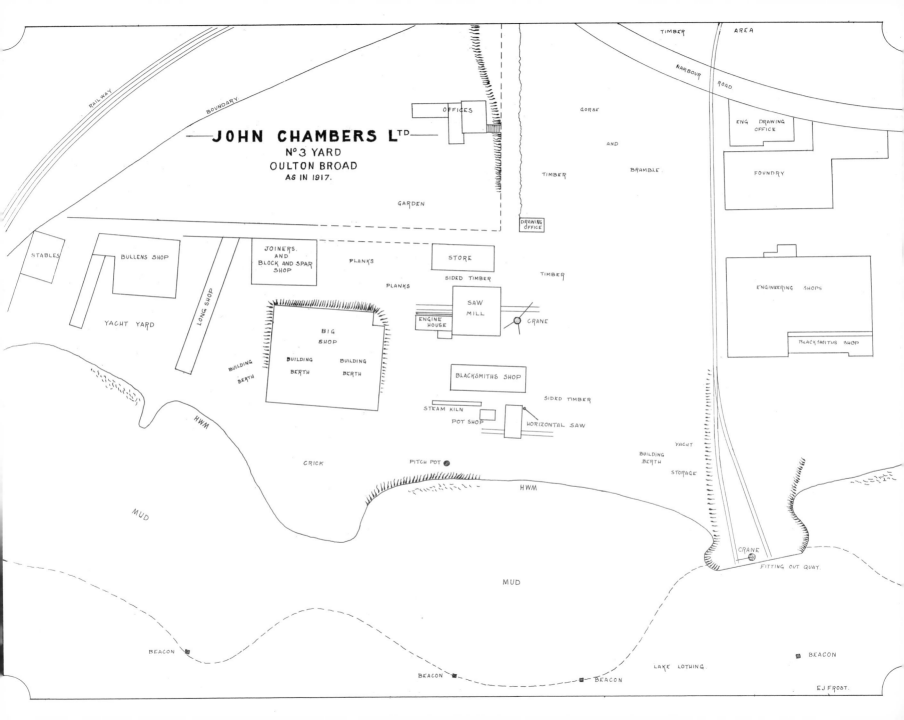

This Indenture Witnesseth

That Edward James Frost of No 89 Bevan Street Lowestoft in the County of Suffolk, aged fifteen by and with the consent of his father Edward Frost, of the same place, Sawyer, as well as of his own free will doth put himself Apprentice to John Chambers Limited a Limited Liability Company having their Registered Office at the Road Shipyard Laundry Lane Lowestoft in the County of Suffolk, trading and carrying on business under the name or style of "John Chambers Limited" Shipbuilders and Engineers and to their assigns to learn their Art trade or business and with them after the Manner of an Apprentice to serve from the twenty sixth day of April one thousand ninehundred and sixteen

until the full End and Term of **Seven** Years and from thence next following to be fully complete and ended **During** which Term the said Apprentice his Masters faithfully shall serve their secrets keep their lawful commands everywhere gladly do he shall do no damage to his said Masters nor see to be done of others but to the best of his power shall prevent or forthwith give warning to his said Masters of the same he shall not waste the Goods of his said Masters nor lend them unlawfully to any he shall not do any act whereby his said Masters may have any loss with their own goods or others during the said Term without Licence of his said Masters shall neither buy nor sell nor absent himself from his said Masters service day or night unlawfully But in all things as a faithful Apprentice he shall behave himself towards his said Masters and all theirs during the said Term **And** the said

Edward Frost hereby Covenants with the said John Chambers Limited that he will do no act to prevent or delay the faithful performance of the terms of this Indenture by the said Apprentice but will in all lawful ways assist in the performance of the same, as far as is in his power, and the said John Chambers Limited in consideration of this Indenture and of the good and faithful service of the said Apprentice shall teach and instruct or cause to be taught and instructed

their said Apprentice in the Art trade or business of a Shipwright and also of a Boatbuilder and Blockmaker as far as may be practicable and convenient

and shall and will pay to the said apprentice the wages as follows that is to say the sum of four shillings per week during the first year the sum of five shillings per week during the second year the sum of six shillings per week during the third year the sum of seven shillings per week during the fourth year the sum of eight shillings per week during the fifth year the sum of nine shillings per week during the sixth year and the sum of ten shillings per week during the seventh and last year of the said term to be paid in proportion to the time the said apprentice may labor in his said Masters employ and the said Edward Frost hereby covenants to find unto the said Apprentice sufficient meat drink lodging and all other necessaries during the said term

And for the true performance of all and every the said Covenants and Agreements either of the said Parties bindeth himself unto the other by these Presents **In Witness** whereof the parties above named have hereunto set their Hands and Seals the fourteenth day of September in the year of Our Lord One Thousand Nine Hundred and sixteen

Signed sealed and delivered by the above named ⎫
Edward James Frost and Edward Frost ⎬
in the presence of, ⎭

A. G. Plant
138 Denmark Road
Lowestoft

Warrington & C° London

Edward James Frost

Edward Frost

TWO SHILLINGS SIX PENCE
26 5 16

Introduction

IN THE course of the following story of the building of a wooden steam drifter I have tried to be as factual as possible when speaking of the methods of putting these vessels together.

The reason that I chose *Formidable* is simply that she and the *Implacable*, which were side by side in the big shop at the yard, were among the last of the orthodox steam drifters built of wood in East Anglia. I myself worked on them before the advent of the standard drifters, on which work was begun in 1917. The methods I have described and the terminology I have used were those employed in Lowestoft, and in particular in Chambers' yards. Both methods and jargon differed from port to port and even from yard to yard.

H. Reynolds, who had the Oulton Broad yard before Chambers took it over in 1910, would never chop wood off where they thought it better left on. Whereas Chambers would bade the stem back to four-and-a-half inches up to just below the sheer height, Reynolds would leave it considerably wider, with rounded corners, producing a stem which was not so pretty to look at but was perhaps a little stronger. The shipbuilders all had different ideas.

Formidable was built in 1917 and I began to draw my illustrations almost fifty years later. I am in fact one of the last shipwrights to work on the building of this particular type of vessel, the building of which was fairly representative of shipbuilding in East Anglia as it had been done for a great many years and on many different types of vessel. I must ask the reader to bear with me when I say that I do not claim all my drawings are perfect, because they have been done from memory.

I was apprenticed in 1916 to John Chambers Ltd., the other parties to the indenture being my father, Edward Frost, and myself. The terms of my apprenticeship were "to learn the art, trade, or business of a shipwright and also of a Boatbuilder and Blockmaker as far as may be practicable and convenient".

The firm "agreed to pay the said apprentice wages or remuneration as follows, that is to say, the sum of four shillings per week during the first year, and the sum of five shillings per week during the second year, and the sum of six shillings per week during the third year, the sum of seven shillings per week during the fourth year, the sum of eight shillings per week during the fifth year, the sum of nine shillings per week during the sixth year, and the sum of ten shillings per week during the seventh and last year of the said term to be paid in proportion to the time the said apprentice may labour in his said master's employ".

I actually started work on the yard on 26th April, 1916, the day after the bombardment of Lowestoft by a squadron of German battle-cruisers, so you could say that I had a good send off. I was fourteen years of age, having left school at the age of thirteen.

I served my time on John Chambers' No. 3 yard, on the north side of Lake Lothing, on the seaward side of the bridge carrying the Beccles to Lowestoft railway line at Oulton Broad. Mr Horace Jenner, an elderly shipwright, was foreman. He had started to serve his time about 1856.

With the development of the standard drifters Mr Jenner retired and his eldest son George, also a shipwright, became foreman. There was also a younger son, Horace, with whom I worked. These man were all first-class shipwrights, and I am proud to have been associated with them.

Looking back after all these years I realise how fortunate I was in being able to work on that yard, among those men and boys and under that management. It was, to me at any rate, almost seven years of happiness. I say almost, as before I came out of my time the regulations were altered in regard to apprenticeships so that if one had served more than five years before reaching the age of 21 one could come out of one's time on reaching that age, and so on my 21st birthday I ended my apprenticeship, having served six years and five months.

It really was almost seven years of happiness. In all my life since, and I have travelled fairly extensively and worked on many kinds of projects, I have never come across another environment such as that on Chambers No. 3 yard. It still stands out in my mind as an example of the way in which people can work happily, for that is what we did. I never heard many angry words, except of course during bouts of horseplay among the boys and some of the men at times, but that was a feature of the yards locally at that time, and was accepted. Even with that there was generally something to laugh about.

The hours were long, the work was hard, and there was an allotted amount to be done per day on many of the jobs. The wages were small, but we were content, except for thoughts of the men at the front and at sea.

I can only hope that in this book I will have been able to retain for all time some sort of vision of the way in which this work was done by the shipwrights and other shipyard workers of the past, before I, too, embark on the last great voyage.

E. J. Frost.

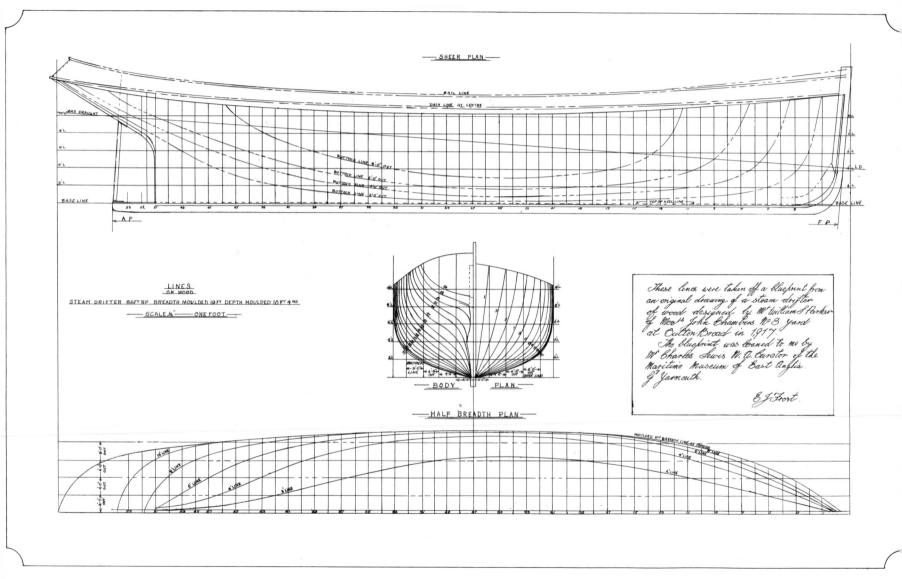

SHEER PLAN

RAIL LINE

DECK LINE AT CENTRE

LOAD DRAUGHT

BUTTOCK LINE 8'0" OUT
BUTTOCK LINE 6'0" OUT
BUTTOCK LINE 4'0" OUT
BUTTOCK LINE 2'0" OUT

BASE LINE

TOP OF KEEL LINE

BASE LINE

A P

F P

LINES
OF WOOD

STEAM DRIFTER 86FT BP BREADTH MOULDED 19 FT DEPTH MOULDED 10 FT 4 INS

SCALE ¼" ONE FOOT

BODY PLAN

These lines were taken off a blueprint from
an original drawing of a steam drifter
of wood designed by Mr William S Parker
& Messrs John Chambers No 3 yard
at Oulton Broad in 1917.

The blueprint was loaned to me by
Mr Charles Lewis M. O. Curator of the
Maritime Museum of East Anglia
Gt Yarmouth.

E J Frost

HALF BREADTH PLAN

MOULDED HF BREADTH LINE AT TOPSIDE

10 LINE
8 LINE
6 LINE
4 LINE
2 LINE

From Tree to Sea

Name	Off No.	No.	Signal Letters	Material	Nett tons
Formidable	139977	LT 100.	GYRE	Wood	40

HP	Built	Owner
33	1917	Edward Catchpole, Kessingland

Olsen's Nautical Almanack 1939

BUILT in 1917 at Oulton Broad, Lowestoft, the *Formidable* was one of the last orthodox steam drifters to be built on Chambers No. 3 yard before the advent of the standard drifter, and was the ultimate in her class of vessel.

About 88 feet in length overall, 19 feet in beam and with a depth of 9 feet 9 inches, she was fitted with a two-fired Riley boiler, a Crabtree engine, and an Elliott and Garrood steam capstan No 5947.

Classed A1 at Lloyds, she was regarded as ideal for the job for which she was built, running economically at a speed of nine knots. She would carry 300 crans of herrings, about 52½ tons, reasonably well with her nets up out of the hold. A 300-cran shot was extremely rare, however.

Preliminaries

When an owner contacted the shipbuilder he would have in mind the class of vessel required. At the time *Formidable* was ordered Chambers were able to offer to build two classes, the 420 and the "Dreadnought altered", the latter being slightly smaller than the 420 and with a counter stern. This feature was at that time going out of favour, one of the reasons being that with the rapid growth of the fishing fleet that type of stern had become very vulnerable as the stanchions went well down into the hull; in the event of a collision in which stanchions were broken a quite considerable amount of work would need to be done to replace them. With a tug stern the covering board, which in itself was a fairly substantial piece of oak, would take the blow and so minimise the possible damage, considerably reducing the fishing time lost.

Later the 420 design was used by the Admiralty as a basic design for the construction of standard drifters of wood, of which John Chambers' No. 3 yard became parent. The dimensions of these vessels were 94 feet 3 inches length overall, 19 feet 11 inches beam, 10 feet 4½ inches depth.

The moulds from which *Formidable* was built had been in use for some time, but I will just touch the fringes of what happens after the draughtsman has finished his plans of the ship, consisting of sheer plan, or profile, deck plan and half-breadth plan. These would be passed over to the loftsman, himself a shipwright, who would then start to develop the drawings up to full size on the mould loft floor by measurement, the medium used being french chalk. The floor would be blackened with a matt finish in preparation for this work, becoming a huge blackboard.

Should the loft not be long enough to accommodate the full length of the vessel, the afterbody as it was called would be laid off first, then the forebody on top of that; sections would be drawn in the centre. These would all be drawn on a very precise base line and would appear no more than a maze of white lines to the uninitiated.

When laying off, the loftsman would put down fore and after perpendiculars, water levels, buttocks, bowlines, sections and diagonals, from loft offsets given to him by the draughtsman. To fair the ship, all these lines should intersect at the dimensions given, the loftsman very soon detecting any discrepancy, as everthing would now be magnified to full size.

Every frame would be drawn in the case of a boat with frames of unequal dimensions, and in this type of fishing craft this was usually the case. The lines were fixed by the use of pliable but fair battens, usually made of pitchpine, which were faired into the proposed line and held in position by weights and nails placed on each side of the batten. The required line was then marked off by the use of sharpened chalk, while the straight lines were snapped in using the chalkline.

The moulds which I have mentioned were then made up to the shape of the lines drawn on the floor. These moulds would all be made from half-inch planed deal, the frame moulds being made up from three or four pieces in order to get round the curves, the pieces being scarphed together where a joint had to be made. The joints would be splayed one on to the other in the same way that a small boat's plank would be scarphed and fastened with copper tacks. Water levels and sur marks would be transferred to the mould from the floor, after which the mould would be numbered and varnished. It could then be used for quite a number of years without any alteration in shape. I would think that the moulds used to mould out *Formidable*'s frames were made during 1912-13.

Choosing the timber

OAK was the timber used mostly in drifters built at Lowestoft because of its strength, durability, adaptability, and availability. Most of the oak used in the local yards was obtained within a radius of about fifteen to twenty miles, much of it being brought to the yard by Chambers' own horse drawn "gill" or steam traction engine. Some, however, was delivered, usually through Messrs. Darby of Beccles, by rail.

The timber used in *Formidable* for frames, plank and stringers would most probably have been sided for at least twelve months. It would have been lying stacked flick above flick, with separation sticks in between each one, in order to help the wood to season, by which I mean simply drying out, shrinking and hardening.

When buying standing trees Mr William Parker, the wood yard manager and draughtsman, an expert in these matters, would get on his cycle, go out into the country, visit the various sources of timber for sale and decide what to buy, then purchase his choice.

Felling would take place during the winter, when there was the least sap flowing in the tree. The fellers, who were expert at the job, used the axe and crosscut saw for this purpose.

In the case of the oak, Mr Parker would have chosen two kinds, one of which would be the common or pedunculate oak, very often to be found (in fact in Suffolk most often to be found) growing in the hedgerows. The other kind would be sessile or durmast oak, usually to be found in a wood.

It was as if nature or providence, call it what you will, sensed that mankind would need to build ships. The common oak, by virtue of the fact that the lateral shoots were the strongest, would produce timber ideal in shape for use in ship's frames or as knees. These bent and twisted branches were called wrongs; wrong in this case simply means bent and twisted. In the durmast oak, however, the terminal shoots are the strongest, and this tree would produce a tall straight trunk and reasonably straight branches, the trunk being ideal for a keel, kelson, planks or stringers. There is very little difference in the texture of the wood.

The common oak, however, was more prolific than the durmast by virtue of the fact that birds such as rooks are able to carry the acorns of the common oak by the footstalk of the cup, dropping some on the way at times and thereby helping to keep the supply up. The durmast oak which has sessile flowers cannot benefit by this as there is no footstalk.

The common oak produces acorns almost every year, while the durmast may flower only once in several years. As a consequence of this the durmast oak has almost ceased to exist in England, I understand, except for some in the north-west of the country.

When felling in the hedgerow great care would have to be taken not to let the tree harm the hedge or to let it fall into the roadway, if possible. It would have to be chopped at a considered angle in order to make it fall exactly where required.

We had some eight or ten men felling when the standard drifters were built and these men kept both Nos 1 and 3 yards supplied. Two apprentices were detailed off to go into the country with a set of moulds to mark the wrongs for cutting up; this would ensure that they were cut into useful lengths and with a minimum of waste, and that the utmost use was made of the available timber. We would also help generally, especially when cleaning and trimming the tree up ready for loading. When doing this job we were said to be "snedding" the tree.

When cleared we were left with the bole, wrongs, boat knees and bends, the residue being the top hamper.

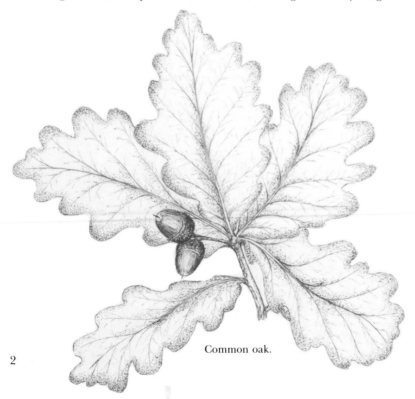

Common oak.

Loading the gill. Two horses would travel with a big gill, the second horse helping to pull uphill and to brake the gill when going downhill.

I enjoyed this job, although in the winter it was a taste of the great outdoors in the true sense. I had to walk sometimes eight miles to work and eight miles home again, yet I loved it. It could be snowing or raining, it didn't make any difference. I enjoyed foggy weather when one could hear the clip, clip, of the axes or the sound of the crosscut saw, men talking or breathing heavily because of their exertions, and at times feel or hear the dripping of water from branches. How wonderful it all was, except for one thing; on the cry of "timber!" one would hear that beautiful tree, possibly two, three or even four hundred years old, come crashing to the ground, two tons of it possibly; then I couldn't help feeling a little twinge of sadness.

The fellers worked under a rugged foreman nicknamed "Scammary" Nunn. They were on piecework and tried to fell so many trees per day, but of course this depended on the size of the tree at ground level. The trees were always chopped as low as possible, as even a few inches would rob the tree of much of its value if it could not be used to the best advantage.

It is still possible to see the bases of some of these trees that were felled sixty years ago.

I believe that the fellers were paid by the cube, while we two apprentices each received three shillings extra per week for the job, which in those days wasn't bad on top of our apprentices' pay.

I'll never forget the smell of freshly chopped oak, a lovely smell I always think, or the acrid smell of wood burning. Sometimes we could smell a farm; this was lovely to me.

When in the country we had a makeshift tent for meals, etc., and usually had a fire to warm our tea, which in those days was carried in a blue enamelled can, the lid of which was used as a cup. My own can was of plain tin plate. Enamelled ones had gone out of production because of the war, and I had mine made at Mr Whiting's, a ship's tinsmith with a shop in Bevan Street, Lowestoft. He used to make ship's lamps and cooking utensils.

Our meals, usually sandwiches, generally of meat on Mondays and perhaps egg on most other days, were carried in a red handkerchief generally, although some of the men on the yard, shipwrights mostly, carried a rectangular basket with a hinged lid on it.

3

Transporting the timber

Both Chambers' No. 1 and No. 3 yards had two horses each. In our case, No. 3 yard, these were Tinker and Boxer. These were fairly big animals and very much attached to the horseman, Mr "Hino" Crickmore, as indeed he was to them. I sometimes wondered how anybody would have fared had they interfered with them.

"Hino" knew exactly what was going on in those horses' minds, and they seemed as if they could read his thoughts. Boxer was the elder of the two, and perhaps because of that the quieter one.

The yard cat, who by the way revelled in the name of Tiddleybobs, used to like to ride on Boxer's back at times. Tiddleybobs earned his living by keeping mice down. If it were not for him I expect certain areas of the yard would have been swarming with them, for at that time there were no canteen facilities, so people had to sit down just anywhere to get their meals. A few privileged ones would sit in the engine house if the driver of the engine, Mr Tiger Flegg, would allow them. A few would sit in the Blacksmith's shop and so on, dropping crumbs all over the place; without the cat the mice would have had a good time.

Should there be days when the horses were not needed on the yard, they would take a gill into the country to bring trees home. One had to keep a wary eye on things when a horse was pulling the shaft down. If a tree had been loaded and the ground was bad it would be necessary to hire two more horses from the nearest farm. My goodness, what a wonderful sight that was,

especially if the day was a bit misty; the four giant animals straining to get the load on to the hard road, they would be steaming as they struggled, with the horseman quietly speaking a word of encouragement to them now and again. Whips were never used, Mr Crickmore never even had one. When the hard road or pan was reached one had to stand clear until they were calmed down, after which the two hired horses would return to the farm while the two yard horses would be prepared for the journey home.

Experience had taught the horseman where to sling the bole in order to get the correct balance. With a big tree it was usual to have the rear end a little on the heavy side.

On a level road or going uphill the two horses would pull, but on going downhill it was a different matter. A timber gill had no brakes, and at the top of a hill the horses would be stopped and the leading horse taken to the rear, where a rope would be secured to a sling chain on the end of the tree, the other end of the rope being secured to the bottom of the horse's collar. The second horseman, Mr Chipperfield, would hold this horse back so he would act as an anchor while the leading horse would steer the load down the hill.

There were three hills in Oulton Broad on which this would have to be done on coming in from the south; first there was the bridge at Carlton Colville station (later renamed Oulton Broad South), then the lock bridge and lastly the approach to the yard in Harbour Road from Bridge Road. It was a nuisance, but nevertheless it had to be done.

One thing in the horses' favour in those days was the fact that the roads were not so slippery as they are today, as they were just made up of hoggin.

With the war gaining momentum the demand for the use of railway rolling stock gradually increased and so it became harder than ever to get trees into the yard by rail. In addition manpower for felling became harder to get, so the yard depended more and more on its own resources and the management decided to purchase a traction engine from Sawyer's of Wrentham, Suffolk.

This engine, an 8HP Garrett, had been built by Garrett and Son of Leiston, Suffolk, and was in good shape when it arrived at the yard. The driver who brought it to the yard was Mr Harry Flatt, of Wrentham, whose face always reminded me of King George V. Here was yet another staunch man, I always thought. When going after timber on the road Mr Flatt had to have a steersman with him, for whom a steel adjustable pedestal seat was provided on one side of the tender.

A pole wagon with an adjustable rear frame and wheels would be drawn by the engine. Extra coal in a few bags would be carried on the wagon, which was known locally as a timber drug, while roadside ponds would provide any extra boiler feed water that was needed. Like many other engines, the

Garrett had a winding drum fitted to the rear axle, and on arrival at the site the engine would be positioned so as to pull the tree by wire into a suitable position for loading. The drug would then be lined up and a piece of oak plank, carried for the purpose, placed on the end of each bearer, after which the wire would be served round the tree several times. When the engine was started the wire from the winding drum would roll the tree up the ramps on to the wagon. This operation was known as "parbuckling" the tree.

Selection, preparation and sawing

We are now ready to start building the ship. The foreman would have to find seven fairly straight trees, of a good length. Three of these would be needed for the keel, two for the centre keelson, with a further two to be used as side keelsons.

The three for the keel would have to be long enough to make up the length of the vessel between perpendiculars, the after perpendicular being

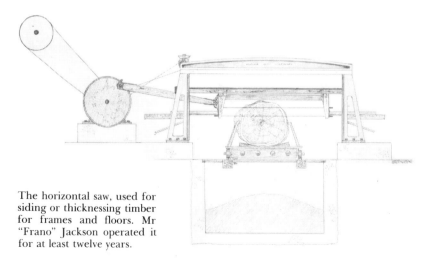

The horizontal saw, used for siding or thicknessing timber for frames and floors. Mr "Frano" Jackson operated it for at least twelve years.

the rudder post, and with an allowance to be made for the scarphs (the overlapping joints between the sections of timber).

The foreman would be looking out for thunder shakes, bad knots, and sap. When he found suitable trees these would be taken to the mill and laid handy under the crane, after which he would consult with the sawyer, himself an experienced man in these matters, about how they were to be cut to the best advantage on the frame saw.

The first tree would be laid firmly on bearers to debark and plumbing would start. Plumbing, or chopping the tree as it was called, entailed simply chopping a flat on what had been chosen to be the underside of the tree when going through the saw. A felling axe would be used because of hard knots.

In my illustration I have shown the sawyer holding a plum-bob to the tree when checking for plumb while chopping was in progress.

After the whole length of the tree was chopped and ready for the saw it would be lifted by the crane on to the first bogie, to which it would be secured with the chopped side down. The bogie, which ran on rails, would

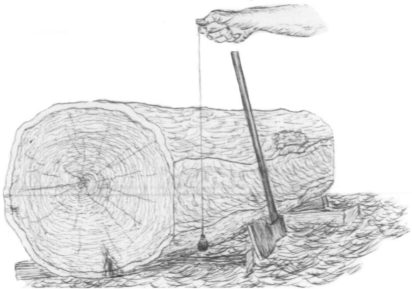

One side of the tree would be chopped plumb, and this would become the bottom and rest on the bogies and rollers of the saw.

6

then carry the tree forward to the saw, where the leading end of the tree would be placed on the bottom roller of the saw.

The saw in question was the frame saw. This had been built in Leipzig; it was a beautifully running machine working with a vertical reciprocating motion. My father was the sawyer and attended this saw for thirty years. The machine was put down during the Boer War, when the yard belonged to Mr H. Reynolds. Two or three German fitters were working on it and the foreman, whose name was Brauer, never tired of telling my father and his mate that "you English are fools and Kruger will drive you all into the sea". After a short spell in Germany on his return home, Mr Brauer made up his mind to return to Britain. He married an Oulton Broad lady and from then on stayed, lived and worked here, so I suppose that after all he didn't think the English were so bad.

Before the tree was loaded on the bogie, which was one of two, one on each side of the saw, my father would have set the saws up in the frame. These would have been the two nearest the centre, separated a distance of eight inches by pieces of wood at the top and bottom of the frame, with two or three other saws set either side at two-and-a-quarter inches apart for plank or at three inches for bilge, topside planks, or stringers. A chalk line would have been snapped on the tree to guide the sawyer in cutting.

With the tree resting on the bottom roller, another roller would be lowered down on to it. Both these rollers were serrated, and they were connected by a chain drive so that when the machine was in motion the two would move together. The top roller was forced down on to the tree by a lever on which was an adjustable weight, and it was by this means that the tree was fed through the frame. These rollers worked by means of a toothed wheel and rack to lift it off the tree. Any difference in the size or shape of the tree was taken up by a jockey pulley on the chain drive.

To start the machine the sawyer operated a lever sticking up from the floor of the mill, throwing a belt from a loose pulley on to a fixed one.

With the tree having been lowered on to the chopped plumb face which now lay perfectly horizontal, it followed that the saw cuts would be plumb and thus cut fair and straight.

The sawyer would be watching the chalk line on the tree and would adjust it slightly to the left or right as required by means of screw cramps on the bogies, the second of which would be reached by the tree after a few minutes. In about an hour the whole tree would have been cut.

Should there have been any bulges on the tree which might impede its progress when going through the frame, these would be chopped off by axe as it moved forward.

When the tree was through, the screws on the bogie would be released and

Boxer dragging a piece of timber down to the horizontal saw.

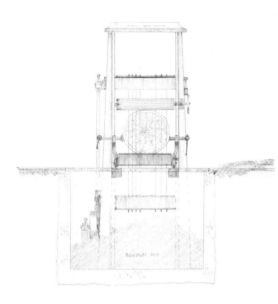

The frame saw, built in Leipzig and installed in 1900. It worked with a reciprocating motion and ran beautifully—I should know as my father operated it for thirty years. Below is the circular saw, used to cut planks after they had been lined out on the flicks by the chargehand shipwright. This type of saw was not sharpened but on getting dull or after striking metal replacement teeth were sprung into place, as seen on the right. These illustrations of the sawmill machinery are all from memory and serve only to give some idea of the appearance of the plant.

this would allow the planks or stringers on the side of the tree to be carried out to the plank area. This area on which the planking flicks were stacked was just outside the big shop and handy for the shipwright who was doing the lining out, as it was called. While waiting to be used this timber would be seasoning.

Meanwhile the keelpiece, as it would now be called, was turned down on its side and again examined for any faults. If there were any doubts about sap or any other unwelcome features the sawyer would call the chargehand shipwright or foreman to come and voice his opinion as to what should be done before the chalkline was snapped on again for the moulded depth cut, which was to be thirteen inches.

The finalised line would now be pencilled in and the piece put through again with two saws set at thirteen inches apart.

The scarphs would now be roughly lined out and cuts would be made into them if there was time in order to ease the work of the shipwright, as after leaving the mill all the work on the remainder of the vessel except for the boring out of the shaft tube would be done entirely by hand. Three pieces of keel would be cut, with the centre piece having a scarph at each end.

Trees would also be put through the saw for the keelsons, planks and stringers.

The mill itself was a single-span building of brick with a corrugated iron roof and with lights set in this at intervals. On each side of the mill was a lean-to open to the mill. The frame saw was pretty well in the middle, while

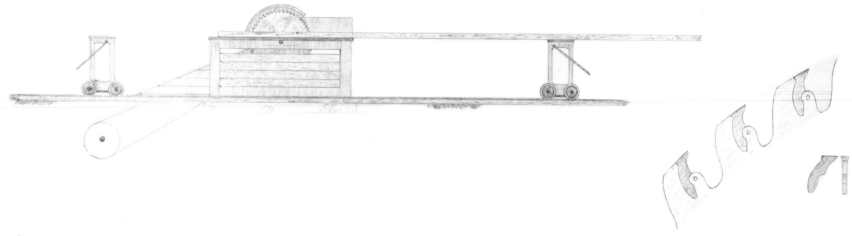

on the north side of that was the planing and spindle machine on which deck deals, etc., were planed and seamed. To the north of this again and in a lean-to was a rack bench consisting of a large circular saw running in the centre of a movable bench on which the timber was carried. The bench, which ran on rollers, was propelled forward by means of a toothed rack underneath it, while to the south of the frame saw was a circular saw on which planks were cut to the plankmaker's lining.

In the south lean-to was the saw sharpening area and, in an enlarged part of the lean-to, the band saw.

All the saws in the mill were driven from an underground shaft motivated by a Robey engine with a locomotive-type boiler. The Robey was an under-drive compound engine, similar to a railway locomotive, and had a flywheel 6 feet 10 inches in diameter on which the driving belt ran, the wheel running partly in a floor pit.

This engine was originally at a box factory at the top of Howard Street, Lowestoft, and was purchased by John Chambers after a fire at the factory. The engine also drove our old-fashioned generator, which was on a bed in front of the cylinder heads of the engine.

The whole thing was in its own house attached to the mill, with the engine exhaust passing through a metal chimney up through the roof. Also through the roof above the fire box there passed the steam pipe for a locomotive-type bell whistle by which the driver, a local man with the nickname of "Tiger" Flegg, gave the signal for work to start and stop. The boiler fuel was largely wood, mainly plank rippings cut up short to suit the furnace.

My father, a very gentle and kind man and very much liked by everybody, was also very lithe and extremely strong. Strangely Mr Ben Bird, the mill foreman, was of the very same stature and temperament, and they worked very closely together. They were both about 5 feet 6 inches in height. I never saw them beaten at carrying timber, some of which was extremely heavy, perhaps the full width of the tree.

When carrying planks out of the mill Dad and Ben would usually be at what we would call the back end. They would lift the back end first, well in the timber; it was customary to lift timber this way, as if it was done the

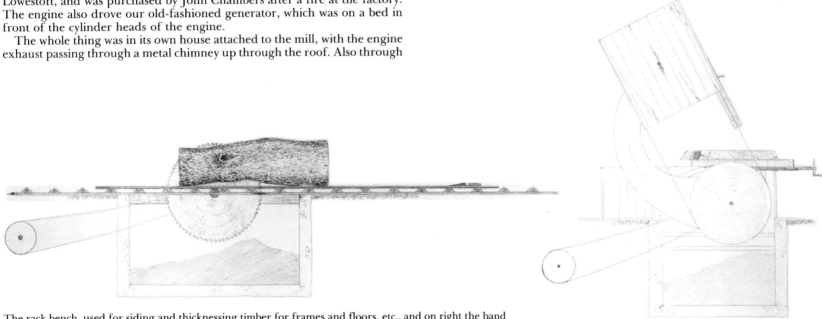

The rack bench, used for siding and thicknessing timber for frames and floors, etc., and on right the band saw, used to cut timber requiring curves and varying bevels such as that for floors and frames.

reverse way it was awkward and dangerous. The fore end would usually be lifted by three or four other men, with the overhang on the first two men's shoulders to help them. The fore end men were mostly ex-fishermen who had very little shipyard experience, and allowance was made for this.

The mill had been built by the local firm of Warnes and Sons. Mr Fred Warnes, a very young man at that time and now aged ninety, never ceases to praise my father whenever I meet him, telling me that he was the nicest man he ever knew. What a father I was blessed with!

The two-ton king post crane unloading timber at the saw-mill.

10

Laying the Keel

The first essential to the actual construction of the vessel was the laying of the keel blocks; two shipwrights and possibly two apprentices would be detailed off for the job. The blocks consisted of pieces of old timber baulk or keel, etc., cut to length to suit the circumstances. These blocks would be used repeatedly for many years.

Oak or elm slab would first be laid on the earth floor of the shop to take each block. The fore and after blocks would then be laid to the height specified by the foreman, to ensure that the ship would fit comfortably under the roof trusses, at the same time leaving ample room for the men to work under the ship's bottom. The intermediate blocks would then be laid and the capping pieces of these "boned" in, as it was called, by means of three pieces of board of equal width, one placed on the fore blocks, another on the after blocks, and the third one sighted in on each individual capping piece. Thus the shipwright would ensure that all the blocks were evenly related one to the other. These keel blocks were laid alternately athwartships and fore and aft.

The blocks were tapered from bottom to top to make it as easy as possible to work the garboard strake and caulk it. After laying stakes would be driven into the ground and nailed to the bottom blocks.

The pieces comprising the keel would now be brought into the shop and laid on temporary blocks so that work could start on making it up. The keel would if possible have been chosen from trees that had been lying about for some time and so would be somewhat seasoned. If the pieces had been left lying about after cutting, they could have been inclined to bend either one way or another. If a piece of eight inches by thirteen inches oak casts much, it would have taken much more than our primitive arrangements to get it back, so it was taken straight from the saw to the shop. With moisture in the timber there was less likelihood of the keel splitting when fastening scarphs or floors.

The shipwrights would now re-mark the scarph to their own satisfaction and trim off any surplus wood with the adze. Then they would square the ends of the scarph across the keel, a standing bevel being allowed on the vertical snibs. After planing and checking for square the two scarph cuts would be offered together. Any adjustment needed would be made, and when both scarphs fitted satisfactorily they would be tarred, after which they would be offered together again, held together by G-screws vertically, and pulled together fore and aft by the use of shifting cramps as we called them on cleats G-screwed to the keel itself. One would see the tar oozing out of the joint.

Before fastening could be started it would be necessary to lay what was known as the station batten on the keel and to transfer the frame stations from that on to the keel, thus ensuring that none of the bolts securing the scarphs would come in the way of a floor seating, stations at 19 inches.

While all this work was going on, the keel would be lying on its side and holes would be bored for four one-inch galvanised bolts in each scarph. These bolts would be driven from the bottom face of the keel and punched up so that they were clear of the face. Two three-eighth-inch by seven-inch galvanised dump bolts would also be driven at each end of the scarph.

The through bolts which had been driven tightly would be cut off, generally by one of the apprentices, and clenched on to a galvanized washer, the clench being on top of the keel and in between floors.

The base line could now be drawn and the bottom edges of the keel could be rounded. This was achieved by trimming the corner of the keel with the adze and then using the jack plane. The round extended an inch and a quarter up the side and under the bottom of the keel.

Cutting the rabbet could now be started, a separate station stick being provided for each station. These sticks went with the moulds and were numbered accordingly. They would each be let in at their respective stations by the use of the chisel, after which they would all be joined up by chisel, adze and plane, the keel being rolled over as required. The extreme fore and after ends of the rabbet were left until after the stem and stern post had been erected.

One further job remained to be done, and that was to secure the sand band. This was a length of five-inch by three-quarter-inch steel, flat on one side and convex in shape on the other, fastened to the underside of the keel. Countersunk holes would have been drilled at regular intervals along the bar, staggered on both sides of the middle line, and the bar coated with bitumastic. The countersinking of the holes ensured that there were no projections along the bottom of the keel on which nets might catch. Smacks did not have sand bands, because of the risk of chafing the trawl warp should they have to shoot with the warp passing under the bottom.

When all was ready the keel would be rolled over on to the prepared blocks, and plumbed up. The fore and after ends would now be secured by shores, one on each side of it, after which a line would be stretched for the full length of the keel with a distance piece, say half-inch, set in at each end. The line would be stretched on the side of the keel from which it would be furthest away and work could now be started to straighten up the keel and secure it.

This was achieved by setting shores and setting the keel over towards the line, using a third half-inch distance piece to gauge it. When straightened,

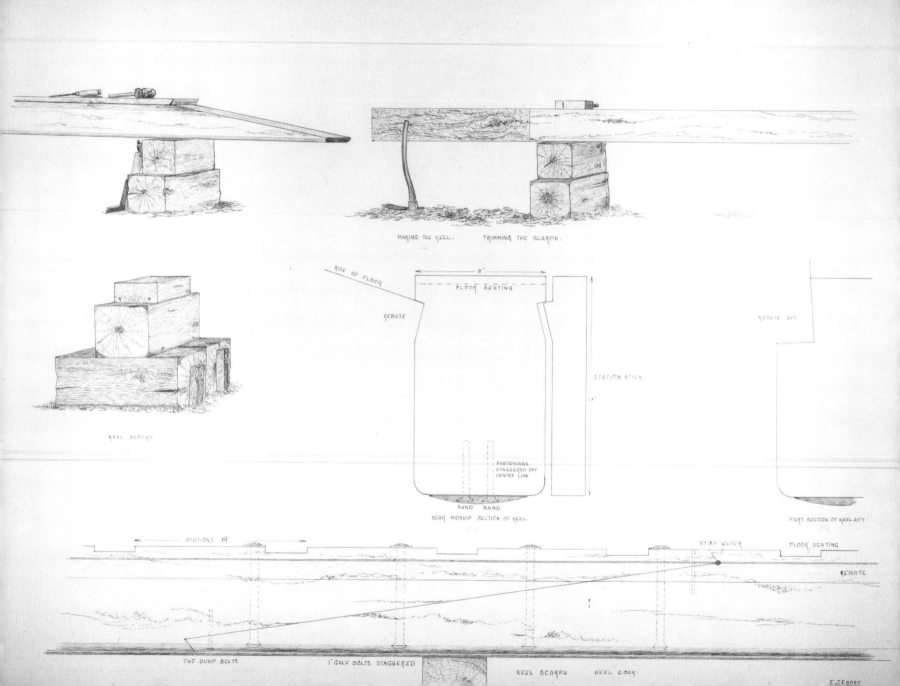

MAKING THE KEEL. TRIMMING THE SCARPH.

KEEL BLOCKS

RIBE OF FLOOR

FLOOR SEATING

REBATE

REBATE AFT

STATION STICK

FASTENINGS
STAGGERED OFF
CENTRE LINE

SAND BAND

NEAR MIDSHIP SECTION OF KEEL.

PART SECTION OF KEEL AFT.

STATIONS 19

STOP WATER

FLOOR SEATING

REBATE

TWO DUMP BOLTS

1" GALV BOLTS STAGGERED

KEEL SCARPH

KEEL OAK.

E. J. FROST

further shores would be set to hold the keel securely in place. These shores would not be touched again until the hull of the vessel was advanced far enough to ensure that the keel would remain straight; preferably they were not removed until just before launching.

One further job remained and that was to drive stopwaters in each of the scarphs at the apex of the top angle, to prevent any water that might enter the scarph from entering the vessel. These stopwaters were of deal about seven-eighths inch diameter and were driven tight. The length of the scarph was 5 feet 5 inches, that is five times the depth of the keel.

After laying, the keel would be given a coat of tar or paint to conserve some of the moisture in it and to prevent the timber from opening and cracking. The timber was less likely to split when driving bolts if it was a bit moist. In my illustrations I have left it bare to give the impression of timber.

Stem and apron

One of the senior apprentices would be detailed off to make the stem and apron. He got ready to receive these from the mill, while the two shipwrights who made the keel would now start to make preparations to construct the stern, this job being generally reserved for two of the best tradesmen.

The stem and the apron would both have been cut on the frame saw and laid by the fore end of the ship. The stem mould would now be laid on the stem to check for shape, and the centre lines, bearding line and sheer height transferred. The fitting together of the two components started by offering them together, any irregularities being noted, and then they were separated for trimming and fitting by adze, plane and perhaps a saw kerf, after which the "bading", as the bearding was called locally, was started.

The face of the stem was left for a width of four-and-a-half inches up to just below sheer height, from where to the stem head it was expanded to six inches. The forefoot also was gradually expanded to the full width of the keel, eight inches, the hard edges in the case of the stem having a small arris, while the forefoot gradually assumed the round on the keel.

The top expansion of the stem is shewn clearly in my illustration of the tizzard bolt.

The bading would be taken to the full width of the stem at the rabbet line. With the completion of this, the stem and apron could be brought together and coupled up with G-screws, and boring for the fastening commenced. One-inch galvanized bolts were used and these would be started in the centre on the face of the stem, but allowed to cant about three-quarters of an inch each on the after side of the apron, one to port and one to starboard alternately. This not only made for a more rigid job but lessened considerably the risk of the whole thing splitting, which it might tend to do with the bolts all in one line. These were screw bolts, screwed up on the apron with the heads just a fraction below the face of the stem.

In the event of the stem being damaged in collision its removal was a comparatively simple matter. The stemband would have to be removed, together with the tie irons, and of course the bolts would have to be punched back, the most difficult job of all. After a new stem had been fitted the whole of the "hooding ends" would have to be recaulked, of course, all very straightforward jobs. To do a job of this sort the ship would have to be either slipped or dry docked.

With the stem and apron assembled together, preparations would begin to step it, after the rabbet had been cut. The base of the stem would be cut to the line decided by the base of the stem mould and squared athwartships,

Bading the stem; bading was a local term meaning bearding.

13

two mortices would be cut in the keel and two tenons on the base of the stem with the second cut, these two tenons being of fairly substantial dimensions.

So now we are ready, except for putting a bar through the stem about a foot from the base and giving both the top of the keel and the base of the stem a liberal coat of tar. A small silver coin might be dropped into one of the mortices for luck; this would disappear in the tar.

Chain blocks would have been slung from a spar across two roof trusses, a sling chain put round stem and apron, and lifting into position commenced. After the stem was positioned a sling chain would be slipped over each end of the bar and left hanging under the keel; and wedges and slivers would be slipped into the loop of the chain and driven home to ensure that everything was set down tight. As the chain tightened tar would come oozing out of the joints. Then the whole would be shored plumb, the rake of the stem being checked by a "horning" batten taken from a given station to sheer height.

In the event of the apron being cut from a piece of timber an inch or so over the eight inches required in width, this extra wood would have been left on except for that part standing above sheer height. This upper part would have been brought down to the same width as the stem.

As the stem is now in position, horned and plumbed, a mould can be made for the stem knee. A suitable piece of oak would be found in the shape of a

Left: Fastening off the stem and apron, which were both of English oak.
Below: A section of the stem and apron at about the level of the waterline, showing how the fastenings were canted to port and starboard alternately.

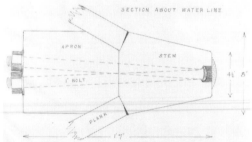

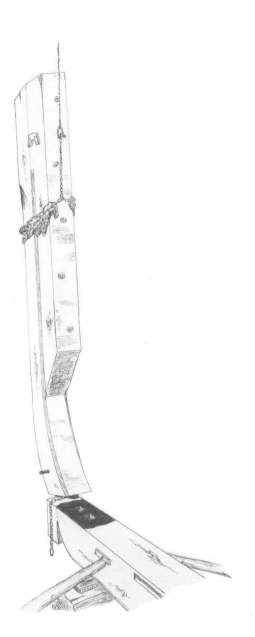

crook, sided to eight inches, moulded out and cut on the band saw.

It would then be fitted between the bottom splay on the apron, the after side of the stem, and the top of the keel. It would be held in position with shifting cramps, and boring for the fastenings could be started. One-inch bolts would be used, staggered as much as possible, the top one passing through knee, splay on apron, and stem, with the others through stem, knee and keel, till the whole was secured. The tie irons could then be fitted and fastened, one on each side, bitumastic covered, let in flush, and with through bolts fastening, driven from alternate sides, cut off by cold chisel and clenched.

Jack Payne, a year or so my senior, could have been the apprentice concerned. He was a fine chap and we have been life-long friends. I am very glad to have known and worked with him.

I helped to make the stem of the *Implacable* and later that of the smack *Challenger*, for which I also made the keel.

Stepping the stem. It was almost traditional to place a silver coin for luck in one of the mortices after tarring; the coin would disappear into the tar, but it would be there for the life of the vessel, and one always hoped it would bring her good luck.

15

The stem and apron and stem knee erected on the keel. The deadwood, of English elm, and the stern-post and stern timbers are also erected.

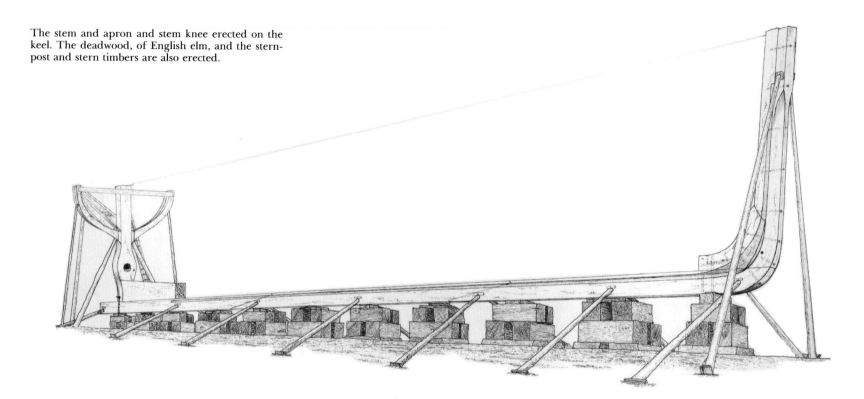

Stern Post and Deadwood

The oak tree from which the stern post would be cut would have to be clear of sap and a fairly good girth as the expansion of the propeller boss would have to be got from it. Again the sawyer would manipulate the timber so that when it left the mill there would be a minimum of work for the shipwrights to perform with the adze. The sawyer would know how close to go to the various marks without endangering the work of the shipwright in any way. After being cut on the frame saw the post would be transported by various means down to the stern of the ship.

The mould would be laid on and the various relevant marks transferred from it to the post, after which work would begin with the adze and plane.

After a time it would have become almost unrecognisable, having been planed with great care until it was quite smooth. The mould would be laid on again and the various water levels, etc, marked on, and the shaft hole would be marked. The base of the stern post was square both ways.

The cutting of the shaft hole would be effected by boring a series of holes just touching one another with a one-inch auger, about a quarter-inch inside the line. When these holes were connected the core would fall out, and all the rough projections would then be trimmed back with a big gouge.

The mortices would be cut in the keel after the tenons had been cut on the foot of the stern post, and the post would then be ready for the two stern timbers to be bolted on, one on each side of the post. These determined the angle of the counter and were its main support, being fastened by means of through screw bolts passing through timbers and post. Fillings were bolted in between the two timbers, with a space left at the site of the rudder trunk.

Preparations would be made to heave the post into position, using two-ton blocks. We used the old-fashioned type of chain blocks in those days.

As in the case of the stem, a liberal supply of tar would be put on the base of the post, on to the keel and into the mortices. If somebody felt in a generous mood, perhaps another small silver coin would be popped into a mortice.

We used to heave up good weights sometimes on the roof trusses, which although of timber were fairly substantial. Mr George Knights, our foreman joiner during the period about which I am writing, had helped to build the shop, and his work was usually "safe as houses".

After it had been lowered on to the keel the post would be hove down tight in the same way as the stem, by means of a bar through it, a sling chain on each end of this bar, and packings and wedges in the loop under the keel; and shored with a shore each side up into the tuck and another shore set about three quarters of the way up under the stern timbers to support them. It would then be plumbed, and all these shores would be left until the ship itself was far enough advanced to ensure that nothing could possibly move.

The tie irons would be fitted only after the deadwood was fastened.

Deadwood

At Chambers we usually used elm for the deadwood, which was made up of two pieces, one on top of the other. It would be high enough for the tube chocks to be fitted directly on top of it.

The deadwood, although a large baulk of timber, was fairly easy to fit. When fitted, it would be well secured with shifting cramps, after which boring would be started for the fastenings, consisting of lengths of one-inch galvanized iron driven through into the keel and stopping about three-quarters inch clear of the sandband, at about two-foot centres and staggered alternately off the centre line of the keel. Some bolts would come into the stern post, driven at an angle and with a washer let in on the after side of the stern post on which the bolt would be cut off and clinched. We didn't have heads made on these bolts, because as they were driven tight the top of the bolt would expand sufficiently to form a head.

When driving some of these larger bolts two men would strike the bolt, and so ensure that it kept moving. If a bolt was allowed to stop it would be difficult to start it again. A tin of grease was always available when boring for and driving these bolts. To ensure that a bolt kept moving either a 7 lb or a 10 lb sledge hammer would usually be used, and sometimes in the case of a smack three men would drive 1,2,3,1,2,3,1,2,3, using a fairly fast tempo; a bolt wouldn't be allowed to rest until it was home.

Usually holes were bored a sixteenth of an inch smaller than the bolt, but in the case of a very long bolt, sometimes up to five or six feet long, holes would be bored the same size as the bolt for part of the way. Even then the friction would make it hard to drive the bolt home.

Although these bolts were simply a plain piece of galvanised rod cut to length, normally by chisel, the end would have to be hammered round slightly in order to make sure that the bolt had a lead and that there were no projections. Shipwrights always checked all bolts automatically to make sure that this was the case.

Tube chocks

As soon as the deadwood was finished it would be necessary to start the tube chocks, followed by the stern post knee on top of them, and so get the whole of the interior of the ship completed in that area before framing up could be started.

At John Chambers the tube chocks were in two pieces. These would be of oak and each one would be hollowed down the middle using a curved adze

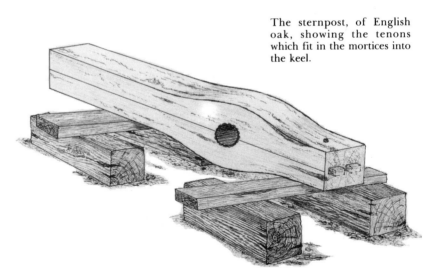

The sternpost, of English oak, showing the tenons which fit in the mortices into the keel.

17

First cut in shaft tube.

First cut in tube chocks.

Stern post, deadwood, tube chocks and stern post knee.

18

and gouges, the hole thus left between the two being about three-quarters of an inch smaller than the size of the shaft tube. The hole would be roughly gouged out in order to allow the boring bar to be put through it later.

When ready, the bottom half of the chocks would be bolted down directly to the deadwood, while the top half would be fastened to the bottom half by means of seven-eighths inch galvanized screw bolts through the sides of each piece. When doing this job the shipwrights had to take very great care to ensure that these bolts were clear of the cutters on the boring bar. If one did foul, it could cause a great deal of trouble, bearing in mind that by the time it was required to bore for the tube the hull of the vessel would be well advanced and any obstruction in the tube chocks hard to get at.

With these bolts in and screwed down tightly, all was ready for the stern post knee. This knee, of oak as in the case of the stem knee and again in the shape of a crutch, was cut to a right angle on the after and bottom sides, while the face of it would usually be cut in a curve; see my illustration. Unlike the stem knee, the stern post knee would be cut or sided a bit wider in order to allow for more intricate fastening because of the tube. Through bolts were used in the stern post.

With this job completed, framing up could start and the stern shipwrights could be allowed to get on with their work abaft the stern post. We will leave the stern shipwrights now for a while and start frame making and framing up.

I mentioned earlier the wrongs that were cut from the felled trees and it was from these that much of the timber for frame making came. Sometimes a bent, twisted and short bole would have to be used for floors, and it was in this case that Tinker or Boxer would be seen dragging a piece of timber down the yard to the horizontal saw.

This was the only saw on the yard with an overhead drive, although it was motivated by the same engine as the other saws. It stood in its own little mill and was operated by one "Frano" Jackson, a batchelor who lived on the Rock Estate at Oulton Broad, and whose brother Stuart "Hilly" Jackson was one of the best shipwrights I ever knew—he was senior apprentice when I started.

I have shown this little mill in my illustration of Boxer. It was simply a little wooden edifice built of slabs and with a corrugated iron roof.

When "Frano" received a piece of timber he would check it for stability and on occasion chop off a projection here and there. When it was ready he would lift it with his own little crane on to the bench, calling on Ben or my father if he needed help.

Once it was on the bench he would "dog" it by the use of "dogs" fitted to the bench, move it into position and prepare the saws, two in number. If he was going to cut frame stuff, as it was called, the saws would be set for four

inch and the resulting slabs would be said to have been four inch sided. If, however, he was to cut floors then these would be five inch sided; smacks were a bit heavier scantling than this.

When it was on the bench he would set the saw in motion, using a lever pulling a belt from a loose to a fast pulley. The saw operated by means of a con-rod from a revolving wheel with side pin to the saw frame, which I suppose had a stroke of about two feet. It would not be long getting through the timbers, though sometimes there were obstructions in the trees. Barbed wire was common, while sometimes there would be stones, or bricks, once even a brass spring gun which the tree had grown over in a crutch many years ago.

With the timber through the saw, "Frano" would lay it out to the best of his ability to await the shipwright or chargehand who would be moulding it out.

"Frano" was a nice chap, very wiry and quite a character, with a flair for a bit of leg-pulling and a great interest in horses and pigs. He owned one of the first and several of the latter.

In addition to the horizontal saw we had a rack bench in a lean-to built on the north side of the mill, and it was on this saw that most of the smaller wrongs were cut. The wrongs being cut on this saw would be sided four inches, after which they would be laid out by Mr Alf Nicholls, the sawyer in charge of the rack bench, in readiness to be moulded out.

Moulding out and cutting frames

The chargehand shipwright was usually responsible for moulding out frames. This was a job that could be picked up and then dropped at will, so long as there was enough work lying about for the saw mill to get on with, unlike lining out plank, which job one of the shipwrights would be doing constantly once planking up had been started.

And the chargehand would be looking round the frame piece area for suitable pieces for the mould in his hands. Starting from the futtock, he would probably have to find five pieces altogether for each side of the frame, ten in all. The floor that would connect them together would have to be found first, and that would be laid by the horizontal saw where the five-inch stuff was lying. We called nearly all timber other than the planking "stuff".

When he had found a suitable floor he would mark it out with a race knife, race on the number of the frame and any sur marks and water levels, if any were shown.

Next he would find the futtock which would eventually be fastened to this particular floor, transfer the number and side of the frame, also sur marks.

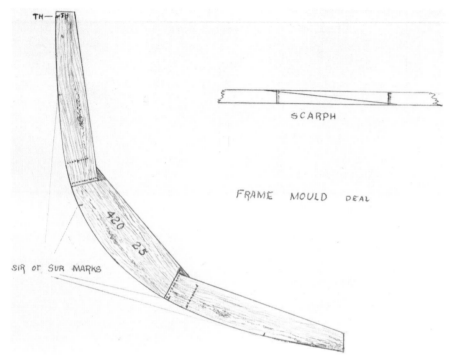

SCARPH

FRAME MOULD DEAL

SIR or SUR MARKS

The frame mould, made of deal.

He would go on to find the rest of the frame pieces, mould them and in every case transfer the relevant marks.

The side on which the mould was laid became the moulded side and the marks which the race knife left became the moulded edge.

Almost from the time the chargehand started to mould out, the saw mill hands would have started picking the timber up and getting it into the mill for cutting. This would be done on the bandsaw; my father used to cut a lot of the frames out, having four or five labourers helping to carry and move the stuff.

On the bandsaw bench, which moved when a handle was turned, provision had been made for a board under the shaft leading to the bevel turning handle. On this board the numbers of the frame would be marked, together with the numbers of the various sur marks appertaining to that particular frame. Into the side of the bench itself a bar was screwed; this bar

was slightly curved at the end and pointed so that as the bevel handle was turned and the bench moved the pointer would sooner or later arrive at a certain mark.

When a piece of floor or frame was lifted on to the bench to be cut, the bevel turner, as he was called, would have to be in his place and ready. On the saw being started and cutting into the wood the bevel turner would turn the bevel handle at a speed consistent with the speed at which the wood was being moved. It follows that a pretty reliable man would be put on that job, otherwise the cut would be erratic.

A Mr John Downing was bevel turner at this time. He was a former Dr Barnardo's boy, deeply religious, who had come to Lowestoft to become a smacksman but like many other fishermen who were over military age found himself in a shipyard sooner or later doing unskilled work. My father always seemed pleased to have him working with him when turning out frames, as he could be relied upon to stop and start instantly with the starting and stopping of the saw. The bevel had to be turned gradually from sur mark to sur mark as cutting proceeded.

When several pieces had been cut they would be taken into the big shop and stacked either to port or starboard of the keel in readiness for the boys to start frame making.

Fitting floors

There were five different kinds of frames in a drifter of wood. These were floor frames, foot frames, fashion frame, shadow frames, and cant frames.

The floors, which extended right across the keel, were cut from five-inch timber. If possible when moulding out the chargehand would try to find a piece of stuff which would allow as much length of floor as he could get to extend on either side of the ship, on each alternate frame.

To fit the floors to the keel the score would have to be cut. A base line would have already been drawn on the keel, this being also the top of the rabbet. This line was an inch and a quarter down from the top of the keel, and the score which would have been marked out earlier from the station batten would now be checked before actually having a cut made in it five-eighths of an inch deep. This would be done by the use of saw, adze and slice, this latter tool being a very wide chisel which would leave a reasonably level surface in the score on which to bed the floor.

The moulding edge of the floor would be checked by use of the mould and any uneven places in the saw cut defined by use of a plane, with which the shipwright would plane a little arris. Sur marks would now be nicked in the edge of the timber by means of a saw.

All the floors would have to be checked and fitted down before framing up could be started. The floors were quite deep at the throat with a gradual taper towards top height, or TH. From the moulded edge to the inside of the floor and frame was called the moulded depth.

Frame making

The frames were usually made by young apprentices. The first thing to be done was to check each piece for fairness by laying the mould on it. In the event of any unevenness, as with the floors, a little arris would be planed on and this would indicate a lump, as it was called.

The frame number and sur marks would also be checked, and if everything was found to be in order these sur marks could be nicked in with the saw.

This work would start with the futtock, and the same procedure would now take place with the second piece and so on right up to the sheer or top height, bolting No. 2 piece to the futtock and No. 3 to No. 2 as the work progressed. This was achieved by means of G-screws to clamp No. 2 piece to

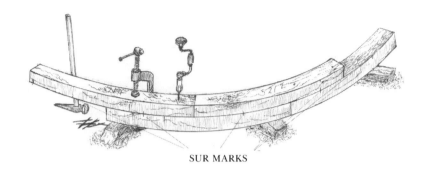

SUR MARKS

Frame making. The frames were of English oak, four inches sided.

the futtock with the edges of the timber concurring and with each sur mark exactly opposite its counterpart.

Two holes would now be bored in each piece by brace and what we called a full-quarter bit, that is five-sixteenths, and pieces of three-eighths inch steel rod cut by the apprentices and then rounded up a little at the driving end used as fastenings. These bolts would be driven by a maul.

The first tools that an apprentice bought were usually a ball pein hammer and cold chisel for use on jobs such as these.

When fitting one piece of frame to another a mark would be taken at it by measurement, the end of the frame would be cut and the piece could then usually be saw kerfed to its final position, sur mark to sur mark.

Framing up

A stage consisting of stage deals resting on barrels would be rigged up across the keel and framing up would be started at the first keel score, at the fore end of the deadwood.

The particular floor of this station would be laid in the centre after end of the stage, ready to receive the two sides of the frames which would now be put into position and fastened to the floor, thus making the complete frame, bearing in mind that they had already been cut and fitted to the floor.

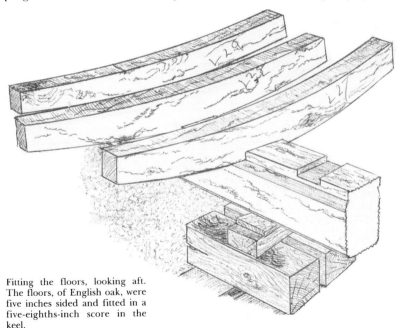

Fitting the floors, looking aft. The floors, of English oak, were five inches sided and fitted in a five-eighths-inch score in the keel.

21

A numbered cross spall, consisting of a seven inches by one-inch deal board, would now be fastened at sheer height by two Nettlefold brads at each end. The length of this cross spall was the moulded breadth at that particular frame. The number of the frame would be raced on it and a very precise centre line cut into it on the top edge.

The spall was fixed on the foreside of the frame in the after body and on the after side of the frame in the fore body. Two temporary shoring cleats would be nailed about three feet below sheer height, while on the after side of this first frame two further cleats would be fastened to support it, as it would be leaning aft owing to the declivity.

The frame would be manhandled up into position, then secured to the keel by means of "shifters" which would be screwed on to floor and keel after the floor had dropped into its prepared seating. The four temporary shores would be set from the ground, two of which would be one on each side with the other two supporting the after side, and with the frame being square with the keel both athwartships and vertically.

Between the apron and sternpost a spunyarn line would have been hung on the centre line of the ship, and on this would have been threaded an ordinary metal washer with a plumb line attached. It was a simple matter to plumb the frame athwartships by straining the one side up and easing the other down until centre was attained.

This operation would be continued, moving the stage forward as the work progressed, the only difference being the changeover of spalls at amidships from fore to after side of the frame. No further shoring on the after side was

Marking piece number five for cutting to fit on the end of piece number three.

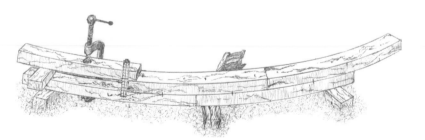

Framing up, looking aft, starting with the first floor frame at the fore end of the deadwood.

required as all the frames were now secured one to the other by a span, one each side. This gave them the support needed fore and aft. Used on ship after ship, these spans were pieces of two inches by one-inch oak long enough to cover the stations and with Nettlefold brads at each end of the span to secure frame to frame.

Additional security was obtained by laying a piece of oak on the top of the floors, temporarily of course, and putting shifters on here and there.

When nearing the fore part of the ship, however, preparations would have to be put in hand to lay the four pieces of keelson in the vessel before framing up could be completed.

Keelson pieces

The keelson or kelson pieces as we called them would have been cut on the frame saw very shortly after the keel was cut. They were of oak, squared nine inches by nine inches.

The two centre pieces were long enough to extend from the stem knee and to overrun the lower part of the deadwood for a short distance, while the side keelsons would be as long as the chosen trees would allow them to be. The function of these side keelsons was not only to strengthen the ship longitudinally but also to support the boiler.

The keelsons would now be brought from the mill area and handled through double doors at the top end of the shop, and into the ship by the stem knee and over the floor and futtock of the frames that had been erected in the fore part of the ship. With this job done it would now be possible to complete all framing up in the fore body.

Other long timbers such as the bilge stringers would have to be passed into the ship later, but it was possible to manoeuvre these between frames.

With reference to the completion of framing up for'ard, the floor frames ended at the after end of the stem knee, and this left two cant frames to be erected on each side of the knee itself. The other frames were squared to the keel, while these were square with the ribband and canted off the centre line. These frames were of one long single piece each and of a moulded depth consistent with Board of Trade requirements, and were spiked directly on to the side of the knee.

During the time that framing up was in progress it was essential to plumb up as the work went on by means of the temporary shores.

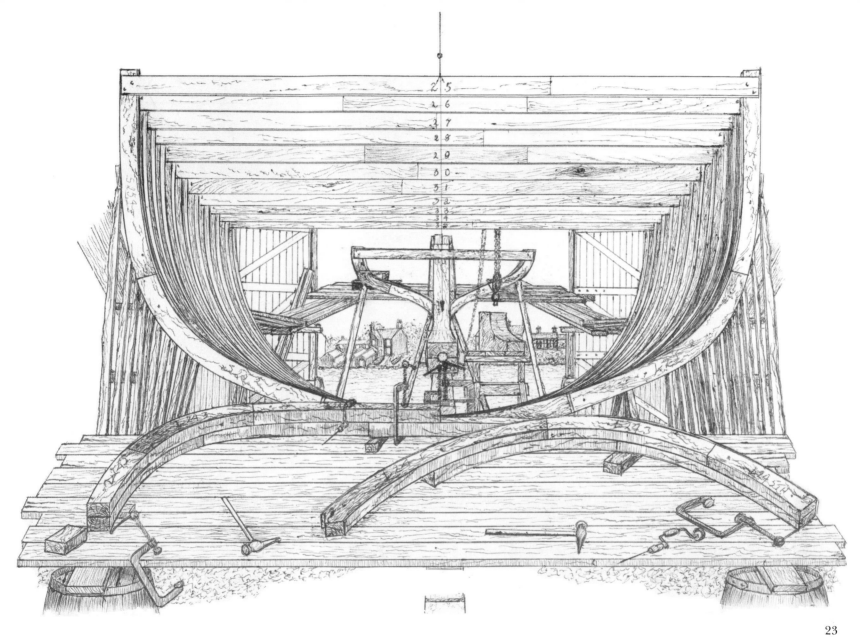

The frames in the after body temporarily shored up, showing the shadow frames, cant frames and fillings resting on the harpin iron. Some of the harpin iron shores and the after stage have been omitted to avoid obliterating the layout of the frames.

24

Stage rigging

With the completion of the framing up of the fore body it would be necessary to rig the stages, as the scaffolding was called, and for this purpose the firm used a number of portable trestles, which you will see illustrated very often in my diagrams. This was common practice in this area of Suffolk at the time for building wooden ships, while for steel ships standards dug into the ground, and fitted with crossbearers on which the stage deals rested, were used. At each end of our wooden ships, where the stages would be too high for trestles, bearers would be hooked on posts in the shop's structure and the stage rested on them.

The deals, which were usually from 20 feet to 22 feet long by nine inches or ten inches wide, would be placed round the ship at about 3 feet 6 inches below sheer height, allowing the people working the topsides enough room to work the lowest planks without altering the stages in any way. Two deals would be used, except aft where the last length would be of three deals each side, while across and under the counter six or seven deals would be used, with two diagonally, as when one was working on the stern a greater area was needed. A shipwright working on the stern would very rarely look down towards his feet, so the stage had to be made reasonably safe, bearing in mind that in those days very little attention was given to making conditions safe for working; it was up to the people concerned to take precautions for themselves.

Below the topside stages people just arranged deals as needed, using the strengthening bars of the trestles as bearers when it was convenient to do so.

On the larger shipyards and in dry docks it was a shipwright's job to rig stages for whatever tradesman needed them. However, the stage just described makes a continuous walkway right round the ship.

Foot frames

With the stages rigged, the work of framing up could continue and a start was made with the first foot frames on the deadwood next to the floor frames and working aft.

I have spoken of water levels being transferred from the mould to the frame. These frames had been made up by the apprentices virtually the same as the others, except that there was no floor fitted, as they were fastened one on each side of the deadwood.

By using the water level on the frame and the WL already marked on the deadwood, we were able to decide exactly where these frames needed to be pitched. The size and shape of the foot would then be drawn on the

deadwood and seating one half-inch deep would be chiselled into it, with the shipwright bringing the two WLs together in doing so.

When ready, the frame would be hove up into position by about three people on the stage and two more on the ground, and these two would offer the foot up into the seating. If it fitted holes would be bored and spikes would be driven through the foot into the deadwood. A shore would then be set up to support the frame, and a span put on from the first floor frame.

The stern timbers and the stages seen from above. The fastenings in the fashion frames and cant frames and fillings are shown in broken lines.

When both sides were erected a cross spall would be put on and the work proceed right aft to the fashion frame, which was fitted and fastened flush with the fore side of the stern post at the "tuck".

The stern

While framing up was going on, work on the stern would also be progressing. With the fashion frame having been erected and fastened off, the position being ruled by the underside of the stern timbers into which the shape of the fashion frame flowed, the shadow frames would be fitted and fastened and shored up, and cross spalls and spans put on. After this the cant frames, of which there were five each side, would be fitted and fastened. These were single timbers four-inch sided and splayed one on to the other at the foot.

Before the cant frames could be fitted, however, the harpin irons would have to be placed in position. These irons consisted of two pieces of one-and-a-half-inch by one-and-a-half-inch angle iron shaped to the curve of the stern and made to fit the vessel at sheer height. After these irons had been secured to the stern timbers and frames on the quarter and shored up to their proper positions from the ground, fitting the cant frames could start. As each frame was fitted it would be secured at the foot and also to the harpin iron by a nettlefold brad through the angle iron.

Oak fillings would be fitted in between the cant frames and the whole would be secured as the work progressed by two galvanised through bolts in each filling and frame.

And so the whole framing up operation is now complete.

Ribbands

The ribbands, which were of five-inch by two-and-a-half-inch pitch pine, sometimes condemned deck deals, started from the hooding end of the stem rabbet. Every frame station was marked on them and indicated by a very lightly cut saw mark, which was numbered, the distance between marks on the ribband having an allowance made for the expansion of the vessel at either bilge or sheer height, depending on which ribband it was. They were in three or four lengths, with another piece of ribband acting as a fishplate.

The bilge ribband would be worked first, to pull the frames down nice and even, also fair, bearing in mind that the frames were already even on the keel and that the bilge was the next nearest point to that. The ribband would be placed so that a bilge strake could be worked before the ribband was

The Big Shop in which the *Formidable* was built.

removed, and each frame was brought into position as the work progressed.

The ribbands would be secured on the apron first by means of two cleat nails driven on to a steel washer, and after that each separate frame would be forced into position. A frame was in position when the midpoint of the frame arrived at the station mark on the ribband itself. This was achieved by having a pair of G-screws lightly screwed on frame and ribband, a shipwright tapping the frame into position with his maul. When in position a cleat nail with a washer under the head would be driven into the frame.

This whole operation had the effect of horning the frames from the centre line at sheer height on the apron and also squaring them with the keel.

After the bilge ribbands had been fastened work would begin on those at sheer height, or as we more commonly called it, "top height". The top ribband was placed so that a topside plank could be worked just below it.

As the work on the ribbands progressed bilge shores would be set and all the temporary shores would be removed. For the first time the whole structure was reasonably rigid.

And so we are ready for the sheer batten, which can now be hung round the ship for the first of four times. The top ribband will not be removed until after two strakes of the topsides have been worked. When necessary the ribbands were removed from the frames by setting wedges in behind them, using the maul.

The planks, called "flicks" in, and just out of, the mill, will now be called strakes. On the shipyard it was "flicks" in the mill, "plank" when laid out, and "strakes" of planking on the ship.

Keelsons

After the frames had been ribbanded up work would be started on the centre keelson, cut from two trees and squared nine inches by nine inches. This would be fitted on to the fore end of the deadwood and up to the after end of the stem knee.

To fit the keelson, or kelson as I prefer to call it, down, a fair area would have to be trimmed by adze for the whole length of the centre kelson along the tops of the floors and for a width of nine inches. When doing this a straightedge would be used to check the seating. When the trimming was completed both centre pieces of kelson would be fitted, or housed down as it was called, after which the timber would be secured by shifting cramps hooked under the keel in readiness for bolting, or as we would say, fastening.

The fore body, ribbanded up and kept plumb by bilge shores. The stages are on portable trestles for most of the length of the ship and can be adjusted to suit the working level required.

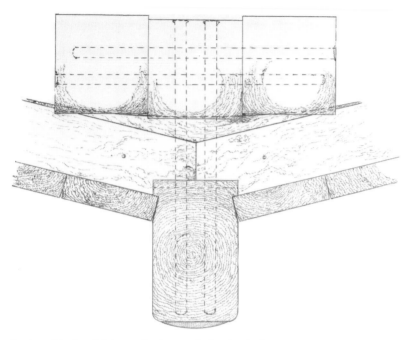

Holes would be bored through kelson and floor and into the keel to within half an inch of the sand band. This would be done by auger, a pod auger generally as this was the type most used in those days. Into these holes would be driven a one-inch galvanized iron bolt, to flush with the top of the kelson,

Pod auger.

Section of keel and kelsons, showing one-inch galvanised bolts staggered in each floor.
The centre and side kelsons in position, seen from above.

one in every floor and each one staggered off centre alternately port and starboard.

Next the two side kelsons were fitted down, this time partly over the frames especially at the after ends where the floors lifted more quickly. These side kelsons, also of nine-inch by nine-inch oak, were started in the area of the engine bed and allowed to go as far forward as the length of the tree from which they were taken would allow.

To fit them down they would be laid directly over where they were to be used and then marked where they had to be slotted down over floors and possibly a bit of frame. After marking, the two pieces of timber would be rolled upside down and sawn at the cross markings, and the wood then taken out by chisel and adze.

After cutting they would be rolled into position, hove together by cramp across the three kelsons and down by cramp hooked under either floor or frame; this procedure was called "housing the timber down". The side

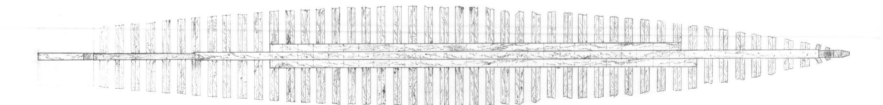

kelsons stood about a three-quarter-inch higher than the centre one, thus reducing the amount of wood to be cut away when fitting.

Hole boring could now be started horizontally through the kelson and side kelsons in between each pair of frames, the holes being drilled alternately from port and starboard, staggered a little on the horizontal plane. A fairly long auger would be used to allow the shipwright to operate, bearing in mind the fact that he would now be boring between the frames. A sledge hammer would be used to drive the bolts, as it was imperative to keep them moving briskly until they were home. Bolts were also driven vertically into alternate floors.

So now we do have a really good foundation for the boiler provided by the keel and three kelsons, in addition to which there will be two side stringers between the kelson and bilge stringers.

The personnel working on the ship were divided into groups while doing these jobs. First there were the men on the stern, then there would be several boys frame making, while some of the other men and boys have been framing up, also ribbanding up and lastly working on the kelsons. But now it is time to split them up into gangs, for planking up is about to be started.

The foreman would detail off three shipwrights and two apprentices to work on the "larboard side", as the elder Mr Jenner called it. Three other shipwrights and two more apprentices would be put to work the starboard side (in planking up you were said to work the starboard side, not to work on the starboard side). The men on the stern would remain where they were, while all other shipwrights and apprentices that were available would be detailed off for the topsides, in this case working both sides. This gang was often called, erroneously I always thought, the "light gang"; some of the heaviest timber, shelves, stringers and beams, etc, were worked into the ship by them, but their working conditions were far superior to those experienced by the people who were planking up. I will explain this a bit later.

The men with whom I worked all had nicknames. I think East Anglia is renowned for its nicknames. I worked with Jack "Saffron" Bunn for a good part of my apprenticeship. He had a younger brother, Ernest "Rock" Bunn, who later worked on our steel yard. Also with me was their cousin, Albert Page, who because he had a bit of a round back became "Camel". Then came Charlie "Grampus" Agus, Wilfrid Canham, Charlie "Mucko" Breach, Frank called "Sammy", "Treacle" or "Chalky" Colby, and Llew Greengrass. There were twins named Tuttle, whom we called "Diddy" and "Lorrie"; as they were so much alike we called "Diddy-Lorrie" when we wanted to speak to either of them. Most people never knew to which one they were speaking. Their proper names were Sidney and Victor, in that order. Others were Stuart "Hilly" Jackson, the senior apprentice at this time, Herbert Briggs,

Jack Payne, George Ayres, Clifford Evans and Gordon Lubbock, none of whom had nicknames, and Walter "Hardo" Harwood. I myself was "Teddie" to my fellow apprentices but "boy Ted" to the men on the yard, as my father was also named Ted. Sometimes I was called "Zero", also, I might add, other things which I won't even even try to mention. Oh, and of course there was Stanley "Dingo" Daniels.

Among the shipwrights were Charlie Castleton, who fought in the Boer War, Jack "Sonny" Barnard, "Horry" or Horace Jenner, Ernie Secret, Jack "Jacka" Pitchers, Herbert "Chy" Page, Albert Oliver, who had been recalled from the Army, Freddy "Nampo" Sampson, sometimes called "Commander" after Commander Sampson, the great wartime flyer, and Old George Wright from Beccles; we used to give him his full title, he was one of the

A group of apprentices at John Chambers' yard. "Boy Ted" is third from the right.

Wrights who were wherry builders, a nice old chap. And then there were my uncle Fred Rouse and his brother Jimmy Rouse, nicknamed "Maggie" after his sister. He was an excellent tradesman in every way and I expect that at that time he was about the best caulker in the port; he had a very good reputation for this work. Unlike Yarmouth, where some men specialised in caulking, at Lowestoft shipwrights did the whole of the work. Then came "Preel" Jillings, Alf "Old Dingo" Daniels, Alf Hammond, who did most of the small boat building at this time on the yard, "Uncle" Jimmy Capps and Percy "Rasputin" Rushmere, so called because of his imagined similarity to the "mad monk". In the case of Jimmy Capps "Uncle" was just an affectionate term used by us all as he was well over retiring age. These are all shipwrights and shipwright apprentices.

I will name some of the other men as I come to them. The deputy foreman on the yard, himself a shipwright, was Mr William "Billy" Coleman. Most people seemed to stand in awe of him, but I always seemed to get on all right with him. Old George Wright from Beccles was positively scared of him. I really liked the work, as you may have guessed by my writings, and I suppose that that attitude helps a bit when working with people who are a bit strict, or should I say more strict than usual, and that description applied to Billy Coleman.

Planking up

A few days before planking up was due to begin a shipwright would begin to line out and to get cut a limited number of planks. Uncle Fred, who used to do a good bit of this, would be selecting plank for length, width and shape. He would look for wood that was clear of sap and defects such as shakes, dead knots, was not too brown, as this could mean the start of decay. He would then line them out, using a pitchpine batten held in position by nails lightly tapped into the oak on each side of it or sometimes by weights.

He would begin by selecting the garboards and as far as possible the following strakes. The strakes, of which there were twenty-two, were generally made up of three pieces, sometimes four. The widths were predetermined and there was a butt board on which the position of the butts was laid out in conformation with the Board of Trade standards and requirements. One of these was that no butt could be near another on the same timber less than three strakes of planking apart. That was a minimum, but of course efforts were made to keep the butts even further apart. They were to be at least five frames apart in adjacent strakes.

The bilge strakes, and also the topsides, had a predetermined position for line, but all the widths of the strakes were worked out to suit the development or form of the ship at the ends and midship section.

The planking, besides making the hull watertight, introduced longitudinal stiffening.

Before planking up could begin the rabbets, which had been finished off along the keel, would have to be connected in the case of the fore end from keel to stem, while aft it would be necessary to trim deadwood, tube chocks, etc., right up to the tuck under the stern. Quite a bit would have to be taken off the deadwood as the planks would be standing on edge all the way up the stern post, but then turning quickly away from there outwards and down towards the ship's bottom.

When all the trimming was completed a stopwater would have to be driven at the junction with the stem knee, stem and keel, and another at the junction of the foreside of the stern post, keel and deadwood.

I remember trimming the deadwood, believe it or not, by the smell, as freshly trimmed elm can smell pretty vile, whereas freshly trimmed or cut oak has rather a pleasant smell, it seems to me. I always delighted in the aroma in the yard sawmill, especially when oak or pitchpine was being cut or pitchpine deck deals were being seamed on the spindle machine.

The planking was of oak, all the fishing craft that I worked on, both smacks and drifters, being planked up with oak. Before my time on the yard, however, I believe some bit of elm was mixed with the oak, especially in H. Reynolds' ships. Both oak and elm are good woods for keeping water out, and when steamed for the prescribed length of time will bend to any shape required in planking up. Elm was best used either above or below water, but when used between wind and water it would tend to rot quickly. Softer kinds of wood can be, and in some places are, used but in East Anglian yards oak was the timber most used.

Just before starting to plank up there would be a scramble by the youngest boys to try to get some of the best tools for their gangs, shifters in the case of those detailed off to work on the topsides and G-screws in the case of both top and bottom, and for a time there would be oil everywhere as well as on the threads as the G-screws were overhauled and prepared by the boys.

Cleats would be made ready. These were pieces of oak cut six inches by four inches by two-and-a-half inches; a hole would be bored in the centre to take a cleat nail, which was of malleable iron three-eighths-inch in diameter with a flat point but a rounded tip. These were made with a fixed washer under a round head; the nail would be about six-and-a-half inches long and used with a loose washer between head and cleat. In addition to this the boys would get two or three hundredweight bags of dump bolts ready, and also some through bolts, and they would see that the supply was maintained throughout the whole operation. This applied to both sides. I don't say that

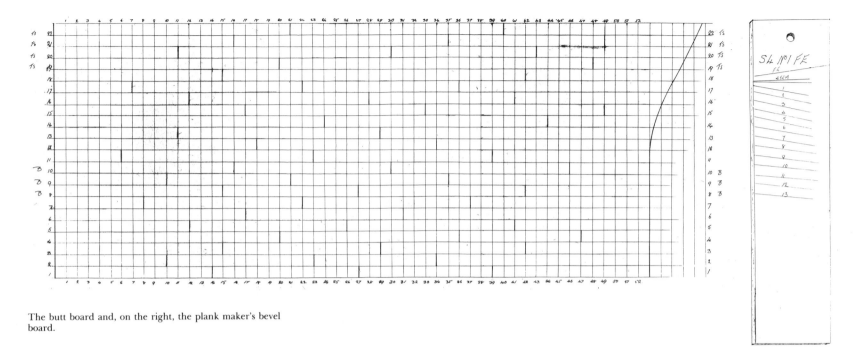

The butt board and, on the right, the plank maker's bevel board.

everything always worked smoothly, but they were risking a cuff or a thump if it didn't, as some of the men we worked with didn't mince matters.

The depot, as it were, for gear was usually near the forepart of the ship and handy to a door. While the gear was being assembled, adze grinding, plane iron sharpening, chisel sharpening, bit sharpening, saw sharpening and brace oiling would have been taking place. It was almost like an army preparing for battle. From now on and for quite a long period complements would be worked; that is, so much work had to be performed each day by every man. This was nothing to do with piecework, and I will describe how this was applied to each job as we come to it. I hasten to add that this didn't apply to all the work but to the principal jobs, at least to those on the cladding of the ship; this was an arrangement between unions and management.

We are now ready to begin trimming down. By some it is called "dubbing" the frames, and this means to fair all the frames one to the other in readiness to secure the planking to them. To do this a good pitchpine batten, usually about one-and-three-quarters inch by seven-eighths inch and about twenty-five or thirty feet long, would be hung first about nine inches from the keel, above the rabbet, using "hutchiks". Any unevenness in the frames could then be seen by casting one's eye along the edge of the batten.

When one could see a hump or any unfairness, a chalk mark would be made on the frame either side of the unfairness or unevenness; the batten would then be set off, probably by wedging a hammer handle down between batten and frame, and the lump as it was termed would be trimmed off with the adze.

The adze is a most ingenious tool. Providing the helve, usually of ash or hickory, is a good fit to the palm of the hand, the adze can be used in any direction without undue fatigue, and the shipwright has absolute control over his adze.

The helve has an oval section, and this in the hand helps to control the

31

blade. One tried not to polish this helve too much, as this could make it swivel in the hand as any highly polished wood will do; it did of course become self-polished through use.

My own adze, a Gilpin No. 2, is in the Maritime Museum at Lowestoft. That is my last adze, of course; with a lot of use and with grinding they soon become worn. When making an adze helve one had to know how to get the blade to set; this was done when fitting the helve in the eye of the adze and was very important. If it was not fitted properly and at the right angle it could become a nuisance and unbalanced; of course one became accustomed to the feel of one's own adze. This was the only tool that I could use with comparative ease in either hand.

Once the frames just above the keel had been trimmed the batten was moved about a foot higher and the frames again trimmed; the operation was repeated at about one-foot centres (closer at the turn of the bilge) right up to the bilge ribband and for the full length of the ship. Meanwhile the same operation was being performed on the topsides. They only trimmed down to the depth of the topside four strakes of planking, or to the shutter as it was called. The planking-up gang would meet the topsides gang at that level.

Trimming down, showing how high spots on the frames are faired by means of fairing batten and adze.

A plank being made on the stools. The batten was used by
the shipwright to get the length and stations from the hull.

As the spots were trimmed and each one faired a chalk mark would be
drawn along the top edge of the batten on each frame. Any unfairness on
the frames between spots could now be seen and trimmed off. Shipwrights'
eyes became trained to detect any unfairness in lines by the very nature of
their work.

Before trimming down was completed the "plankmaker", as the shipwright in each squad or gang who was prepared to go plank making was
called—a matter of mutual choice—would have called for a "lifto". The first
piece of garboard would be lifted on to the stools in readiness to be made up.
If the weather was good these stools would be outside the shop and not too
far from the steam kiln or "kel" as it was called. In bad weather, or in winter,
they would be set up just inside the shop door situated nearest the "kel".

The plankmaker would already have been given the position of the butts
of the strake, as the number of the frame would have been raced on the
inside of the plank and towards the end of it by the liner out.

A "spile" or mould of the shape of the garboard at the forefoot would be
made by the plank maker to fit on the outside edge of the rabbet, in and out
bevels would be taken, and a batten would then be hung on which to get the
length of that particular length of plank. While in position frame stations
would be marked on it, also a pitching spot, which would also be marked on
the spile from a predetermined mark in the rabbet. With the frame station
marks on the batten would also be written the number of each individual
frame and the butt at the end of that particular length.

The bevels would now be taken by the plankmaker and transferred to a
piece of planed board, henceforth to be called the bevel board.

The marks on the batten, including stations and station numbers, would
be transferred to the plank in chalk. All other marks, except "hollowing
marks" which I will explain later, were done with pencil.

The plankmaker will now get help to stand the plank on edge so it can be
wedged upright on the stools with the upper edge of the plank (as it will be
on the ship) at the top; this edge will now be faired and planed square. When
this is done the plank will be laid to suit the shipwright, who will form the
fore end from the spile and trim the bevels from the bevel board on at the
various station marks, after which these spots will all be joined up by the use
of adze and plane. Great care would be taken with the fore end, both with
the shape of it and with the bevels, bearing in mind that it would have to be a
first time fit when the plank was worked hot.

I said the top edge would be planed square; it was on all strakes unless the
plankmaker knew he had to lose or gain something here or there, and of
course he would automatically allow for caulking the seam, and when cutting
butts.

While this preparation was going on the plankmaker would also have been
looking for minor defects in the timber; if he saw any which he wouldn't
have time to remedy himself he would mark them for the "squareberther",
about whom I will write later. The plankmaker would of course attend to
any defects that he saw on the inside of the plank. There would not be a
great number, as the liner-out would have spotted them and most probably
have marked out the plank so that they were cut away when being sawn.

The plankmaker would also have to be very careful to see that he cut the
butt on the right frame. It was always better to measure twice and cut once.

When cutting in the last of the three or four pieces that would go to make
up the strake, the plankmaker would have to wait until the plank was finally

The steam kiln was about 55 feet long, with counterbalanced doors at each end; the doors are open in the picture on the right. The chain tongs were used to pull the planks out for the first few feet as they would be too hot to hold.

worked up before "taking a mark at it", as it was called, on its immediate neighbour, and cutting it off.

When he had got the first piece made up, the plankmaker would come into the shop and call "lifto!" If it was a fairly long and heavy piece, then all hands from both sides would go to help.

The door of the steam kiln would now be pulled up and the two planks would be lifted in and pushed far enough to enable the door to be closed. Steam would have been turned on for some time and the "kel" would be fairly warm. When it was opened steam would come belching out, and one would have to be careful not to get scalded.

Now that the first two planks are in, two further pieces will be lifted on to the stools ready for making up. Similar work is going on the topsides.

The time required for steaming is one hour per inch of thickness of timber. The garboard and all other ordinary strakes are two-and-a-quarter inches thick, the extra quarter of an inch being an allowance for trimming off excess timber and planing up, or as we called it "scrubbing down".

The planks having been placed in the "kel", the youngest apprentice on the job would start to "lay along". This job entailed laying out G-screws, cleats with nails already in them, wedges, a few slivers, a few shores of rough length gauged by the eye, and also some dump bolts. The bolts would be laid handy and would have been rounded up slightly at the point.

Shipwrights would fix a containing piece on to the stem and forefoot using G-screws. A pitching spot would have been marked earlier on the keel; this is the one that I have referred to earlier as being transferred from there to the new garboard.

Tools, that is mauls, braces and bits, reamers, etc., would be placed near to

34

the area in which the work would take place, the braces usually being hung in the nearest trestles to the job, with some consideration given to who would be working where, the leading hands usually being at the vital fore end. Having arrived at the time when the first two planks are about to be "worked", one each side, port and starboard, the word would be given.

The two gangs would gradually gather at the "kel", after having attended to their bodily functions, etc., or had a drink of cold tea from their cans. As the work progressed this interval would be in the nature of a "spell", as a stand-easy was called, each gang knowing that they would be working all-out for the next hour or so. During these few minutes there would often be some good-natured banter.

Before I go any further, let me say that there was never any arguing about who should do what, or when. We worked as a team, and that was the way it had to be in order to accomplish the job, with every man and boy co-operating.

The "kel" door was made to slide up and down between a vertical batten and the ends of the planks forming the side of the "kel". The door was partly balanced by a fairly heavy iron cogwheel or some other weight hung on chains running over two sheaves working over a frame on the guillotine principle.

At the shout of "Ready!" the "kel" door would be slammed up; steam would come belching out, and in summer the man nearest to the "kel" would have to be very careful not to let his face be scalded. This man would be the one to put the "tongs", chain tongs they were called, on to the plank required. The plank numbers and position were marked by chalk on the end facing you; this had to be done as there could be several planks in the "kel" at one time, especially if the topsides were working at the same time, as was usually the case.

A G-screw, one of the smallest in width, weighing about 30 lb., and other useful items in the shipwright's armoury. From left to right are an oak wedge, an oak cleat with its nail of malleable iron, and a hutchik with its Nettlefold brad.

By this time the plank itself would have turned almost blue in places due to the acid in the oak combining with the moisture in the "kel", and this would have turned the chalkmark on the end of the plank a dirty pink. You will find the blue stain if you bite into an acorn. With the tongs safely on the plank, they were made to bite, and with a good heave ho! the plank would come trundling out, steaming hot to the touch, after which the door would be slammed down again until we were ready for the other side.

As far as I can remember there were no preferences as to which side would come first, as both sides would start to fasten off together.

With the plank out of the "kel" we could spread ourselves along it, usually with the shorter chaps at the leading end and the taller ones at the back; this

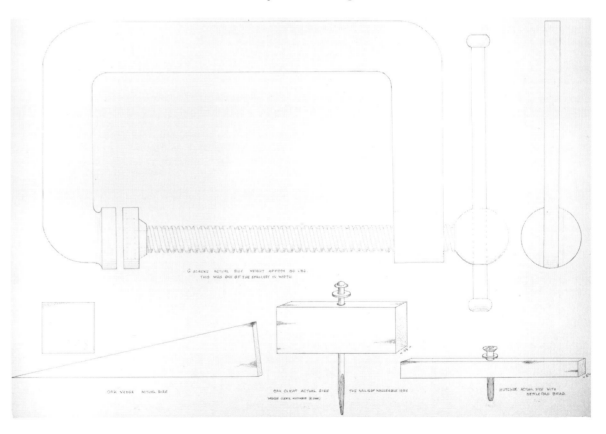

stance gave a tendency to lean forward if anything when carrying; experience taught us how and where to carry. With the plank on our shoulders away we would march into the shop and pass under the ship below the bilge shores; then on our hands and knees with the hot plank on our backs, and so right under the bottom we would edge our way forward, where it would now be handled, and the fore end lifted and pushed into position, bringing the pitching spots on keel and plank together, which would ensure a good fit when finally in position.

Wedges would be driven between the keep and the plank, a shore would be set, a hole bored and reamed, and the first bolt driven into the stem knee, after which the plank would be gently worked, getting G-screws on where possible and slowly forcing it round and twisting it into shape. As soon as it was nearly home a cleat would be nailed into the floor or frame above it wherever it would be an advantage to do this, a wedge would then be set between cleat and plank and driven to force the plank down and home. This would be repeated until the whole of the plank was firmly in position, after which boring for the bolts and driving them would be continued until the fastening was complete. This could not be done in this way on all strakes, as sometimes it would be necessary to leave out some bolts (through bolts, that is) until stringers had been worked inside the vessel.

We used a five-sixteenth, or full quarter bit as we called it, for the dump bolts, which were three-eighths inch in diameter, and a seven-sixteenth bit for the through bolts, which in the planking were half-inch in diameter. We used a British-made five-sixteenth spoon bit for the three-eighth bolts, and we used to improve on these by filing the spoon out so that it became thinner. We would file the nib off at an angle; this had the effect of making the bit cut much faster and longer, as the whole bit was then in effect a nib.

When filled with "cullum," as the swarfe was called, the bit would squeal, on which we would give it a half turn back, then forward again, and with a sharp pull it would come out to be emptied; this would be repeated until the hole reached the depth required.

The hole would be "reamed", that is countersunk, with a "reamer", which was really a large shell or pod gimlet, and the bolt would then be driven, having been tapped round on the edges of the leading end by the boy, using an old anvil or some large piece of iron or steel for this purpose. The reason this was done was that where the bolts were sheared off for length by the manufacturers the end of the bolt might have been compressed a bit, causing it to expand a fraction on each side of the cut; any metal protruding at all could cut a groove on two sides of the hole, thereby possibly causing a leak.

In the butt would be one through bolt and one dump bolt. There would also be a dump bolt and through bolt in the adjacent frame, but in the opposite edge of the plank to those in the butt. These were half-inch through bolts manufactured with a pin head and pilot point. To bore these holes we would use a spiral bit, and we used to try to buy German-made bits as they were machined out to leave just a thin shell, while British bits were left in a thick state and so could not accommodate the cullum as well as the German bits would, in addition to which the British bits were much harder to turn.

When sharpening these bits it was always advisable not to file the outside edge, especially the leading edge, as to do that would lead to jamming and hard work not just for one hole but every hole that one would bore, so particular care was taken when a file was being used. A rat tail file would be used for the inside, and should one have been unfortunate enough to have struck iron, as did happen at times, a flat file would be used across the leading and cutting edge at the end and also at an angle; this had the effect of allowing the bit to cut easy and fast. I might add that it was a pleasure to bore holes in oak with these bits.

To lubricate the bits and also the through bolts the shipwright would use launching fat, which would be carried around in an old paint or treacle tin. One would dip the bit in this most times on pulling the bit from the hole, and this would keep the wall of the hole itself greased. The bits got very hot when being used.

These bits were among the tools that one would not lend if it were possible not to, as they were very precious to the owner, especially so if he had got them up to top cutting pitch. Most people understood this and indeed very rarely asked for the loan of a bit; other tools perhaps, but not bits.

Almost the same thing applied to the firm's augers, some people could sharpen them so that they cut easy while others could not do this, and sometimes the good cutting augers were hidden by the previous user, at times never to come to light again.

Well, we have got our first piece of garboard worked and fastened and the cleats knocked off by sharp blows on one end of them with the maul. This would bend the nail as it was drawing out, but the youngest boy on each side would be straightening cleat nails all the time from now on as part of his duties. The nails were used over and over again. We didn't bore holes for the nails; we always cut the grain when driving them, that is to say the cutting edge was used across the grain.

Now to prepare for the second piece, that is to say, lay the gear and the tools along where the next piece is to be worked, and then repeat the whole operation. We have now entered a phase of the work in which every man and boy will be expected to do so much work per day; the planking up gang

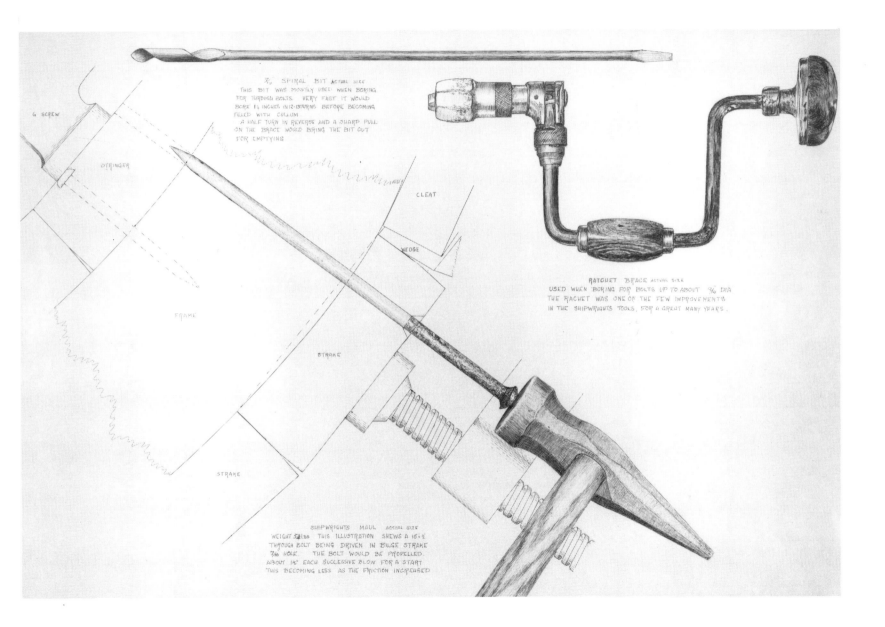

⁵⁄₁₆ SPIRAL BIT ACTUAL SIZE
THIS BIT WAS MOSTLY USED WHEN BORING
FOR THROUGH BOLTS. VERY FAST IT WOULD
BORE 1½ INCHES IN 12-13 TURNS BEFORE BECOMING
FILLED WITH COLLUM.
A HALF TURN IN REVERSE AND A SHARP PULL
ON THE BRACE WOULD BRING THE BIT OUT
FOR EMPTYING

G SCREW

STRINGER

CLEAT

WEDGE

FRAME

STRAKE

STRAKE

RATCHET BRACE ACTUAL SIZE
USED WHEN BORING FOR BOLTS UP TO ABOUT ⁹⁄₁₆ DIA
THE RACHET WAS ONE OF THE FEW IMPROVEMENTS
IN THE SHIPWRIGHTS TOOLS, FOR A GREAT MANY YEARS.

SHIPWRIGHTS MAUL ACTUAL SIZE
WEIGHT 5½ LBS THIS ILLUSTRATION SHEWS A 15 × ½
THROUGH BOLT BEING DRIVEN IN BILGE STRAKE
⁷⁄₁₆ HOLE. THE BOLT WOULD BE PROPELLED
ABOUT ¼" EACH SUCCESSIVE BLOW FOR A START
THIS BECOMING LESS AS THE FRICTION INCREASED

The gear laid along ready to work a plank.

will be expected to work one strake and a piece per day, fastened off and completed.

As the garboard becomes wider towards the after end three bolts instead of two would be used in the frames and correspondingly in the deadwood.

During the summer we would start at 6 a.m. and work till 8 a.m., then a half-hour for breakfast; starting again at 8.30 a.m. and carrying on till 12.30 p.m., when we would have a dinner interval of an hour, starting again at 1.30 p.m. and working until 5 p.m., when unless overtime was being worked the yard closed for the day, except for the office where closing time was 5.30 p.m. The office staff started at 9 a.m., the hours in the office being constant all the year round. Work finished at 1 p.m. on Saturdays.

On the yard the working hours were reduced by quarter-hours at each end of the day; for a period we would start work at 6.15 a.m. and leave off at 4.45 p.m.; and in mid winter we would start at 6.30 a.m. and leave off at 4.30 p.m. Although the hours were reduced one was expected to produce the same amount of work as in a full-length day; strangely enough this used to happen, as far as I could see, the only reason for this being that as the temperatures were lower one was able and inclined to work much harder.

It was only the shipwrights who benefited by this reduction of hours, as at the period about which I am writing they were the only people on these yards who were in a union. The other workpeople had nobody to negotiate for anything for them, and for several years prior to this period their wages were extremely low. When my father married his wages were eighteen shillings (90p) per week and he was a first-class sawyer; at that time shipwrights' wages were about thirty-two shillings (£1.60) per week, quite a substantial difference.

We used to clock on when we arrived at work in the morning and again before starting work after dinner, and would clock off when ready to go home in the evening. Should one be two minutes late when clocking on one would be said to have "lost a quarter", that is to say one would have lost a quarter of an hour's pay.

Should any man or boy be persistently late the management would want to know why. But as that sort of thing only used to occur when there was an illness in a man's family or something similar, then an allowance would be made; the management were very understanding and a friendly atmosphere always seemed to pervade the yard.

Before the time clocks were installed a system of circular numbered brass tallies was used. Each tally hung on its own numbered hook, and on arrival at work one would unhook the tally and drop it into a receptacle provided. The timekeeper would replace them on the hooks, making a note in the register at the same time.

There were no annual holidays in those days for the workmen in shipyards. Statutory holidays such as Christmas Day and Boxing Day were unpaid days.

To offset some of this, if I remember rightly we did receive our full wages during the winter when we worked shorter hours, and as we turned out a full complement of work I suppose that this was justified.

Shortly after the period of which I have written things did begin to improve, in many ways. For one thing, fairly substantial war bonuses were paid.

I must return to the planking up: we have worked and fastened off the garboard. Although dump bolts were used in the ordinary plank except for butts, where there was a stringer opposite a plank, such as the stringer which occurs between the kelson and bilge, every other bolt would be a through bolt.

When the bilge was arrived at three-inch planks were used. These would be hollowed about one quarter of an inch by the plankmaker by means of his adze to allow the plank to fit snugly to the frame; the shipwright would use his own judgment about how much to take out. In the bilges every other bolt was a through bolt going through the stringers.

The inside of the frames in the bilge area would need to be faired to receive the three bilge stringers. The top edge of the top stringer would be chamfered half an inch each way and so would the bottom standing edge of the bottom strake of bilge. This same chamfer was put on the top and bottom bilge strakes, but as these planks were gradually reduced to two-and-a-quarter inches at each end of the vessel the chamfer was allowed to peter out towards the ends.

When working these planks, if one should be a bit stubborn when it was required to get it down snug to its neighbour it might be necessary to reinforce the cleats in the area by doubling them; it was essential that the planks were set tightly together, not only to do the job properly but also to prevent a draught coming through the seam. If it did, the plank would shrink very quickly in that area and that could make it more difficult to caulk.

One area in particular was more affected by draught than all the others, and this was up in the tuck just where the plank leaves the stern timbers to turn down the stern post. It was generally very difficult to get a good fit at that spot, and to make matters worse being at the after end of the ship it was also close to the big doors of the shop, which we would mostly require to be open, especially in the summer. If there was a very slight gap, this could increase in width rapidly before it was possible to caulk the seams; we used to try to overcome this by stopping the draught if possible.

The edges of the plank were always scrutinised by the plankmaker for fairness before he would take account of the plank to go next to it. Should there be any kind of unfairness in the edge he would place a little arris to suit the line on it and then chisel the plank back for fairness. This did not, however, need to be done very often. After this was done he could carry on preparing the next strake of planking.

When arriving at the bilges at least one bilge strake would have to be worked before a bilge ribband was removed. We would also work the first inside bilge stringer strake. Before a bilge ribband could be removed fresh bilge shores would have to be set up to the first bilge strakes and these would remain, except for caulking above one at a time, until the day the ship was listed for launching.

So the work would progress, with one little difference; the after piece of planking in each strake would be worked after end first and cut in on the next piece forward.

In the meantime work on the topside was progressing also. Although heavier, these planks were easier to work. In the first place one could work

in a standing position except right under the quarters of the vessel, and secondly there was not a great deal of shape or twist in the ship except under the stern, and as the turn was very gradual there was nothing difficult about working plank there.

When two strakes had been worked so the butts had been overlapped the ribbands could be removed, topside shores could be set and the crosspalls could be removed from the frames. It was now possible to rig the inside stages.

The leading hand on the topsides would decide on the level of these and strong oak spans would be nailed on the inside of two frames each side, at intervals to suit the length of the stage deals to be used, the oak spans being fastened with flatpoints or a spike with a washer under the head. Cross bearers made out of pieces of oak plank ripping would generally be used as bearers, being cut in and stood on edge on the spans and wedged in between frames, after which the stage of two deals would be laid right round the inside of the vessel.

There were four strakes of topsides, the bottom one three inches thick and the top three strakes four inches thick.

By this time the people working under the bottom would be drawing up close, until eventually there would be only the shutter left to work. This was a strake which would be fitted in between the bottom strake of the topsides and the last but one strake of the bottom planking.

For the shutter the plankmaker would get the lengths and stations on his batten, including the frame numbers as before, the difference this time being that he would take the distances between the top and bottom plank and write these on his bevel board. He would need to check on the bevels of these two planks to ensure that when the shutter was being worked it would tighten slightly as it was driven home.

Before taking the measurements he would have looked along the plank edges to see if they were fair. Should there be any unevenness he would have faired the outer corners of the aperture with his jack plane and would have chiselled any standing wood off.

All this matter would now be transferred to the chosen planks and a continuous line drawn over any marks shown, after which the plank would be taken into the mill and cut to the lines. These planks were cut on a circular saw, operated by Mr Frank Easter.

Mr Easter was a true countryman. He would tell some interesting stories on the "lore of the land" when he had a chance.

With the plank sawn it would be carried out to the stools, where the plank maker would fair it and seam it, after which it would be put in the "kel". When hot enough it would be removed from the "kel", taken into the shop

and passed up to the ship, entered at the fore end and then gradually hammered home by the shipwrights as they worked their way aft. It was not possible to get G-screws on this plank.

When using the maul on the shutter the plank itself would not be hit, another piece of short oak being held to the plank by one of the shipwrights. Should the plank be a little tight in any place it would be eased a little by the use of a chisel.

All the butts of the planks were cut about three-eighths of an inch from the centre of the frame, usually on the far side piece from the end of the plank, and this gave the butt seam a good backing for caulking.

While planking up was going on one would hear the sounds of a pair of G-screws crashing to the ground or on to the stage, the squeal of the bits and the clunck! clunck! clunck! of the face of a maul as it struck a bolt. One might hear, too, the sound of preparations being made for another plank to be worked, intermingled with whistling, singing or even swearing, and often, I am pleased to say, laughter. Some of these chaps were very droll and amusing, some witty—they really were—and it was a laughing happy atmosphere that pervaded the scene. I suppose you could say that I was happy at my work.

Shelves and stringers

The shelf was the only longitudinal stiffener on the inside of the vessel that was scarphed, other than the centre kelson. The scarph was two feet eleven inches in length, and cut with the top and bottom ends to the butts in the same way as the keel scarphs.

A first-class straight-grained piece of oak would be chosen for this component, as it could be very dainty to work. When selecting it the foreman would make sure that the first length, and therefore the scarph, would come well aft of the luff of the bow. If he possibly could, and it usually worked out that way, he would try to get both port and starboard pieces from one tree, in addition to which he would make sure that he got each side in three pieces.

When steaming it the shipwrights would ask for a little more steam pressure than usual. It would need to be pliable as it would require a bit of nursing to get it round safely. It had to be hauled up and over into the ship by means of a tackle, or handy billy as we used to call it.

The shelf would be chamfered on the bottom inside edge, and the fore end would need to be cut with two bevels to fit the apron.

The starboard side was the one usually worked first, partly because this was the nearest and therefore could be the hottest. Spans would have been

A plank is worked.

fastened on the inside of various pairs of frames, and pieces of plank ripping laid from the topsides on the port side down on to these spans which were fixed so that when the shelf was home it should be exactly in the right place, or at any rate needing very little adjustment to put it in the right place, that is four inches below sheer height.

Before actually working the shelf round into the ship a length of clean inch-and-a-quarter oak would be G-screwed on to the outside of it in the form of a lamination, as unlike the outside strakes, which would be pulled round from timber to timber and then supported by the cramps, the shelf has no support except the bearers on which it rests and slides until it reaches the vessel's side. When working the plank we would do it very gently and carefully, as if it was worked carelessly it could be very easily broken, bearing in mind that it was hot and soft.

It would be necessary to hold it forward to the apron, and this was done by using a light shifting cramp on the end of the scarph. Other cramps were put on over the topsides and shelf, and so the whole would be very gently hove home into its final position. Just before reaching home the laminating piece would have to be removed. It was generally with relief that it was seen to be home; by now it would have cooled down considerably and of course have started to harden.

The stringers were merely spiked to the frames, but became of its size the shelf was through bolted. The first part of the shelf was difficult to work because of the hull curvature, but the rest were easy as they had very easy bends.

The second piece would now be in the "kel" and the third piece on the stools. The fore scarphs on these would be marked out from a mould taken from the after scarph of the previous length. The after end of the third length would be tapered slightly and undercut; that is to say, it would have a little wood taken from the under lower side.

The scarphs were fastened by spikes at the top and bottom ends, while the body of the scarph was through bolted alternately from above and below, also through the ship's side, thus making a good sound job of the whole thing.

Below the shelf were placed two pitchpine or oak stringers, each of them ten by three inches, running the full length of the ship. Unlike the shelf, these were butted together and spiked as they were worked. Also unlike the shelf, they were comparatively easy and safe to work as being of pitch pine they were more resilient and there was less danger of the fore pieces giving as they were hove home.

Between the top and bottom stringers on every fifth frame a three-quarter-inch distance piece was placed. This had the effect of keeping the two pieces apart, allowing ventilation between the timbers. This gap had to be filled in in the way of the coal bunkers, for obvious reasons, and if this was not done fine coal which fell through the gap would work its way along to the pump sumps.

The crew themselves would block the apertures that occurred in the way of their bunks. This was understandable, as I expect the smell would be pretty vile at times.

We have now arrived at the stage where all through bolting could be completed, except for the various components which still have to be fitted as the work progresses.

Boring for through bolts when the planking up was finished and completing this bolting could sometimes be a dangerous business as one could not see inside the ship from the outside.

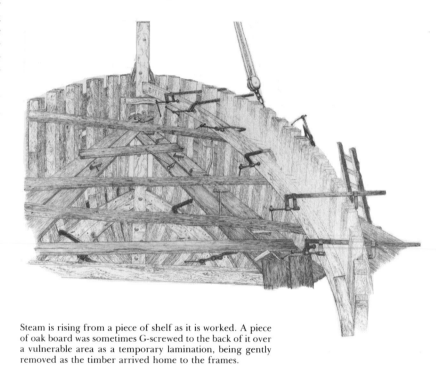

Steam is rising from a piece of shelf as it is worked. A piece of oak board was sometimes G-screwed to the back of it over a vulnerable area as a temporary lamination, being gently removed as the timber arrived home to the frames.

My uncle Mr Fred Rouse had the misfortune to have a bit enter his boot, continue right up between his toes, and come out of the top of his boot; this was a seven-sixteenths inch bit. He was working inside the ship in the bunker area, while one of my other uncles, Mr Tom Frost, also a shipwright, was boring for the bolts from the outside. Once the bit came through and penetrated the boot it was impossible for Fred Rouse to get away, and Uncle Tom, not knowing the bit was through because of boring into the boot, kept on boring. Two of Fred's toes were very badly cut.

It would only be possible to stop the man boring on the outside of the vessel by shouting to other people, in the hope that they would immediately realise what was happening and stop the hole borer quickly.

This sort of accident did not happen often as the bolts were usually driven as the work progressed.

It was also necessary at this stage to take extra care generally when working inside the ship, as by now there would be dozens of these pilot-pointed bolts sticking up in the ship either in butts or stringers, and if you slipped and fell on them a nasty injury could result.

I remember a miracle happening one day. "Treacle" Colby fell off the inside stage among these points and he never got a scratch; he missed them all.

In those days most of us wore heavy boots with plenty of nails in the sole in addition to heel irons, so it was an easy matter to slip on the hard oak.

Before leaving the planking up I would like to tell one little story which will give the reader an idea of the way some of these chaps' minds worked. When working planks, the ease with which they could be worked depended on the quantity and quality of the steam in the "kel", and on some days things would not go too well.

Now it was one of the duties of the old nightwatchman, John Blogg, to start the boiler fire at about 4 a.m. One day which had been particularly bad steam-wise he was spotted coming on duty and the shipwrights began to harangue the old chap, who could give no explanation of why the steam was bad. It was nothing to do with him, he said, failing to see that he was having his leg pulled.

All he could say was that he couldn't get the old varmint to start, referring to the fire.

"Well, John, was it the same water that was in the boiler yesterday?" asked one of the shipwrights, Charlie Castleton.

"Why yes", says John.

"Well," says Charlie, "No wonder we couldn't get any b----- steam, the steam was all biled outa that water yesterday!"

Ready for the beams.

Scrubbing down

With planking up completed, two other operations would be started, one of which was called scrubbing down.

For this purpose the whole length of the keel would have been marked off in nine or ten-foot lengths, depending on the number of people available. In between each pair of marks would be chalked the name of a man or boy who had taken part in the planking up. Each man or boy would be responsible for the scrubbing down and caulking of his own berth.

The tools needed for the job were adze, maul, punch, two or three handplanes, oil stone, oil feeder, hammer and screwdriver, these last two to adjust the plane iron and back iron. The first thing to do was to prepare the tools, as the complement per day scrubbed down would be seven strakes and a piece, the piece being say two inches on the bottom edge of the eighth plank.

The adze, and as many hand plane irons as one had, would be ground and one's maul would be checked to see that the wedging of the head was sound. There would also be a check on the withe punch, as through usage the heads of these tools could be expanded and rolled back, making the punch dangerous; a piece could fly off if not knocked or ground off beforehand.

Before starting on the actual job the bottom of the shop in the vicinity of the ship would have to be cleared of debris and rubbish left over from planking up.

The men worked in pairs to "punch up", the man in No. 1 berth swinging the maul to punch up his own bolts with the man from No. 2 berth holding the withe punch on the heads. Enough bolts would be punched up to enable the No. 1 man to complete a full day's complement, after which the No. 1 man would hold the punch on the bolt heads in No. 2 berth, with the No. 2 man swinging the maul.

Right round the ship the men co-operated in pairs, punching up and rigging stages, as these had to be adjusted on the way up the vessel's side. The men from the bottom scrubbed down and caulked all the way up to sheer height while the men who worked the topsides were now on other work, as I will explain in due course.

Punching up under the bottom was usually achieved by kneeling on one knee, with the body bent over sideways, and swinging the maul just clear of the ground; one had to give it a good powerful swing, of course, in order to move the bolt. It was not much use using a maul of less than six pounds in weight.

If one was a bit unsteady and missed the punch and hit the plank, and this also applied when driving the bolts, the maul face would leave an imprint. This was said to be writing one's name on the plank, a thing which everybody tried to avoid because of the embarrassment.

One thing that always seemed a little unfair to me was the fact that the men towards midships had a much larger area to plane than those towards the ends of the vessel, and a good deal of it had to be done in adverse conditions. Even so I never heard anybody complain; I don't suppose many of them gave it a thought.

With the heads of the bolts punched up (we used to reckon about three-eighths clearance to be enough) trimming could be started and any projecting edges would be trimmed off. Trimming was comparatively easy as when using the adze the arms would be lowered a bit, but it was a different matter when one started to plane the plank as one would have to force the plane upwards and forwards. Oak is a hard and at times a coarse timber, so one would have to work really hard at it, and we used to make it a bit easier for ourselves by using the adze carefully when trimming.

Almost all of us used a Gilpin No. 2 adze. Anything smaller than this was virtually useless as we depended on the weight of the tool to help with the cutting, any adze larger than the No. 2 we would have found a bit akward, I think.

Sometimes one would come across a bit of crossgrain in the plank, and this might mean turning the adze and aiming it upwards directly at your own face. Should a tiny chip be left hanging from a previous blow it could deflect the edge of the adze, perhaps with dire consequences, if one was not very careful. I remember this happening to Mr Charles Cator, one of my fellow apprentices, when working on Chambers No. 1 yard at Lowestoft; his adze slipped over a chip and cut the bridge of his nose very badly.

The first day under the bottom was the worst; the next day you would be eight strakes away from the keel and able to work in a more relaxed position. And so onward we would go punching, trimming and planing, until at last you could see a vast difference in the appearance of the ship. What a transformation! Now she looks really something!

Some people could work faster than others, which sometimes created a problem when it came to raising stages. It would be better for all if the stages could be reorganized in unison, but this was not always possible.

One compensating factor about the job, to my mind, was the lovely aroma of the cut oak.

The difference in appearance of the vessel's planking before and after being scrubbed down.

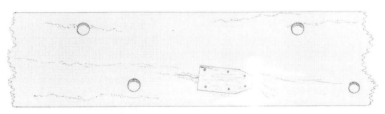

The appearance of a knot before and after squareberthing.

Square berthing

A short while after "scrubbing down" had started one of the older shipwrights would be detailed off for square berthing. This consisted of inspecting all planks for previously undetected faults, which would have become plainly visible once the planks had been planed.

Should the square berther see a bad knot, for instance, he would chisel out an area which extended to just beyond the edges of the knot and to a depth of about five-eighths of an inch, plug the knot if necessary, and then fit a piece of oak after spreading white lead on the bottom of the cut. The new piece would be fastened with galvanised cut nails, punched down, and the projecting wood trimmed off and planed up neatly.

Should the square berther see a good knot with a crack, usually in the form of a cross, in the centre of it, he would caulk it with a little caulking cotton using a spike iron and hand mallet. This would later be payed up with pitch.

Any unused bolt holes would most probably be pointed out to the shipwright in whose berth he was working, and the shipwright would drive the bolt unless it had been left out for any specific reason. The square berther would also be looking to see if any fastening had been forgotten, and if he found any he would call the shipwright's attention to it; most probably he would bore and drive them himself if he was not too pushed.

The hull would be scrutinised most carefully at this stage as this would be the last chance to put right any omissions. Any shakes that were seen would be done by the square berther, unless he thought that any of these should be left to the shipwright.

A shipwright who was known to be pretty thorough at his work, usually an elderly man, would be chosen for this job. Such a man was "Uncle" Jimmy Capps, a nice old chap with a strawberry complexion, a little white beard and a happy nature. He always wore a peaked cap and a carnation in his buttonhole in the evening and on Sundays. I suppose it was his cheery nature that earned him the nickname of "Uncle" throughout the port. He was from one of the very old Beach families of Lowestoft, and although a shipwright he was often in the crew of the pulling and sailing lifeboat when he was a younger man. Jimmy never knew what it was to be shipmates with one of them new-fangled engines.

The square berther worked by himself and attended to both sides of the ship.

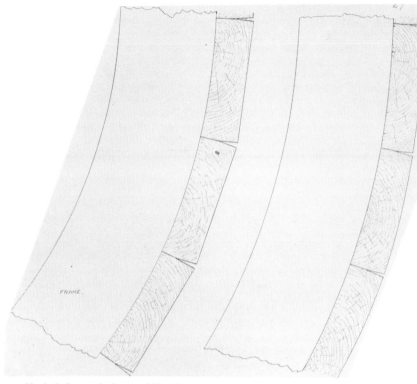

Planks before and after scrubbing down.

Caulking

With the scrubbing down completed, preparations would be put in hand for caulking the vessel down. The bottom of the shop would again be cleared of chips, shavings and other debris, which would be placed near to the pitch pot, not far from the shop and near the river bank.

46

The temporary staging that had been used for scrubbing down would be brought down to ground level again, the scrubbing down gear would be put away into our tool boxes and the caulking gear brought out. There would be a general overhaul of caulking mallets, adjustment and setting on of rings mostly, and a certain amount of trimming up of caulking irons. It was better to see that all one's gear was in working order since, as with the previous job, it was to be hoped that the stages could be raised more or less in unison.

The same man who had scrubbed down a berth would be the one to caulk it and pay it up. The men would work at slightly different speeds, but it was possible for all of them to reach the complement per day, which was ninety feet. The amount to be done per day must have been arrived at with the slower men in mind; men like "Maggie" Rouse could finish the complement quite easily.

Each shipwright would have prepared himself for spinning the oakum by getting a piece of old canvas tarpaulin about two feet by one which he would wrap around his knee and the top part of his leg to protect his dungarees from the Stockholm tar in the oakum. It was essential to keep the oakum clean, so in one corner of the shop a rough board floor had been laid, with a rough seat or form nailed round by the walls.

The oakum would be brought into the shop in bales of about three-quarters of a hundredweight, surrounded by wooden battens kept in place by a tightly fastened wire. When the bales were being opened there would be a rush for the battens by the pigeon fanciers among the shipwrights.

The shipwrights would be seated around the floor either on the form or on their own individual caulking boxes according to preference, each with oakum from the bale tucked under the left arm. They would begin to tease the oakum out by gentle tugs with the right hand, rolling the material backwards and forwards between hand and right knee, at the same time feeding it forward with the left hand.

Eventually a long continuous thread of oakum about one-and-a-quarter to one-and-a-half inches in diameter would be formed, and this they dropped into an old paint drum which had been burnt out clean or into an old apple barrel.

Spinning would start at 6 a.m. and continue until breakfast at 8 a.m. After two hours' spinning (and, I might add, yarning, as this was a job that didn't need a great deal of mental concentration) enough oakum would have been spun to cover a good deal of the day's work; a little more might be spun later in the day.

After breakfast a start would be made, some oakum having been put into the men's oil boxes and saturated with engine oil taken from a can brought in by one of the young lads. This oil was sometimes hard to obtain, but one

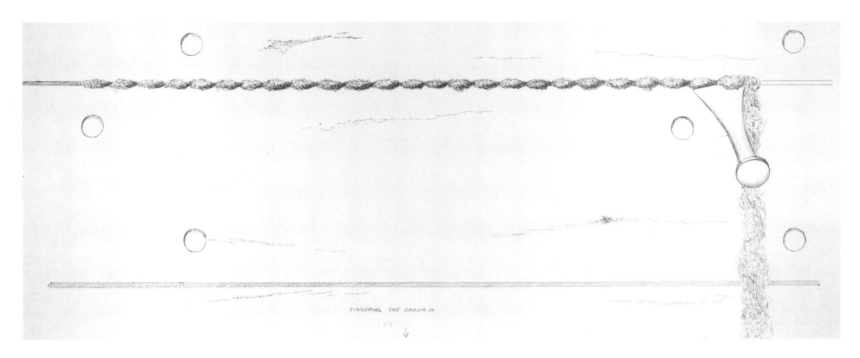

FINGERING THE OAKUM IN

Fingering the oakum in.

could not caulk without lubricating the caulking irons at intervals to prevent the Stockholm tar in the oakum sticking to the irons. An oil box would be cut out of a solid piece of beech generally. I believe that years ago they could be a bit more elaborate.

While two or three threads depending on the seam was the order of the day overside, it was generally reckoned to try to caulk three or more into the garboard. The complement for the days' work was ninety feet; nine seams would be expected caulked and payed up, if one was caulking a ten-foot berth.

Right under the bottom the shipwright would be on one knee to finger the oakum into the garboard seam and the next two or three seams. To do the rest he could perhaps sit on his caulking box as the floor of the ship began to rise. Fingering the oakum into the seam consisted of pushing in the oakum in a series of tight little loops, and this was done by picking up enough

oakum between the forefinger of your left hand and the caulking iron, then giving the iron a short sharp tap with the caulking mallet for each loop to jam it in. The blade of the caulking iron was held in the left hand between finger and thumb, bringing the head of the iron close to the underside of one's wrist, the mallet being held in the right hand.

Some men would like to caulk in good lengths, even the length of the berth, while others would do it in shorter lengths. Either way, one had to ensure continuity of the thread.

Under the bottom one could work with one knee on the ground and head bent over to enable one to get as high as possible. To drive the oakum up into the seam one would have to get a good swing on the mallet and slam it on to the iron; and to give you some idea of the swing, it was possible at times to hit the ship's bottom at the end of the back stroke.

If for some reason or other you did manage to hit your wrist with the edge

47

of the mallet hoop it would leave you with a nasty aching bruise. This sort of thing used to happen more towards the end of the day, when one was tiring. With the first thread in one would usually open the next seam above and then go back to the first seam for the next thread. It was when the oakum was being made in that the heaviest blows would be made.

When one came to the extreme end of the berth it would be necessary to continue for at least four inches into your neighbour's berth. If he had been there first you would find that he had caulked four inches in your own, but in any case you would caulk over this and into his berth.

When starting a seam or ending one, if no work had been done on either side of it one would leave a piece of the thread hanging. This "tail" was an indication to your neighbour that you had already caulked that thread into that seam. With another thread there would be two tails, and so on; but however many it was, one would caulk them in and then overrun with one's own work and thus ensure continuity.

When it came to butts one would turn up the butt seam, go right up through the butt, then turn into the original direction for several inches in the seam above. Some would go the full length remaining of the berth, then start again at the other end of the berth, turn down through the butt again and along the seam below.

If a fresh seam was found to be very tight, as was sometimes the case, it would have to be opened with the reaming iron, which was made expressly for this purpose. This iron was simply a steel wedge which forced the seam open.

After the threads had been caulked in a crease iron could be used. This would take in any loose hairs and leave the oakum regulated as in the crease of a pair of trousers. The crease irons were in several sizes and were used according to the width of the seam. The oakum would be "made in" about a quarter of an inch from the outside edge of the plank with making irons.

Before going on to paying up we used to horse the garboard up using a horse iron, which was held by a steel "withe" in the hand of the shipwright from the neighbouring berth while you struck it hard with a large hooped mallet called a beetle. As with the punching up each shipwright would take his turn, but it was customary for you to use the beetle when horsing up your own berth. At that period the garboard was regarded as being very important indeed.

When caulking our clothes would gradually become impregnated with the smell of Stockholm tar. This was the aroma in which we worked, and to my nostrils at any rate it was a lovely smell. It was not very long before I learned of the healing properties of Stockholm tar; whenever we suffered a cut or graze on the hand we would wrap either spun yarn or oakum round the wound and then it would heal very quickly.

Before paying up could be started the chargehand shipwright, Billy Coleman, would test the garboard and the butts of the work that newcomers had done, using his own mallet and iron. All the berths of the apprentices would be examined, more especially the berth of an apprentice who had never caulked over the side before; "over the side" being the expression used when discussing any aspect of caulking the vessel's hull. Should he detect any softness he would mark the area with chalk on each side of the seam and would see that this was put right before he would allow the caulker to pay up.

It would be an affront to the older shipwrights to test their berths.

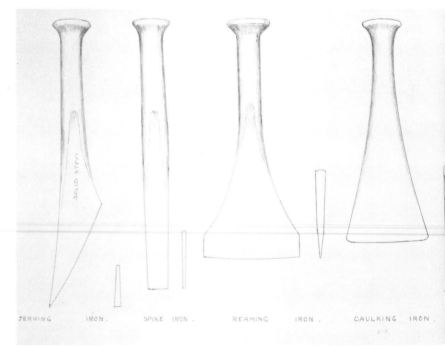

JERRING IRON. SPIKE IRON. REAMING IRON. CAULKING IRON.

A caulking mallet of lignum vitae, with its shaft of hickory. The mallet would weigh about five pounds complete with shaft. On the far right is an oil box, with a section of the box through its middle.

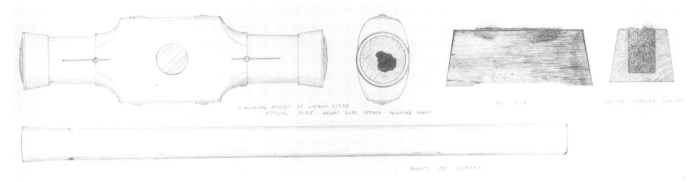

CAULKING MALLET OF LIGNUM VITAE
ACTUAL SIZE WEIGHT 5LBS. APPROX INCLUDING SHAFT

OIL BOX

SECTION THROUGH CENTRE

SHAFT OF HICKORY

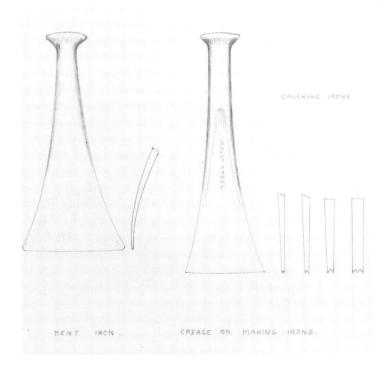

CAULKING IRONS

BENT IRON.

CREASE OR MAKING IRONS.

One disconcerting thing that used to happen at times was that after several hours of holding one's arms overhead and slogging away, for that is what it was, the caulking iron would drop a little and by the time your mallet hit it the iron could be in such a position as to cut the edge of the seam. This was bad and unsightly, and everybody did their best to avoid this.

By the time you reached the bilge you would be standing and the job would be transformed. It would be a pleasure, if such work can be pleasurable, to be one of the shipwrights caulking the ship's hull. One thing you could not avoid noticing when caulking was the sharp "clink", "clink" of the caulking mallets, which are mostly made of lignum vitae. There seemed to be a bit of prestige in having a good mallet; the "clink" was called "ringing". A really good mallet would have its slits just right; there were two holes through the mallet, one on each side of the shaft, and slits cut away from these which would help the mallet to ring. Tapered hoops for the mallet were better than the parallel hoops that were sometimes used, as they were lighter and more sleek.

If one had a good mallet one would take pride in this, keeping it polished and oiled. By and large one's caulking gear was well looked after; when not in use the irons would be cleaned and oiled, then wrapped in canvas and stowed away in the caulking box, which was used to sit on when one was between kneeling and standing over the side or when caulking on deck.

Clinking or clenching through bolts

With the completion of scrubbing down, "clinking" as it was called could be started, as by this time all through bolts used in fastening would have been put in and punched up. Two or three of the younger boys would have

49

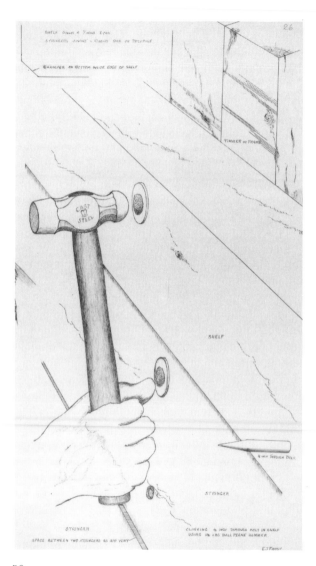

Clinking a half-inch through bolt in shelf using a one-and-a-half-pound ball pein hammer.

been detailed off to clink or clench these while the caulking of the vessel was in progress.

Clinking entailed putting a half-inch galvanized washer over the point of the bolt, which would be sticking up into the vessel about two-and-a-half inches, ensuring that the washer was down on to the timber or stringer; then with a hammer and cold chisel one would start to cut the bolt off by cutting into it all the way round, and when cut sufficiently one could knock it backwards and forwards and so break it off; after that one would use the ball pein of the hammer to clink it, striking the bolt continuously and expanding it over the washer—one would use a circular motion when doing this and by so doing expand it evenly. When the "clink" was big enough we would use the face of the hammer to finish it off.

On occasion one would come across a crystalised bolt which would shatter and fly when being hammered. When this happened we found that smearing a little grease on the metal would help the bolt to lend itself to the clinking process. Why this was so I do not know.

Compo

One other job would have to be done between scrubbing down and paying up, and this was filling the reamed space left over the bolt heads with cement and sand compo. This was flushed up to the surface of the plank, and when the ship was completed you would have a difficult job to see where the bolt heads were. This mixture of sand, cement and water was of about the same consistency as that used for bricklaying today.

The job would be done by some of the semi-skilled hands from the mill, usually in the evenings, on Saturday afternoons and sometimes on Sundays. The material would be pressed in over the bolthead by means of a small trowel sometimes known as a spud trowel and then flushed up. It was essential that the job was done before paying up.

Paying up

We are now ready to pay up, so we will go along to the pitch pot for the pitch. The pitch in the pot would be bubbling hot, one of the younger apprentices having been sent along to light the fire under the pot, which was like a huge copper standing on four legs, earlier in the day. Wood scraps, chips and shavings cleared from the bottom of the shop would provide plenty of fuel. A large sheet of thin iron plate would be used as a lid to the pot; it was essential to keep rain from the boiling pitch as even a drop of water falling on to it would cause a minor explosion.

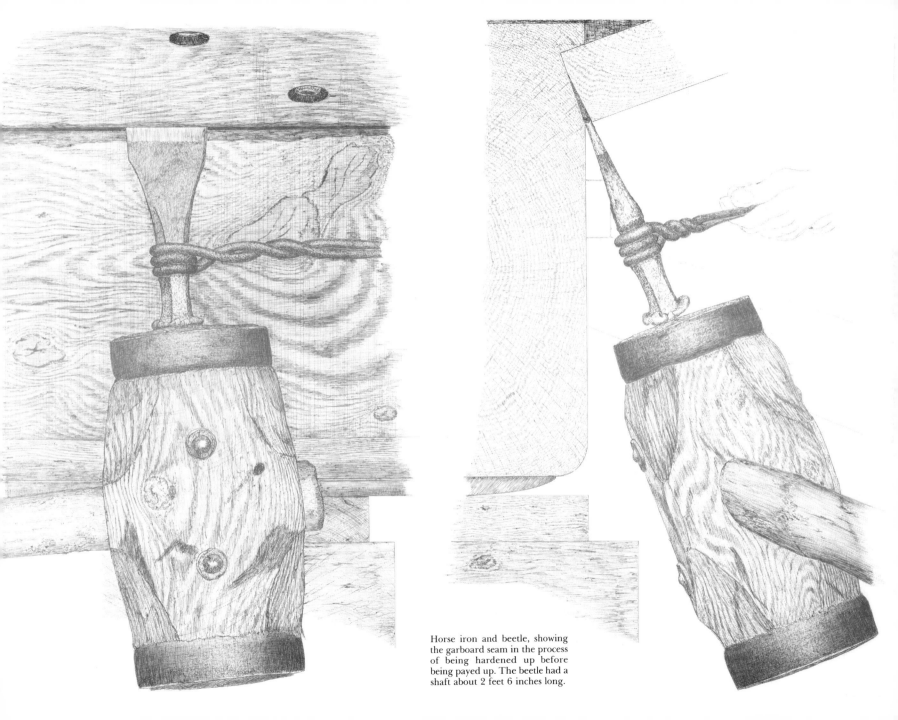

Horse iron and beetle, showing the garboard seam in the process of being hardened up before being payed up. The beetle had a shaft about 2 feet 6 inches long.

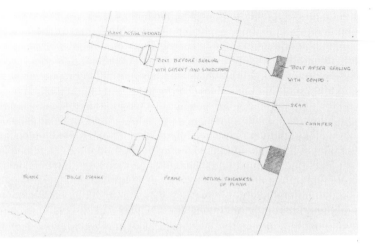

Top left labels: PLANK ACTUAL THICKNESS · BOLT BEFORE SEALING WITH CEMENT AND SAND COMPO · BOLT AFTER SEALING WITH COMPO · SEAM · CHAMFER · FRAME · BILGE STRAKE · FRAME · ACTUAL THICKNESS OF PLANK

It would usually be about mid-afternoon when paying up started. We would make our way to the pitch pot, which would be bubbling, pick out a clean bucket (the boy would have burned some of them out) and then choose a medium used mop, which was the means by which we would get the pitch into the seam. We would try to avoid a new mop as these would be messy. One thing we used to vie with each other in, was paying up as cleanly as possible. We would try, too, not to get a badly used one or too small a one; a half-worn one was the best.

By the pot would be a large cup-shaped ladle on a long handle, and with this we would fill the bucket of our choice with the boiling pitch, then hurry off into the shop, scramble under the bottom, get down on our knees again and begin the actual paying up, plunging the mop into the pitch and saturating it, then lifting it to the seam and pushing the mop backwards and forwards vigorously, at the same time giving the handle a twist back and forth with the wrist; this had the effect of forcing the hot pitch up into the seam, where in seconds it would be cooling, consolidating. One would try to

The pitch mop and bucket used in paying up. The mop had a handle about 3 feet 6 inches long.

Top left: A section of the bilge and side planking showing bolts before and after sealing with cement and sand compo.

Opposite: The pitch pot. The pitch mops and ladles were kept in the little brick building, known as "the pot shop", which was used also by the night watchman.

'THE PITCH POT'

do this work as effectively and cleanly as possible, but it had to be done quickly.

When we had finished we would return the mop and bucket to the pitch pot, where the boy would attend to it as he began his preparations for the next day. Some of the boys, especially during the winter, would pop some potatoes into the pot, where they would soon roast; and with a little salt, by golly! they were lovely!

On occasion the pitch pot would catch fire. My goodness! The flames and smoke were terrific when that happened, but we used to overcome that by placing the thin plate over it—and if flames still flickered round the edges we would throw over it wet sacks which we used to keep lying handy for this purpose.

After paying up, should there still be some time before knocking off time, we would adjourn to the spinning corner and spin oakum until five o'clock in readiness for the morrow's complement.

Scraping

After paying up the surplus pitch would have to be scraped off the plank. Once again the men from the sawmill and any other of the few labourers who cared to would come along to do the job after working hours; the overtime money would be very acceptable.

A good bit of preparation would have to be made, especially during the summer, when the skin of the face and hands would get hot and without some precaution the pitch dust would stick to the skin. The men would wear their oldest or most worn dungarees, wristbands and trouser leg bottoms would have spunyarn tied round to prevent the pitch dust getting up sleeves or trousers, wrappers (or as they would be called today, scarves) would be put round the neck. A liberal supply of river mud would be smeared on the face and hands, so that at the end of the day when the mud was washed off the pitch dust would come off with it. A red handkerchief would be draped round the face, particularly over the nostrils.

The tools that the men would use for scraping were usually worn-out flat files which had been flattened and expanded at the end and then bent over at right angles about one-and-a-half inches from the end. They were used by pressing the sharpened end to the vessel's hull and pulling it along over the plank, scraping the pitch off.

One-third of the vessel would be done from a kneeling position under the hull, working overhead. The whole operation would be done as neatly as possible, and when the job was complete the vessel would be ready for the first coat of tar.

54

This is how the seams appeared after paying up and after the excess pitch had been scraped off with a file scraper hooked at the end.

Tools

The first tools that an apprentice bought would be a hammer and cold chisel, and these would be followed later by a saw, jackplane and one or two handplanes, although sometimes one of the men would make a boy one of these. Mr Horry Jenner made my first one for me and this I still have. Later the apprentice would acquire a ratchet brace, a bit or two and a shipwright's bevel.

Possibly after this would come an adze, then would come the maul, generally second-hand as the newer types did not seem to balance properly. There was a source of supply of these in Lowestoft which were perfectly made and very cheap; I have never seen them beaten for shape, size, or durability. To follow on would most probably be the caulking mallet and a set of caulking irons. When buying the mallet of lignum vitae it would be necessary to get one of the shipwrights to help you to chose it. We preferred one which had some heart in it, the very dark green wood.

The irons would be jerring iron or jerry iron as we called it, reaming iron, caulking iron, bent iron, spike iron, one-eighth-inch crease iron, three-sixteenth crease iron, and a quarter-inch double crease.

We would make our own caulking box, usually from a piece of ceiling stuff, this was three-quarter by seven-inch planed all round deal, and we would make an oil box, usually from a piece of beech. An oilstone would also be needed, and for our purpose carborundum was the best.

We usually bought our tools from Frosts of Norwich, and their representative would come to the yard monthly to collect money from us for the tools that had been supplied. It was amazing what some of the boys would get up to in order to avoid meeting him, especially if they had already spent the money their mother or father had given to them for this purpose. They would either disappear into the dunnican, as the toilet was called, or hide in some other place. On one occasion Sammy went up on to the roof of the shop, where he concealed himself between the two pitched roofs, and there he stayed until he received the tipoff that the coast was clear.

I have a 1912 catalogue from Melluish, of Fetter Lane, London, from which I will quote some prices: Hammer 1s. 6d., chisel 10d., 26" straight backed handsaw 5s. 6d., skew backed handsaw 7s., smoothing planes 3s. 6d. to 4s. 6d., Jack plane 5s., best quality 10 inch English ratchet brace 6s., boring bits 1/4" 10d., 1 1/2" 2s. 6d., shipwright's bevel 1s. 3d., a No. 2. Gilpin adze 2s. 9d., adze helve 9d., oil stone 4s. 3d., shipwright's maul 7d. per pound, lignum vitae caulking mallet 4s. 3d., white bright steel caulking tools, straight 1s., single crease 1s. 1d., double crease 1s. 2d., handsaw file 3d., double-ended file 6d., reamer gimlet 1s. 2d., hammer handle 2 1/2d., and a

hickory maul shaft is shown as costing 6d. Prices rose only slowly between 1912 and 1916 but quite fast thereafter.

By today's standards it is most surprising how many tools could be bought for a few shillings. I have a small school gardening notebook in which I kept a record of some tools that I bought in 1916; there were fourteen tools, the total cost of which was £1 11s. 8d.

		£	s.	d.
May 23rd	1 pair pincers.		1.	8.
May 23rd	1 boat bevel.		1.	2.
June 7th	1 4 1/2" handsaw file.			5.
June 7th	1 carborundum stone.		3.	3.
June 7th	1 spike iron.		1.	3.
June 7th	1 reaming iron.		1.	7.
June 7th	1 sharp iron.		1.	3.
June 7th	1 bent iron.		1.	4.
June 7th	1 1/8" crease iron.		1.	3.
June 7th	1 3/16" crease iron.		1.	6.
June 7th	1 1/16" crease iron.		1.	4.
June 18th	ratchet brace.		7.	0.
June 18th	1 cold chisel.		1.	3.
June 18th	1 compass saw.		1.	11.
June 18th	1 caulking mallet and shaft.		5.	6.
	Total	£1.	11.	8.

The bits which we used when planking up were usually bought from a private source, if I remember rightly somebody in Hull. These had been made in Germany and were superior to anything that we could buy in Lowestoft at that time. The bits that we used for through bolts were from the same source. Should a bit need lengthening one of our blacksmiths would do it for us; we would ask him to "lay it on" for us, specifying the length required.

Other tools that a boy would need were chisels. An ordinary one-inch firmer chisel was priced at 9d., a nest of compass saws with handle at 2s. 9d., while a marking gauge would cost 8d.

The augers used by everybody were for the most part owned by the firm. With the advent of the standard drifters many new augers were bought, and among them were a good few screw augers which had never been very much sought after before.

All cramps, G-screws and shifters belonged to the firm.

FRAME

SECTION THRU
SHEER STRAKE

SHEER BATTEN

NOTCHER

DISTANCE
PIECE

SHEER BATTEN
RIBAND BATTEN (HATCHING)

CAULKING AND PAYING UP

E J FROST

Sheer batten

After scrubbing down was completed it was possible for the topside people to hang the sheer batten round the vessel—for the second time.

Hutchiks were nailed on the top strake far enough down to allow for the depth of the sheer batten to sit above the nail, with at least a half-inch clearance to allow for adjustment between nail and top of plank. The batten, in three pieces or lengths on each side of the ship, was of pitch pine half-inch by three inches, painted grey and used over and over again.

This time round it would be hung by the shipwrights with the top edge at TH mark, from a quarter to a half-inch from the top outside edge of the top strake. A distance piece would be placed between the plank and the hutchik and the brad driven home, after which adjustments would be made and the line faired in by eye by the shipwrights on the job; when completed a message would be sent to the foreman shipwright that he was wanted to "look" the sheer in. The batten would then be looked at from every angle. It is impossible to see the sheer of a vessel from close alongside, so whoever is looking the sheer in along the top edge of the batten would have to be as far away as was practicable. To make this possible ladders were placed against the walls of the shop at strategic points.

The foreman would use the ladders and various other vantage points, contorting himself into some strange positions at times, while beckoning or waving away the shipwright on the job (who would all the time be trying to keep below the line of vision) either to tap the batten up a little or to tap it down a little. This went on until after a while it was faired right round the ship to the foreman's satisfaction. Then and only then was the line quickly pencilled in before the batten could be disturbed.

With the completion of the line, the battens would be carefully taken down from the ship and put back on the rack provided for them, on which they were laid flat.

Shipwrights would now use a jack plane to plane an arris on the top corner of the sheer strake down to the pencilled-in line, leaving it permanently marked.

Knightheads and stanchions

After the sheerline had been finalised and clearly defined by the use of the plane, everything done to the vessel above the line would be done in relation to it. Those things which were to be fitted down such as beams, knightheads and stanchions were all fitted and fastened in relation to the sheerline.

The knightheads were of oak, four and a half inches by one foot ten inches by five feet; and, if the timber would allow, a little longer. One of the cant frames might possibly have to be trimmed to receive the knighthead, which would be dropped in between topsides, shelf and stringers, leaving at least two feet above the sheer line. Packings were fitted between the knighthead, or bollard timber as it was called years ago, and the shelf and stringers, after which the whole would be through bolted.

One of the functions of knightheads in sailing ships was to resist the crosspull of the bowsprit. In a drifter it strengthened the bow rail and carried the hawsepipe. The fore and after sides of the timber and also the inner face were planed above deck level, a half-inch bead being put on the inner corners.

The stanchions, also of oak, five inches by four-and-a-half inches at sheer height and four-and-a-half inches by four-and-a-half inches at rail height, were also planed on the fore and after sides together with the inner corners. The stanchions were also left two feet above the sheer line.

The stanchions varied in shape below the sheer line, more especially at the after end of the vessel, each unit being moulded out individually. Shipwrights would plane and bead the top ends of the stanchions unless the joiners were short of work, when the joiners would do it. Shipwrights fitted and fastened them, whatever the case, our own workforce usually taking about two-and-a-half days on the job altogether.

The stanchion would extend about three feet below sheer line into the ship. In relation to the vessel itself the stanchions would be square with the

Moulding out stanchions.

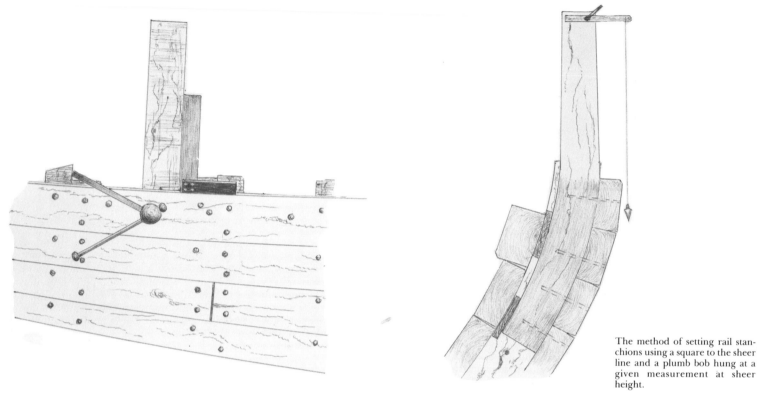

The method of setting rail stanchions using a square to the sheer line and a plumb bob hung at a given measurement at sheer height.

sheer, and thwartships leaning slightly inboard to a given dimension. Odd stanchions would be set up along the ship's side at their stations, a batten would be secured to them at rail height and the intermediate stanchions would then be set up at their stations to the batten, which would have been faired.

Methods of fitting stanchions varied considerably from yard to yard. On our own yard we would fit the stanchions into the ship before anything else was fitted after the sheer line had been defined. As a consequence of this we could see to fit the stanchions snug to the side of the ship, and this method was also better for fitting the packings though it meant that later on the covering board would have to be fitted in and around the stanchions. At Sam Richards' yard at Lowestoft they would fit the stanchions after the covering

board, which meant that a hole had to be cut through the covering board to accommodate the stanchions. When using Richards' method it would be difficult to see if the stanchion was fitting the ship's side properly, and I personally preferred our own method. I believe that on Colby's yard stanchions were dropped through the covering board; Mr Jack Colby had been foreman shipwright at Richards at one time and evidently preferred their method.

The stanchions were secured by using three dump bolts, so that in the event of a stanchion having to be replaced through damage no other fastening would have to be disturbed.

The stanchions were at approximately three-foot centres, according to timber or frame spacing, except that from abreast of the foremast aft for about one-quarter of the ship's length they would be at about half that spacing. Because of the sheer any water that came aboard collected in this area, putting a fairly considerable outboard pressure on the bulwark, hence the need for closing the stanchions together.

Another reason for increasing the number of stanchions in this area was to resist pressure from other vessels when a large number of boats were trying to get up to the market at the same time, with their engines running full ahead and with a rope ashore on a bollard and round the ship's capstan with the steam turned on. A steel boat with a flaring bow could exert a great deal of pressure on one or two stanchions, due to her own curvature, hence the need for additional strength in the wooden vessel. There were a number of market inspectors, uniformed men employed by the Great Eastern Railway, whose job it was to try to direct the movement of the vessels, but among the skippers were those who did not wish to be so directed, and so it would become almost impossible for drifters already at market and who had finished landing to go astern to get out. To help overcome this difficulty the inspectors were armed with a small axe which they carried in a belt in much the same way as a fireman would carry his, and in the event of a skipper refusing to give way the inspector would jump down on to the lower landing, where the bollards were situated, and chop away the rope of the offending vessel; after this was done it would be almost impossible for the vessel to get up to the market by engine power alone. As I have said, it was a fantastic sight some days.

Beams

The oak beams were moulded out by the foreman or chargehand shipwright. They had to be chosen very carefully from the timber available, and were cut usually on the frame saw from timber previously sided for this purpose. After cutting they would be brought into the shop.

To set them out on the vessel it would be necessary to lay plank rippings or pieces of ribband across the vessel at intervals of about eight feet to support the beam batten on to which the beam spacing had been picked up off the mould loft floor. The batten was made up from three separate overlapping battens laid on the centre line of the ship, with the fore end of the fore piece touching the after side of the apron at sheer height.

The main hatch beams were seven inches wide by six inches deep in the centre, and the camber on these gave the sheer line in the middle of the ship, which was less than the sheer on the topsides. There was less camber on the underside of the beam, so they were tapered off to five inches at the ends, allowing approximately an inch cutaway on the shelf.

All the other beams and half-beams were cut to the same camber relatively. The centre dimension was six inches by five inches, and then five inches by five inches as these beams progressively became shorter and were spaced more closely.

There were only two big beams near the middle of the vessel, together with one steel or iron beam as we called it. These withstood most of the squeezing to which the boat was subjected when in dock. There was one more iron beam right across the ship in the space between boiler and engine. All the rest of the beams in the hold, the boiler and engine spaces were half-beams, which together with the deck formed a horizontal longtitudinal stiffener.

The main hatch beams on which the main hatch coamings would be fitted

A race knife, used to line out timber. It would leave a very small groove in the surface of the timber.

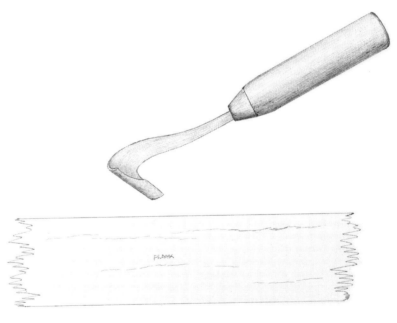

PLANK

59

and fastened would be fitted first. Before fitting, each beam would be laid on stools on the ground to be chamfered. The chamfer would be put on the two bottom corners of the beam unless there was a bulkhead to be fastened to one side of the beam, in which case only one chamfer would be put on. The chamfer would be "drawn by", as we put it, in pencil say to half an inch, after which it would be trimmed by adze and then planed by jack plane, stopping about three inches from the shelf by turning the ends of the chamfer outwards.

The length, bevels, position of shelf seating, and any fitting marks round timbers would all be set out on a mould extending the width of the vessel or alternatively on a batten with a board at each end. This would be taken down to the beam, the marks would be transferred and the beam would be cut accordingly.

When the beam was fitted it would sit on the shelf with the camber at sheer height, leaving four inches on the shelf and a lip of about one-and-a-quarter inches extending downwards on the inside of the shelf. It would have been cut to fit, and fit it nearly always did; usually very little would need to be done to make it fit after it had been hove on board and manoeuvred into position, though sometimes one would have to do a little sawing or chiseling.

Usually the fore main hatch beam would be fitted first. Marks would have been horned from the centre of the apron, at sheer height and on to the shelf, and when fitted this beam would be perfectly square with the centre line of the ship, to which all the other beams would be adjusted.

The beams would be fitted down on to the shelf so that the camber at the ends coincided with the sheer line. To make sure that it did, a straight edge would be run out over the end of the beam on to the line. There would not be enough visible camber on the end of the beam for this not to work. Usually a straight-backed handsaw would be used for this purpose; a saw cut would be made across any standing wood on the sheer strake down to the sheer line, the back of the saw being laid in the cut.

When in position the beam was completely self supporting, having been moulded out with a greater depth in the centre of it with that object in view. It would be fastened by two pilot-pointed bolts driven down through it into the shelf on which it rested, and later a knee would be fitted at each end of it. The main hatch beam would later also have an iron knee fitted from the underside of it to the vessel's side.

As the beams became shorter fore and aft, and also of smaller scantling, it was possible to heave them aboard the ship and mark them for cutting at the exact position for which they were destined. They were hove on board by means of a tackle hooked into a sling chain slung round a spar bearing on the roof trusses.

60

Should a beam come between timbers it would be cut half an inch short of the vessel's side at each end.

In addition to the wooden beams there were two metal beams which we spoke of as iron beams, though actually they were of steel, "T"-bar in section of half-inch thickness, six inches across the flat by four-and-a-half inches in depth. They were fitted in the way of the boiler as oak beams would have suffered from the heat. These beams rested on top of the shelf, with the flanges of the "T" fitted down into fillings which came flush with the camber. The iron beams were also fastened by pilot-pointed bolts driven down into the shelf, the holes in the flange having been countersunk to fit the underside of the head, leaving the heads flush.

One of the beams crossed the ship fore side of the boiler, while the other was located between boiler and engine, placed in each case so as not to impede the fitting of either engine or boiler.

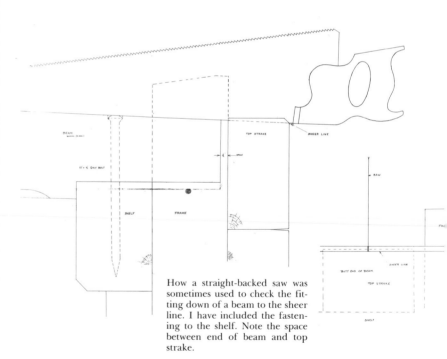

How a straight-backed saw was sometimes used to check the fitting down of a beam to the sheer line. I have included the fastening to the shelf. Note the space between end of beam and top strake.

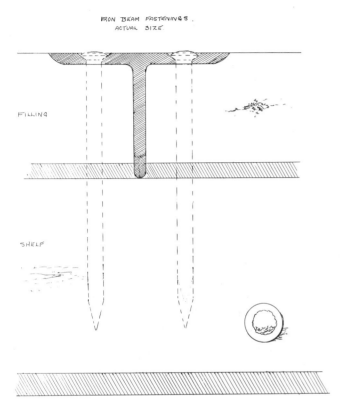

FILLING

SHELF

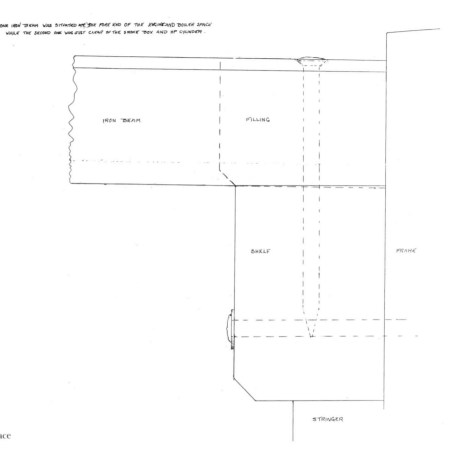

ONE IRON BEAM WAS SITUATED AT THE FORE END OF THE ENGINE AND BOILER SPACE
WHILE THE SECOND ONE WAS JUST CLEAR OF THE SMOKE BOX AND HP CYLINDER.

IRON BEAM

FILLING

SHELF

FRAME

STRINGER

Iron beam fastenings. One iron beam was situated at the fore end of the engine and boiler space and the second one was just clear of the smokebox and HP cylinder.

Breasthook, knees and fillings

With the completion of the fitting of the main beams two or three apprentices would be set to work on the breasthook and knees. These were of oak selected for shape and angle from the stuff available. They would be sided four inches.

The breasthook would need to be taken from a good crutch or crook in the tree, and the boy on the job would first of all make a mould which would embrace the after side of the apron and the inside faces of the knightheads and any timbers in the area. He would take all relevant bevels and mark them on the mould at the point at which they were taken, after which he would go in search of the chargehand shipwright, who would choose a

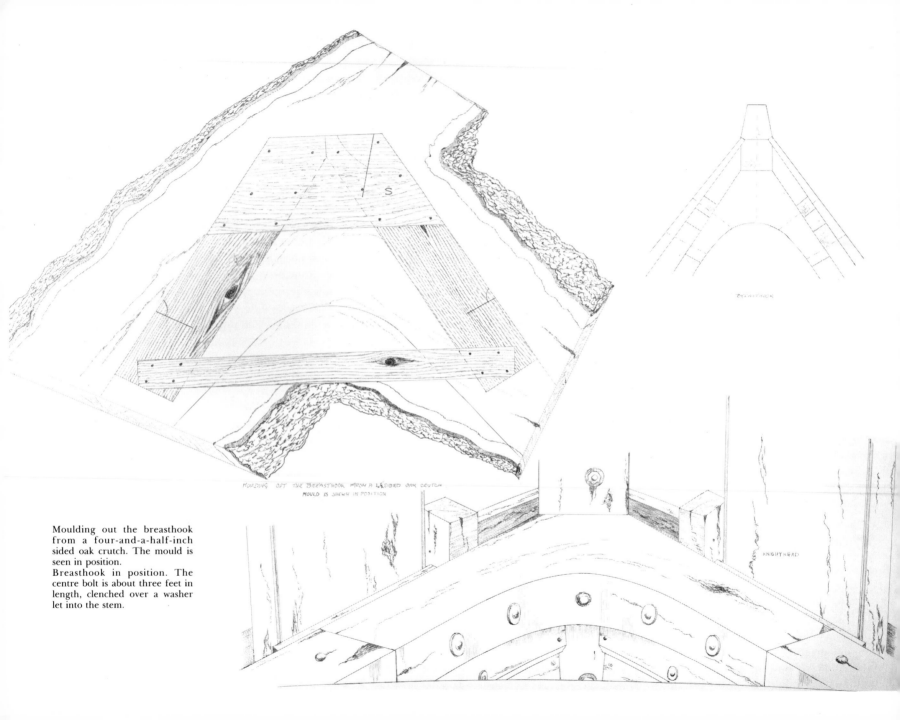

Moulding out the breasthook from a four-and-a-half-inch sided oak crutch. The mould is seen in position.
Breasthook in position. The centre bolt is about three feet in length, clenched over a washer let into the stem.

suitable piece of oak for the job and mould it out. The chargehand would be searching for a sound piece of timber absolutely clear of sap and straight grain; the perfect crutch if possible.

The chargehand would then inform the people in the mill of what had been done, and as soon as possible help would be forthcoming to carry the piece to the bandsaw, and in a very short time a breasthook would have been produced.

The apprentice would then get back on to the vessel to receive the breasthook when it was hove up to him, and with a few resounding words of banter ringing in his ears he would be left to his own devices. After a time with adze, chisel, saw and plane he would have fitted the breasthook ready for fastening, not forgetting the chamfer which would have to be put on the bottom inside edge.

It would then be held firmly in place with shifters round stem and apron and a pair of G-screws on each wing out to the top strake while the apprentice bored a hole from the centre of the stem, using a pilot spline to guide him. Sometimes one would have to bore a smaller pilot hole from each way when the area in which the hole will eventually be is limited, and in this case it would have to be dead centre of stem and centre of breasthook. The hole would be for a seven-eighths-inch galvanised iron bolt specially made to the apprentice's instructions with a head and pilot point. The bolt would be driven from inside the ship, after which it was cut off and clinched on a washer let in the face of the stem.

When boring for the centre bolt it would be advisable to run a seven-eighths-inch auger into the bolthole for a few inches, as with a very tight seven-eighths bolt in a piece of timber sided four-and-a-half inches there would be a chance of the timber cracking when the foc's'le got hot.

Two half-inch through bolts would also be driven from the outside of the vessel through timber and/or knighthead on each side. After punching up these would be cut off and clinched on the inside of the breasthook.

For the knees the tip of the timber on the beam would be fastened with galvanised spikes, then two half-inch through bolts would be used to fasten the knee to the beam. Through the ship's side, timbers, and the tail of the knee would be driven two half-inch through bolts. These were all cut off and clinched on the inside face of the knee.

All the knees finished flush with the top of the beam. Where a knee came short of the next beam a filling would be used between the tail end of the knee and the beam, fitting tight and bolted directly down to the shelf. Those knees in the fore body were fitted on the after side of the beams, while those in the after body were fitted on the fore side.

Once again nature lent herself to the job as the shape of the vessel made the angle of the knees obtuse, and this was the way that most of the crutches were formed. We would make a mould for the knees, then take it to the chargehand, who would choose the stuff and mould it out so we could get it cut out on the bandsaw. We used to take great pride in fitting these knees, and did our best to make them fit snugly.

These were termed rising knees.

Iron or hanging knees

The iron knees, of which there were eight—four on each side of the vessel—were in themselves quite a good tie, and I would say helped to prevent the vessel from working, especially when rolling. They were fastened pretty substantially.

They were sometimes made up from three-and-a-half inches by three-quarters inch flat mild steel, but three inches was the minimum width allowed.

We would make up the moulds, from any old board that we could find lying around, to embrace the beam, shelf, stringers and timber. Should the beam not be in line with the timber we would have to cant the mould, keeping the horizontal arm of the knee in the centre of the beam. It was very rarely, however, that we had to resort to a dolly or dummy timber for a bolt. After the mould had been made up for shape, on the opposite side to that which we would call the moulding edge we would fix bevel chocks which would define the bevel of the knee under the beam and also the bevels of the vertical part of the knee in relation to the ship's side.

When making the knee the smith would shape, set, and twist the hot iron to the mould and bevel chocks. To do this he would have to put it on the forge several times. I have illustrated a knee on the anvil, showing the smith checking it for bevel by overrunning his steel or brass rule over the bevelled chock and the still-hot knee itself.

When they were ready we would collect the knees, take them aboard and offer them up, that is to say we would hang the knee up to the beam with G-screws to see if it fitted properly. We might find a need to cut away a little piece of wood, usually on the bottom edge of the stringers or something like that, to make it fit snugly, but usually they were not far out if one had made the mould properly.

If the knee fitted properly, we would draw a pencil mark right round the knee, then decide on where the holes for the bolts were to be bored, and after due consideration we would take the knee down and mark the holes and bore them, hopefully not striking iron; if one did it was almost sure to be a frame bolt.

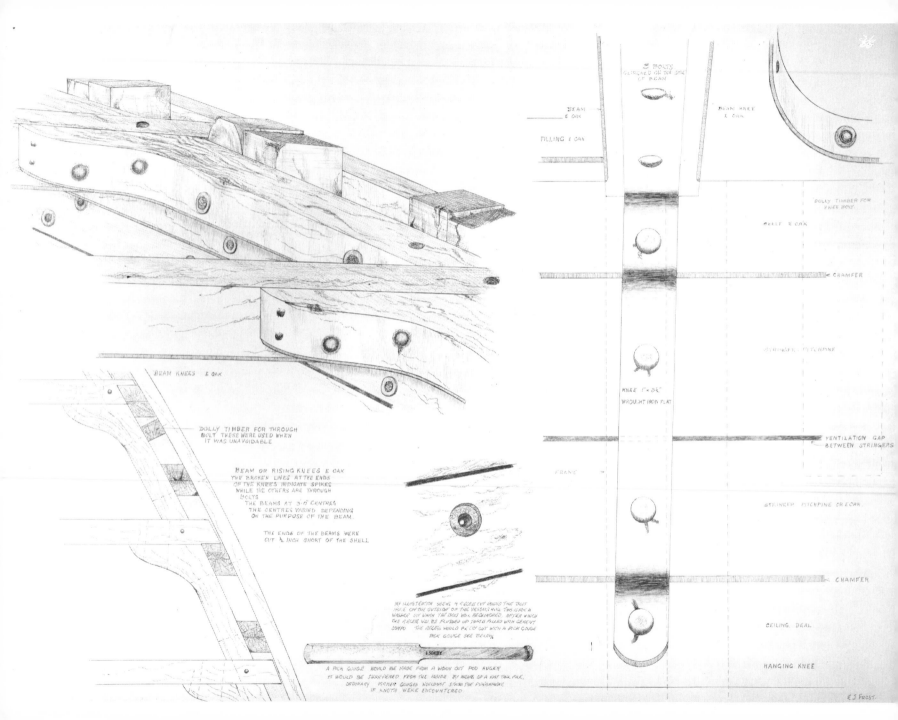

We would then take the lengths of all the bolts and, allowing enough length for cutting off and clenching, write them down on a piece of board. This was taken to the blacksmith who had made the knee, and who would almost invariably say, "Right you are, Edward, I'll make them as soon as I can for you."

The knee would then have to be offered up again and the holes marked for drilling by dipping the end of a piece of tube into white paint and then pushing the tube through the holes in the timber. It would leave a white circle on the knee where the holes were to be drilled. When the knee had been taken down again we would mark the centre of the hole permanently by means of a centre punch and hammer, leaving a tiny pop-hole for the point of the drill to enter.

Back into the blacksmiths' shop for Mr Sid Bessey, the driller, to perform his part of the operation. He might say, "Drop it there, Ted, and I'll do it as soon as I can." And he was as good as his word.

During the making up process and and when still warm the knee would be laid in a tray of black bitumastic in order to give it a complete coating of this preservative.

There would probably be two apprentices on this job, and as there were eight knees we were able to get on with the job somewhere or other while waiting for the blacksmith and driller. One job would be to prepare the bolt holes for clenching the bolts; to do this we would mark round the holes in the beam and topsides by hammering on a galvanised washer placed over the hole, leaving a mark round it. Inside the mark we would gouge out a recess for a washer. All the bolt heads would be on the knee itself inside the vessel.

The recess for the washer would be cut out with what we called a pick gouge, made up usually of a piece of broken-off or spoiled auger sharpened on the inside. It being all steel, a hammer could be used with it. It would be sharpened in the same way as an ordinary inside sharpened gouge, and would stand a lot more knocking about than an ordinary gouge would; it would stand up to work that would break an ordinary gouge.

With the knee drilled and the bolts made, the next thing to do was to hang it up for the last time and to start to drive the bolts, which would have been made with a pilot point and round head. The bolts, which were driven one-sixteenth inch tight in the wood, would be stopped when about an inch from the knee and a spunyarn grummet would be wrapped round the bolt just under the head; should any of the bolts have become crystallised near the head when being made there was a chance that the head might fly off on impact with the knee, and the grummet would reduce the chances of this happening.

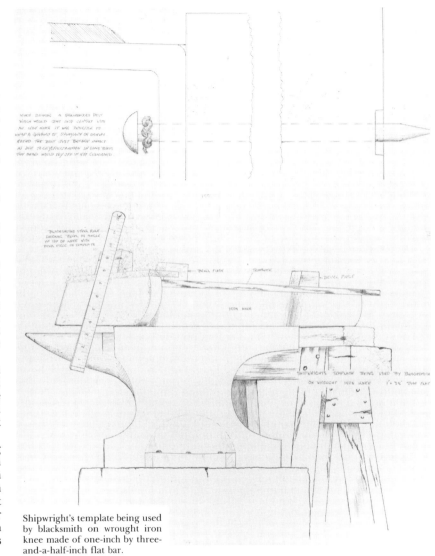

Shipwright's template being used by blacksmith on wrought iron knee made of one-inch by three-and-a-half-inch flat bar.

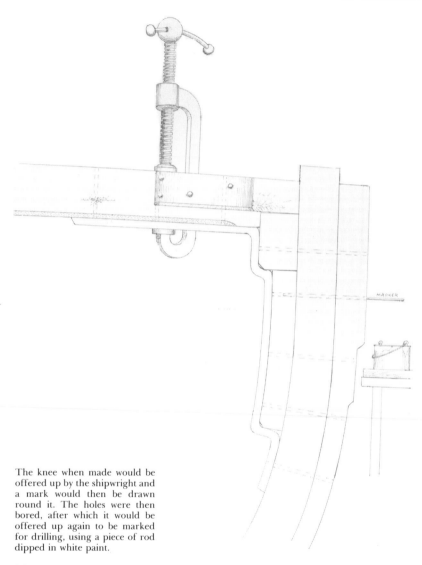

The knee when made would be offered up by the shipwright and a mark would then be drawn round it. The holes were then bored, after which it would be offered up again to be marked for drilling, using a piece of rod dipped in white paint.

After the bolts had been driven home the next operation was to cut them off and clench them, after which the recess in the topsides would be filled flush with compo; it didn't matter about the recesses in the top of the beam as the deck would be laid over them.

As I have just mentioned one of the blacksmiths and our driller in relation to the making of the iron knees, perhaps it would not be amiss at this stage to give a short account of the staff in the blacksmiths' shop at No. 3 yard.

The foreman blacksmith was Mr Billy Womack, who was nearing retirement age when I started my apprenticeship, so I suppose he must have started his time about 1864. He knew a lot of the tricks of the trade, though he was a very quiet man.

Next to him but several years younger was Mr George Hewitt, a Gorleston man who had served his time at Gorleston with Hewitt's Short Blue Fleet. One of the finest men I ever knew, he was an excellent blacksmith and a very staunch man in every way.

Mr Stacy Baine came next, another fine smith who although handicapped by the loss of an eye could do a good job. He was also a very nice sort of man and one with whom I always got on very well; one who always tried to do a good job.

When the standard drifters were started one more blacksmith was taken on, a Mr Ted Hardingham, who had spent almost the whole of his working life on ship's smith's work. I would say that we had a very good staff in the blacksmiths' shop, and this includes the strikers, Mr Jimmy Hickleton, Mr Bertie Saunders, Mr George Simnett of the Salvation Army, and later Mr Freddie Tuttle and Mr Freddie Wilson, not forgetting our driller whom I have already mentioned, Mr Sid Bessey.

With the advent of the standard drifters rudder stocks were forged at Middlesbrough and other places in the North and delivered to Lowestoft and other ports in railway wagons, thus relieving our own blacksmiths of quite a considerable job. A rudder stock of the size required was not really the sort of job to be done by hand.

Chambers' blacksmiths would be called on to do work for other firms at times.

Main hatch coamings

The main hatch coamings were of three-inch sided oak; I cannot remember the exact depth, but I think that they were fifteen or sixteen inches deep and this would leave standing when the deck was laid

66

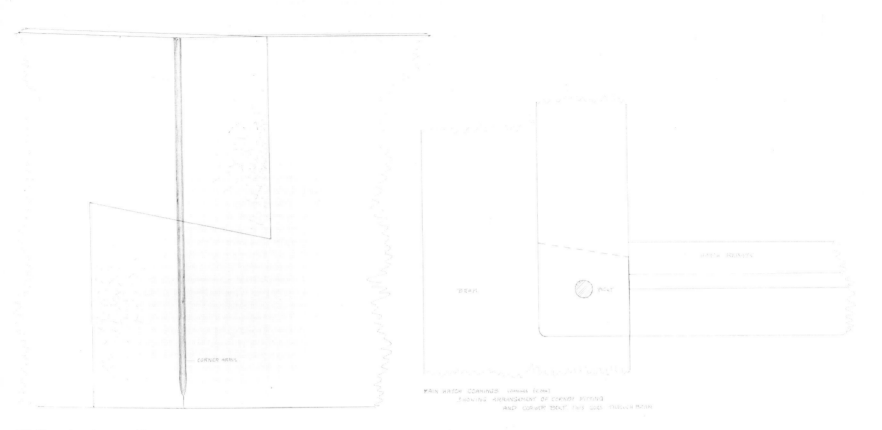

MAIN HATCH COAMINGS COAMINGS (COAM)
SHOWING ARRANGEMENT OF CORNER FITTING
AND CORNER BOLT. THIS GOES THROUGH BEAM.

This illustration gives some idea of the appearance of the fore part of the vessel when the main hatch coamings were fitted. The broken lines indicate the fastenings through the coaming to the beam. The half beams in way of the hatch were fitted up to and fastened to the underside of the coaming in the 420 class; later a rooming off stanchion coincided with each beam.

Main hatch coamings showing arrangement of corner fittings and corner bolt; the latter goes through the beam.

twelve-and-a-half inches, with the headings two or three inches higher in the centre.

The side coamings rested on three beams, on one at the fore end and on two at the after end. On the foremost of the after pair of beams was fitted a third heading, completing the fore end of the after well. No carlins were used as the coamings themselves were considered deep enough and strong enough to do all that was required of them.

At the corners of the hatch when fitting them down the heading would be halved over the side coamings, with the heading itself seated into the side coaming by the method I have shown in my illustrations of the corners of the hatch. The third heading formed the top part of the fore side of the after well, while below the beam the well was completed by pound boards. This heading was simply seated into the side coamings.

The shipwrights on the job would have to be very careful about fitting the joints as it had to be a first-time fit and no shipwright would like to see a bad fit. The coamings were planed on both sides and when ready the whole was assembled after the joints had been given a coating of thick paint; tar would not be used as later the coamings would be painted blue. Through bolts would be driven through the corners down into the beam, while at a specified spacing bolts would also be driven down into the beams through the headings. When all were fastened, the projecting ends could be sawn off and planed flush.

A small round would be planed on the corners nearly down to the deck, and a very small arris planed on all hard edges. A recess would be chiseled out at the top centre of the headings to receive the hatch beam, or strongback as it was sometimes called, after which the whole would be given a coat of grey priming paint to prevent the wood from weather opening in the sunlight coming from the rooflights in the shop.

A two-inch rebate would have been left on the top edge of the side coamings. The inside face of this would have been cut square with the pitch of the headings, and was made to receive the hatches.

Half-beams

Below the main hatch coamings and to the underside of them would be fitted the half-beams of oak, three in number on each side of the ship, cut to camber and with the outboard end increasing in depth from the inboard end to the shelf. The dimensions of the beams were four inches by five inches at the inboard end and five inches by five inches on the shelf, on which they were cut to fit, with the camber true to the sheer line.

They were chamfered on the two lower edges and at the coaming or inboard end a dovetail was cut out for a four by four-inch filling to fit up to

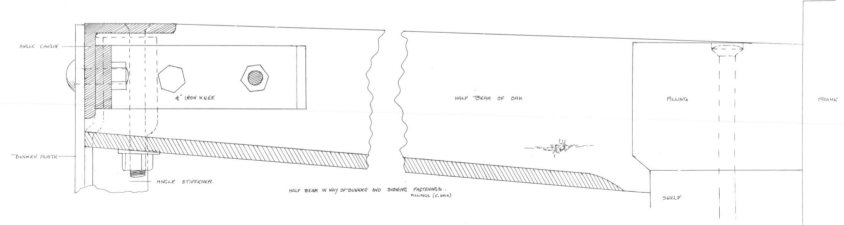

The half beam in way of bunker, showing the fastenings.

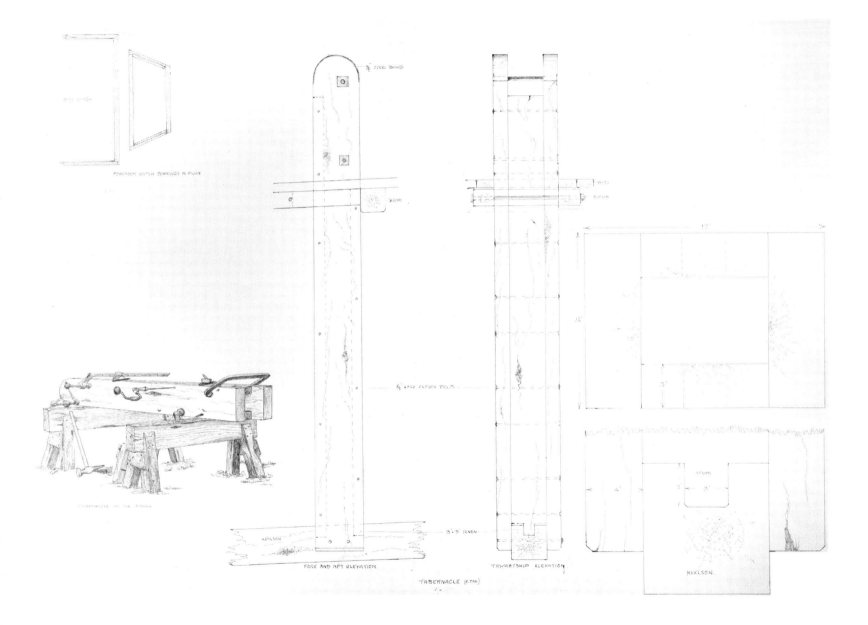

FOKE'SOOM HATCH COAMINGS IN PLAN.

TABERNACLE IN THE STOWN.

¾ STEEL BAND

BEAM

THROAT
CHEEK

TABERNACLE (E.OAK)

FORE AND AFT ELEVATION.

THWARTSHIP ELEVATION.

KEELSON.

KEELSON

3"×3" TENON

5/8" GALV. CARRIGE BOLTS.

THROAT

the underside of the coaming. The half-beams were bolted up to the underside of the coaming, using twelve-inch by half-inch galvanised pilot-pointed bolts, while on the shelf they were bolted down in the usual way. Four by four-inch fillings were then fitted in between each pair of beams and fastened with ordinary three-eighths-inch galvanised dump bolts; this applied to both ends of the beams. At a later stage in the work a rooming off stanchion would be fitted up tight under the beam and in line with the coaming.

More half-beams were fitted over the bunker space and the after end of the engine room. To carry these beams an angle iron carlin was fitted in the case of the coal bunker from the after side of the forward iron beam to the fore side of the iron beam running across the engine room. This angle iron was placed in such a position as to be available to support the coal bunker plates, and holes were drilled in it to take the bolts to hold these plates. These bolts would be in the vertical face of the angle, while in the top flange holes were drilled to receive bolts that would fasten a chequer plate on deck; these bolts would come through chequer plate, deck deals, and angle. The chequer plate was used only in the way of the boiler to cover the space between the coaming and deck, some of which was created by the cylindrical shape of the boiler itself.

On the after side of the engine room iron beam another angle iron carlin was fitted to carry the half beams and to take part of the casing fastenings. It was fastened to the wooden beam at the after end of the engine room, and in this space two half beams were fitted.

All the half beams in these areas were cut as before, with the deeper end cut out to fit down on to the shelf. The inboard end of the beam would be

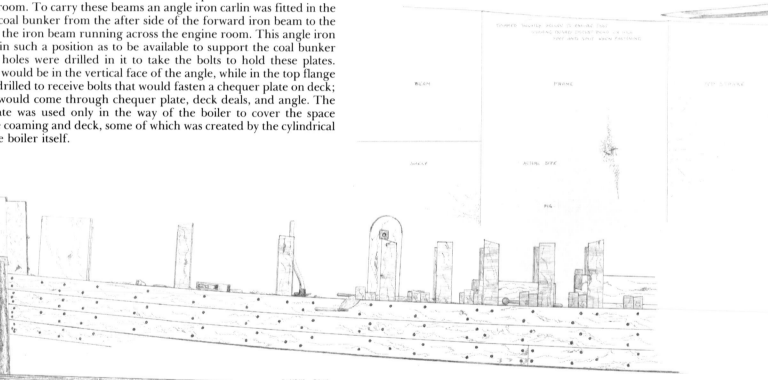

Sheering Down.

70

fitted up under the top flange of the angle bar so as to be flush and was secured to the angle iron by steel lugs set to form right angles and drilled to take half-inch screw bolts through the half beam. Two lugs held the beam, one on each side of it, the lugs in turn being bolted to the carlin.

On the shelf the usual procedure was followed, the beam being fastened down to the shelf with fillings cut in tight between each pair of beams, the fillings themselves being bolted to the shelf. No beam knees were used.

Sheering down

With the beams all in position and fastened, sheering down would be commenced by the top gang. This meant that spots would be faired through on the top strake from beam to sheerline, after which the whole plank would be faired from spot to spot by adze and plane.

Any high spots on knees or fillings would be trimmed off, and when this was done (and it would not take very much time) the vessel would be ready for the timber tops to be sawn off. Crosscut and handsaws would have been sharpened for the job, and where a pair of men or a man and boy were available they would take a crosscut between them and start sawing away, taking care not to let the saw run at all or cut into the top strake. Others would saw singly with the handsaw. The stages both inside and on the outside of the vessel were usually at ideal levels for this operation.

When all the timbers were cut all the cut timbers would be checked with a short straightedge for high spots, and all of them trimmed across with the adze to ensure that there was nothing left on which the future covering board could ride and perhaps split when being bolted down.

From now on the vessel was ready for all work to be performed above the sheer line.

Covering board

For the covering board we made a mould to fit round the stanchions with its top face two-and-a-half inches above the sheerline, the thickness of the covering being two-and-a-half inches. The width was taken from the inside edge of the chamfer which ran round the top outside edge of the top strake to the inside face of the stanchions.

Working now in pairs, we would go out into the planking area to look at the covering board stuff which would be laid out slightly apart from the planking flicks, as this stuff would be sided two-and-a-half inches. After a good look round we would put a chalk mark on the piece we had chosen,

Sawing off timber tops.

and then back into the shop and up on to the stage, taking with us some old boards, usually used material, with which to make up the mould.

This would be made to fit round the apron, knighthead, and as many stanchions as the piece we had chosen would allow. We would let the outboard end run the full width of the last stanchion, where it would be cut flush with the after side of the stanchion, thereby giving the second piece a good clean start. We would then take the mould out and mark the piece out for cutting, with the mould itself helping us to clear any bad places; we would try to work them into a stanchion cutout.

When moulding out any timber it would be marked on the top or narrowed side of the plank, in which case at least as far as sap was concerned the piece would become better rather then worse because of the shape of the tree. The timber would also tend to shed water better that way up, which was why timber was always laid out with the convex of the grain upwards.

With the piece moulded we would get a lift into the mill and have it sawn for shape, most probably on the band saw, which would certainly be used for the inside cut. After cutting we would take it into the shop, put it on the stools and plane both the inner and outer faces, putting a small arris on the outside top edge.

We would lay the mould on the piece to check for shape and to mark off the stanchions, for which we would now cut away the wood, taking care to leave a seam round the three sides of the stanchion. When all was prepared we would heave the piece up on to the stage, then lift it and offer it into place on the vessel. If we had done our job properly it fitted.

The piece might possibly have to be helped into position with a few light taps with the maul here and there, but that was usually all it would need.

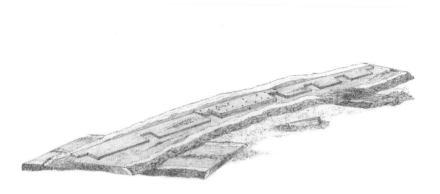

Moulding out a piece of covering board of English oak two-and-a-half inches thick.

Fitting mould round stanchions for a length of covering board. The mould was fitted on packings.

With the piece in position it would be necessary to set it down tightly, to prepare it for fastening. To do this cleats would be G-screwed on to stanchions where it was necessary, to force the covering board down; the whole would be set down tight, using wedges between cleat and covering board, in readiness for fastening.

The fastening consisted of seven-inch dump bolts on the outside edge, driven down into the top strake of planking at about nine-inch centres, with one bolt canted aft and the next one canted for'ad alternately. This method of fastening was termed driving the bolts "on the sosh" on our yard. This dovetailed method of fastening helped to prevent the covering board from lifting when the vessel received a severe blow from another vessel while manoeuvring in harbour, but the primary reason for driving the bolts in this manner was to prevent the covering board from lifting when caulking was

Fastening off the covering board. The broken lines indicate the angle of fastening on the outside edge into the top strake.

done between covering board and top strake. The act of caulking creates a very powerful wedging effect. On the inside edge spikes were used in the beams, knees or fillings, and these would be the same size as those to be used in the deck.

When fitting further pieces of covering board where the vessel's shape is not so round, a piece of board could be laid and supported on the outside of the stanchions and what was known as the "taking a mark at it" method employed for marking out the stanchion apertures; but great care had to be taken when doing this as one could soon gain or lose quite a bit when working on a little curvature.

When shearing down around the stern provision would be made for a four-inch sided covering board. It was very necessary to use a substantial piece of oak in this part of the vessel as nearly all the other timber in this vicinity to which the stern covering board would have to be fastened would have been trimmed to a feather edge, more especially with a tug stern, and as a consequence it became very vulnerable when a number of vessels were moving about at the same time in crowded conditions. Even so, when finished the tug stern was stronger than the counter stern.

The stern covering board would be made up of three pieces, with the two ends of the centre piece and the after ends of the quarter pieces scarphed together. The centre piece of covering board would be moulded out to a mould made on the stern. The piece would be left from fourteen to sixteen inches wide in the centre and then be allowed to taper down gradually to the width of covering board on the vessel's side.

The centre piece would be fitted first, with the scarphs cut on it before fitting. It would be bedded down on "blair" and "hair", the blair consisting of a mixture of coal tar, Stockholm tar, Russian tallow, resin and pitch heated and stirred together. The resultant solution would be waterproof and non-hardening. When this was spread on top of the prepared stern cow hair was thrust into it immediately by the shipwright, using his hands, and this congealed it and prevented it from slowly running away.

After the material was spread the covering board would be lifted into place and hove down tight by means of G-screws and possibly a shifting cramp. Soon the blair and hair would be seen squeezing out, and when this happened the timber was ready to fasten off.

The fastening consisted of galvanised through bolts driven up through planks, stern timbers, cant frames and fillings, punched up and clenched over a washer let into the wood to its own depth. The tapered ends of the planks would be fastened by "flat points", that is flat-pointed galvanised nails, right round the stern.

The next operation would be to fit and fasten the quarter pieces in a like

Bedding down the stern covering board on blair and hair.

manner. A mould would be made to the scarphs at each end of the centre piece, accommodating the shape of the vessel's stern and tapering down to the width of the side covering board.

The covering board stuff was cut on the bandsaw and the inside and outside cuts were square. When the scarphs were cut they would be tried on to the scarphs of the centre piece. These pieces, like the centre piece, would be laid on a good bed of blair and hair and with a good thick coat of tar on the scarphs. They would be hove tightly together and down on to the stern, the G-screws and shifting cramps being very powerful. The scarphs would be spiked together at the ends and through bolted, with the covering board itself through bolted.

The hooding ends of the deck would help to resist pressure on the covering board in the event of a collision or a crush.

We now have all the covering board on, but before leaving it altogether I would mention that in our counter sterned vessels, such as smacks, we also mixed a little horse manure with the blair in order to help to retain it in place initially. In that type of stern there is so much cutting and fitting that some of it could leak away before it had congealed, and if that happened it would be virtually impossible to replace it. Our smacks all had round sterns, and we also built the last counter sterned steam drifters of wood in East Anglia, the *Choice Lass* and *Lydia Long* for Great Yarmouth.

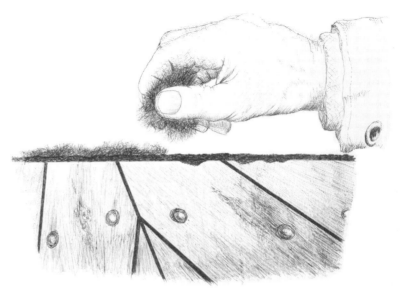

Putting the hair into the blair. The cow hair was taken from a sack and stuck into the blair in tufts by the shipwright, using his fingers.

Fastening off the centre piece of the stern covering board.

Deck laying

This was a job on which as many people as possible would be concentrated in order to get it done quickly; "to get it out of the way" as we said. On our yard the whole operation took two or two-and-a-half days.

Before we could start to lay the deck we had to get the deals prepared. Our sawmill was very well equipped to do this, as we had the frame saw and the planing machine, whch was also fitted with spindles. The baulks from which the deck deals were cut were of pitchpine, delivered to the yard by various means, some by rail, some by road, but also at times by river after arriving in the port by sea.

Although by 1917 the timber trade as we had known it had ceased, previous to the war years one would almost always see at least one ship in the port unloading timber from spring time on. Usually built of wood, these vessels were mostly three-masted barques, but there would a sprinkling of barquentines, brigs, brigantines and snows discharging at either Jewsons or Sauls of Lowestoft.

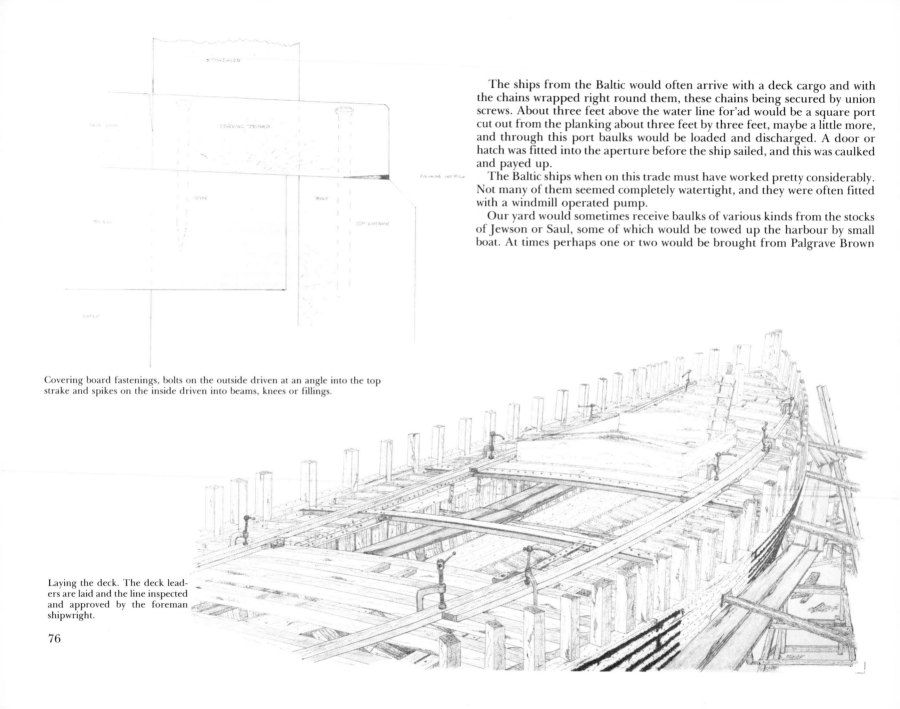

The ships from the Baltic would often arrive with a deck cargo and with the chains wrapped right round them, these chains being secured by union screws. About three feet above the water line for'ad would be a square port cut out from the planking about three feet by three feet, maybe a little more, and through this port baulks would be loaded and discharged. A door or hatch was fitted into the aperture before the ship sailed, and this was caulked and payed up.

The Baltic ships when on this trade must have worked pretty considerably. Not many of them seemed completely watertight, and they were often fitted with a windmill operated pump.

Our yard would sometimes receive baulks of various kinds from the stocks of Jewson or Saul, some of which would be towed up the harbour by small boat. At times perhaps one or two would be brought from Palgrave Brown

Covering board fastenings, bolts on the outside driven at an angle into the top strake and spikes on the inside driven into beams, knees or fillings.

Laying the deck. The deck leaders are laid and the line inspected and approved by the foreman shipwright.

76

of Yarmouth, either by gill or timber drug, in either case drawn by horses. Very often several of these baulks were left chained outside our yard's own boom defence, which consisted of a series of spars chained together end to end and secured for the whole length of the foreshore. As the yard was situated on the north-west side of Lake Lothing, and with the north-west wind making high tides higher than normal, without such a defence as this timber, blocks, etc., would often be blown off the yard and lost.

As these baulks were required the horses would drag them up to the mill, where they would be inspected for nails, staples and stones, and then be laid on the saw bogies and wire-brushed. The saws of the frame would be set up to cut two-and-a-half inches full, then after this cut the flicks would most probably be moved on to the circular saw and rack bench and cut at five inches full, a very little extra being allowed for planing. The deals would then be planed all round and at the same time the spindles would put the seam on.

With the saw cutting and the planing machine humming away there would come a lovely aroma of pitchpine. The deals as they were finished would be taken into the big shop on a truck and stacked ready for use under the west lean-to, together with other timber.

The first thing that we did when laying decks was to choose perhaps three suitable deals long enough to lay completely fore and aft in places overlapping side by side and using the engine room aperture as a guide. These deals were called the leaders; they were allowed to overlap the covering board at each end of the vessel. At the fore and after ends they would be pushed inboard slightly, the fore end slightly more than the after end, and this would put a little curve into the decks.

Many firms laid their deals straight, but we always laid ours in this fashion. This meant that we would have to fit in a tapered piece on the centre line both for'ad and aft. The for'ad piece was cut wide enough to take the centre bollard.

With the leaders laid temporarily one could see a line for the whole length of the vessel. When these were G-screwed in position the foreman would be called in to look at and approve the line. Generally there would be no need for alteration and the work would be proceeded with.

The hooding ends of the deals would be cut to fit the covering board at each end of the ship. When the splay became too long for this to be done joggling would be started, with each successive deal being let into its predecessor about one-and-three-quarters inches and thereafter sawn or trimmed round to the full width of the deal. Both sides of the ship would be treated exactly the same.

The deals would be selected to obviate faults as the work went on, and this

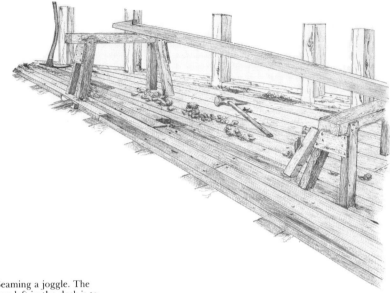

Seaming a joggle. The gap left in the deck is to start the aperture for the rope room hatch.

would tend to leave pieces that could be adapted to any required circumstances. For instance, cut-offs could be used in the way of the bunker rings, or between coaming and engine room space. We would try to do the job with a minimum of waste and at the same time cut out any unwelcome features such as sap or bad knots. The butts would be spaced as far apart as possible.

After three or four deals had been laid side by side these would be set up tightly together and G-screwed down, and then fastening would be started. A series of holes would be bored through the deal, just entering the beam; these would be slightly reamed for the heads of the spikes with which the deals would be fastened.

Several spikes would now be inserted in holes by the individual shipwright, with the cutting edge of the spike standing across the grain of the beam, in order to cut the grain and thus minimise the risk of splitting the

77

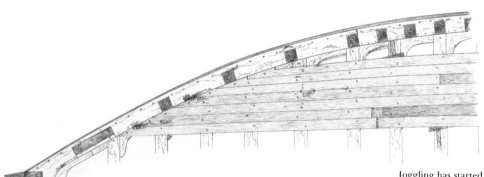

Joggling has started

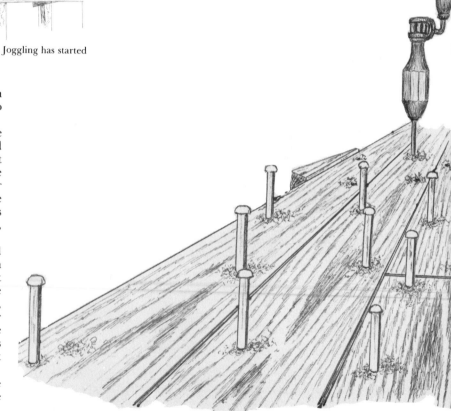

beam. The spikes would be driven flush with the surface of the deal. With these deals securely fastened the struts and wedges would be removed to make way for further deals.

The work would progress fairly rapidly, the only variation being over the iron beams. Except where the fore end of the casing would be fastened across the fore part of the wheelhouse, the deck on that beam and also that on the outer ends of the iron beams across the engine room would be fastened by half-inch purpose-made galvanised deck bolts with a flat circular head and a square on the neck of the bolt beneath the head. Holes would be bored for these bolts up through the holes in the iron beam. After the holes had been bored the shipwright would change the boring bit for a dowel bit, with which he would bore out for the dowels.

The deck bolt would be driven, having first had a little white or red lead and then a grummet of spunyarn put round the neck, after which a half-inch galvanised washer would be put on the bolt, followed by a nut which would be screwed up tightly. Red or white lead would be put on the head of the bolt and a dowel of pitchpine would be driven into the hole, covering the bolt head. These dowels were made by the block and spar maker on his lathe, and you could be sure that they would fit perfectly, the dowel bits were made to a specified size, and it was to this size that the dowels were turned up. With the dowel driven down tightly it was possible to trim it off flush with the deck.

Deals would often be started at a point where a hatch or ring was to be fitted later, thus using short lengths and at the same time giving the shipwright or apprentice a start with the cutting out of the hole.

78

Fastening off: boring for and driving the spikes.

Below right: Punching down spikes, using withe punch and maul.

The deck by now would be assuming a finished look, with struts and wedges being removed, deals being put down, struts being shortened, and shutters being fitted until at last all was finished. The shipwrights and boys would now pair up for punching down, withe punches would be brought out and punching down started, one man holding the punch on the head of each spike while the other would strike the punch with his maul, sending the head of the spike from a quarter of an inch to three-eighths below the surface of the deal.

The spikes would have been staggered in the beam and also staggered from port to starboard in the deal. Great care had to be taken when doing this to see that both sides of the ship finished up properly.

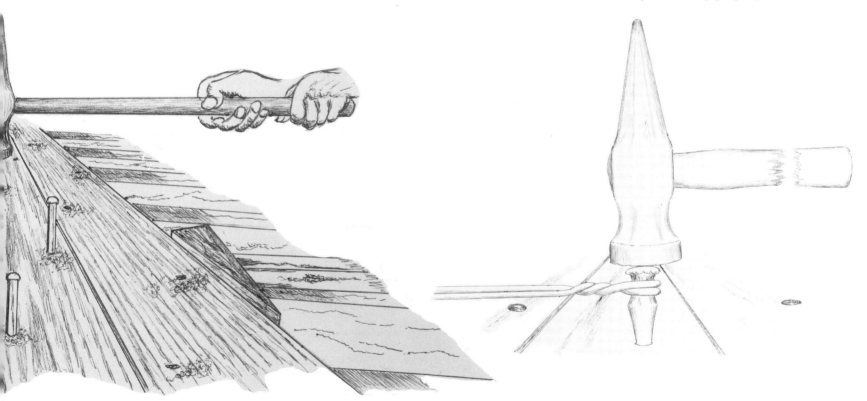

79

With the punching down completed, it remained to trim down. Each shipwright would observe high spots and trim the standing wood off with his adze. There was no need to plane this afterwards as it would be trimmed very well. Being a workboat, a drifter's decks were never planed over the high spots when laying was finished; the pitch when paying up, plus wear and tear, took care of any small irregularities.

Trimming down after punching spikes.

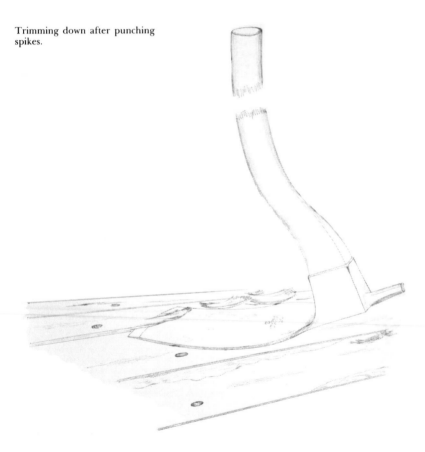

Caulking

Caulking the deck was another of those jobs that required a concentration of men and boys to get it done quickly, both to allow other jobs to proceed and to ensure that caulking was done before the seams filled up with chips, shavings and other rubbish.

It was on deck caulking that an apprentice would get his first feel of a caulking iron and mallet. He would be told how to hold the iron and mallet, and how to choke the oakum into the seam; and once he got started his work would be scrutinised by his neighbours. The boy would not be expected to do a day's complement by any means, but would do what he could, as well as he could. Once he had mastered holding the oakum between finger and iron he would be away, as it was termed.

The boy with his new caulking mallet and irons would feel quite proud of the fact that here he was doing a man's job with the men. This day was usually an event in a shipwright apprentice boy's life; I remember that it was in mine.

Bales of oakum would have been brought from the store into the shop by the younger boys, while some of the older boys, perhaps to show off a bit, who knows? would pick the bales up and show the smaller lads how easy it was to carry a bale on the shoulder up the ladder and dump it on deck. The men might look out of the corners of their eyes now and again and think to themselves, well it's saved me a job.

But they would not let the boys do this if they thought that there was a chance of somebody getting hurt through the carrying up. If they thought that, it would be stopped and the bales would be hove aboard by tackle.

To spin the oakum the same method was used as for caulking over the side, the one difference being that instead of spinning it into a drum or box, it would be balled up, as the deck being freshly laid was quite clean. Spinning would take place from 6.00 a.m. to 8.00 a.m. usually with everybody that was on the job sitting in a group on their own caulking boxes on either the fore or after deck, or wherever some deck has been payed up.

The caulking box was generally about thirteen inches high, depending on the man using it, and it would be about six-and-a-half inches square or thereabouts, depending on the size of timber available when the box was made; this sort of thing was usually made from stock. In the front of the box and in the upper part of it a circular hole about four-and-a-half inches in diameter would be cut for putting caulking irons, oil box, knee canvas, and perhaps a small ball of caulking cotton away into the box when moving or on having finished the job. In the back of the box, and towards the top, would be two smaller holes, large enough to take a piece of one-and-a-half-inch circumference rope, left long enough for a handle; the ends of this rope would generally be finished with a wall and crown knot in the box to stop it pulling through. To carry the box the shipwright would slip the shaft of his caulking mallet through the handle and sling it over his shoulder.

At Yarmouth, where caulking was a specialised job, the caulking box was a rather more elaborate affair, rectangular in shape but with splayed ends and fitted with a curved seat for comfort and stability. I preferred our own square box myself, as one could cant the box when sitting on it and so reach further if necessary.

The berths for deck caulking were not allotted to one as the overside berths were; we simply choose our own, making them eight, nine, or ten feet

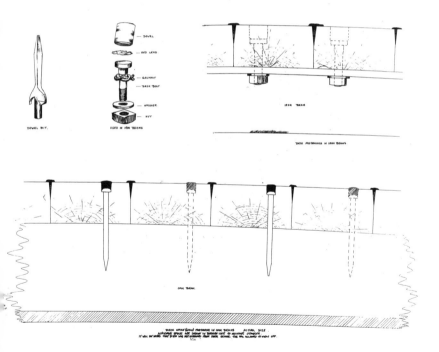

long depending on the circumstances. When one berth was completed one moved on to another, after paying up.

The complement was one hundred and thirty feet per day of two thread caulking. We would generally try to pay up at any time from 3.00 pm onwards. When starting a berth the shipwright would leave a tail standing out of the seam some four or five inches inside his neighbour's berth, and again when one was caulking the second thread in one would overrun into the next berth to ensure continuity.

When caulking one would first finger the oakum in, that is, take the thread between the first finger and iron and choke it into the seam in a series of small loops for as far as one could reach, and then caulk it in. Some people went all over the berth with one thread and then came back to the start of the berth to go over it again with a second thread, with this difference, that it would be necessary to make it in ready to pay up. A crease or making iron would be used, the width of the crease depending on the width of the seam. One would make the oakum in to about a quarter of an inch below the surface of the deck.

When caulking by any coaming or round stanchions a bent iron and a bent crease iron would be used. A spike iron would often be used across the end of a joggle. If a seam or part of it should be very small it would be necessary to ream it first with the reaming iron; if one did not open the seam the oakum might be cut by the sharp edge of the deal.

By three o'clock in the afternoon some of the people on the job would begin to drift towards the pitch pot, which by that time would be bubbling and ready for use. We would ladle a quantity of pitch into an already hot bucket, carry it into the shop and begin very carefully to ascend the ladder with it. When aboard the ship and over the berth one would ladle the pitch from the bucket with a warmed pitch ladle, pour it from the spout, stepping backwards along the seam as one did so, and moving from seam to seam on completion of each.

We would try not to let it overflow, although sometimes it did. When we had been all over the berth we would carefully scrutinise it for places where the pitch had settled and top these up flush.

If I could leave our yard for a bit, while I was at sea I was carpenter for six years of the *Marquesa*, which was fitted with wooden decks over the steel deck, and during this time we had several areas of deck caulked in Buenos Aires. The caulkers specialised in this work in the same way that the Yarmouth caulkers did, but their methods of paying up were quite different from, and better than, ours here in Lowestoft. The Argentine caulkers used a metal funnel, shaped like one of the old-fashioned blue sugar bags, fitted with a fairly long metal handle; inside it, a loose metal rod was used to act as

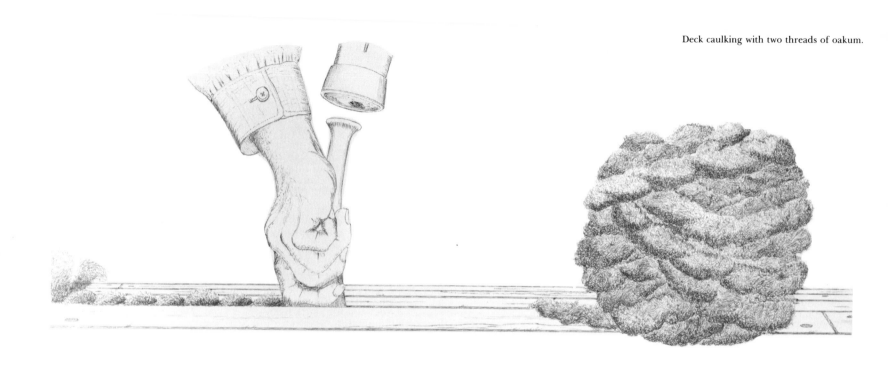

a plug which fitted into a tubular spout brazed into the lower end of the funnel. The funnel would be filled with hot pitch from the bucket, the spout would be laid in the seam to be paid up, and the caulker would then pull the rod up a little and retreat backwards along the seam with the pitch pouring from the spout of the funnel, the rod being adjusted so that the seam filled perfectly, cleanly and with a minimum of waste.

The methods differed from yard to yard. At Chambers a concentrated effort would be made to get the deck caulking done and out of the way, especially on a ship that was laid down in the open.

While on the subject of deck caulking one amusing incident stands out in my mind. We were working on the fore deck of a standard drifter at Chambers during the First World War, and the youngest apprentice had been told to go over to the village to buy mineral waters and cakes as we were working overtime. On returning back on board ship, he just settled himself down on the deck among the caulkers. Now I have said that some of my workmates were poor, and this lad was wearing a jacket that was much too large for him, it having been either his elder brother's or his father's, and as he was sitting on the deck the jacket was spread out behind him like a fantail. Just behind him "Preel" Jillings was working.

"Shift up, so-and-so," says Preel.

"Oh! go so-and-so," says the lad.

"Shift up, I say," says Preel.

"Oh, go to hell," says the wee lad.

Percy didn't speak again but just kept on caulking. Oakum went into that seam, jacket as well. When the boisterous laddie tried to get up he found it impossible to do so as his jacket had been well and truly caulked into the seams. He had to wriggle out of it, and of course it was later cut off half way up the back. The boy never got in Percy's way again.

To work in that trade one had to be strong and adaptable, there is no doubt about that, and if you were not then you could not be a shipwright. I am of course referring to the days when most of this work was performed manually.

Tug stern stanchions and knees

With the caulking on the after deck completed, the two shipwrights who had started the stern would prepare to work on the tug stern stanchions and knees. The outer edge of the bases of these stanchions would be set out by fixing a pliable batten right round the stern, on top of the covering board, to a given dimension in the centre of the ship, and following the contour of the covering board round to the aftermost stanchion on the ship's side.

This line would now be pencilled in and the stanchions set out on it. The first two would be one on each side of the centre line and at a specified distance from it, with the remaining three on each side of the ship spread equal distances to the existing stanchions. With this done the mortices could be set out and the first two cut out. Following this the tenons on each of the two centre stanchions could be cut at the same time as the bevelled base of the stanchion itself.

The inner face of these stanchions and the two sides would have been planed and a half-inch bead put on the two inner edges.

To cut the mortices the shipwright would first bore the core of the mortice out, most probably with an inch twist bit, and thus reduce considerably the amount of chiselling out to be done. The tenon would be cut on the stanchions by the shipwright using his handsaw, after which a very small arris would be chiselled on it to help it when being driven into the mortice.

When all was ready a little tar would be poured into the mortice and the stanchion set up in position and driven home tight by the shipwright using his maul. These first two stanchions would be spiked in position.

It would next be necessary to hang the taffrail harpin irons in position at the underside of taffrail in the centre. They would have been given a little extra spring over and above the natural sheer; a few drifters had been built in the past with the rail height unchanged round the stern, and these never looked right. Richards in particular always used to spring their sterns up quite a bit in the centre, but it could be overdone. The sheer round the stern would first be determined by the use of a batten, after which the harpin iron would be hung to suit this line.

The harpin irons were made up of light angle bar shaped to the contour of the stern, which changed gradually from almost plumb on the ship's side to the angle at the centre of the stern; this would have been picked up from off the mould loft floor initially. Holes would have been drilled in the angle to accommodate a nettlefold brad in each individual stanchion, and as each

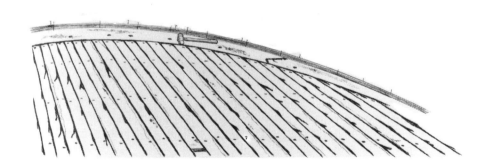

Setting out stanchion mortice line to tug stern.

Mortice and tenon.

stanchion was fitted in turn in the same way as the two centre ones, and made to fit so that it touched the harpin iron at the proper height, it would be temporarily fixed to the iron by means of a brad driven home into the wood. All these stanchions would then be spiked in position.

The stanchion knees would be fitted next, a mould being made for each knee with the relevant bevels marked on it. The knees, which were four-inch sided, would be taken from suitable oak crutches. They were planed, with the two inner edges rounded, and would be fitted to the stanchions, covering board, and deck, after which they would be fastened off. The knee would have been left long enough for it to come up tight under the cavil, which would be fitted on to the top of the knee later.

The knees would be spiked at their outer end, while on both knee and stanchion through bolts would be used. These would be half-inch, driven from the knee through the stanchion and clinched on the back of the stanchion, with the washer let in just below flush before clinching. For the foot of the knee long pilot-pointed bolts would be driven through the deck and down into the stern fillings or cant frames. At this point the harpin irons would be removed and stowed away.

When completed the stern would be quite a substantial job.

I will leave the work on deck for a time and we will go below.

Ceiling

During the time that the deck caulking was in progress some of the youngest boys would have been detailed off to start putting the ceiling in. The ceiling, which was the lining of the ship, was of imported deal three-quarters inch by five or six inches wide, depending on the delivery. It would most probably be of Scandinavian origin, planed on all sides or P.A.R. as it was called, and would smell sweetly.

The work would start at the apron and would be carried right aft as far as the cant frames, the ceiling being fitted tight up under the stringers. The first butt would be cut on the first convenient timber, the length having been got with a batten pushed up tight to the apron, and further butts would be cut to suit the circumstances.

The board to be fastened would be pushed out to the frames as tightly as possible and nailed from timber to timber starting from for'ad in order to draw the plank for'ad and home; it was shored out to the ship's side, and assisted at times with a light tap on the end of the plank with a maul. Galvanised flat points were used as fastening. Each following strake would be set up tight to the previous one before being fastened, and a shutter would be cut in and fitted on arrival at a stringer or the bilge stringers.

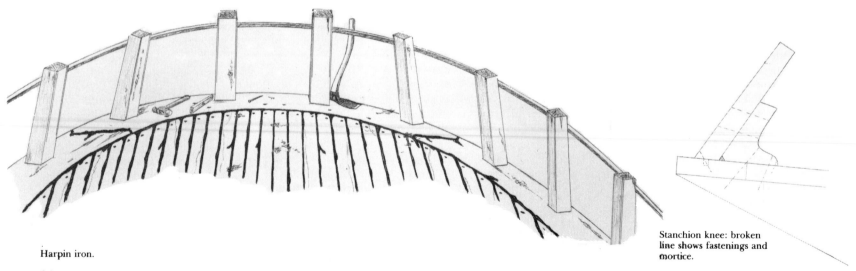

Harpin iron.

Stanchion knee: broken line shows fastenings and mortice.

Tug stern stanchion and knee.

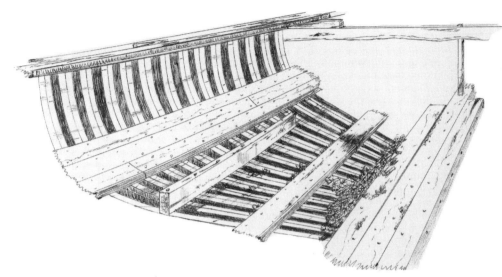

Bunker plate bearer, made of English oak.

The ceiling would be carried down as far as was thought necessary, and this information would be given to the apprentices by the foreman. I remember that when I was doing this job as a young apprentice I would stand back to admire the day's work, and think to myself that this had made her stronger. I don't suppose it had, but I used to like to think it had.

No dressing was applied to the frames before the ceiling was fitted, nor to the underside of the ceiling itself.

Bunker plate bearers

The line for the bearers, which were of English elm, was arrived at by dropping a plumb bob down from the angle iron carlin already in place forming the outer edge of the bunker space, and marking the position of the point of the plumb bob on the frame below. One had to bear in mind that this was the line of the plate, and that the inside face of the timber would be two inches inside this mark, as the bearers would be four inches sided by nine inches deep approximately.

A mould would be made on this line, after which the apprentices on the job would go to see the chargehand shipwright, who would pick out two

suitable pieces; or quite possibly one piece of timber large enough to cut the two bearers from. After moulding out, the piece would be carried in to the bandsaw to be cut to shape and bevel, which was put on to ensure that the bearers would stand plumb when fitted.

After fitting, the bearers would be bolted at every timber on which they stood by means of sixteen-inch by half-inch pilot-pointed galvanised bolts, which would be driven so that the heads were just beneath the surface of the wood.

With bearers in position the base angles would be cut and given a coat of bitumastic, and when ready these would be coach-screwed down on top of the bearers, the tops of which would be given a coat of tar before the angle was put down. The angle would be fitted so that the bunker plate would be pressing outwards against the vertical flange of the angle. Holes for coach screws and bolts were drilled by the driller in the blacksmiths' shop. These coach screws were large coarse-threaded screws, I would think of seven-sixteenth inch gauge, with a square head and were screwed down with a spanner on to a washer on top of the horizontal flange of the angle bar.

Now that the angles were fitted the template for the bunker plates could be made from rough-sawn boards, say four inches by three-eighths, of deal

85

preferably. To make the mould or template, a piece would be clipped to the top and base angles, and holes marked by means of a piece of brass tube dipped in white paint and pushed through the holes in the bars, thus leaving a white circle on the timber ready for boring the hole at that position. The top and bottom splines would be joined by a vertical piece at each end, and the whole would be subdivided up by three other vertical pieces at equal distances apart, allowing for four plates to make up the bulkhead. Bolt holes would be bored in these splines and later transferred to the plates. Provision would also have to be made in the template for the bunker door, located in the after plate on each side of the ship.

When finished the template would be handed over to the foreman blacksmith for the work to proceed. At a later date a template would have to be made for the end plates at each end of the bunker which would be fitted thwartships and from the vertical out to the vessel's side.

Engine bed

To start work on the engine bed it would be necessary to set up the centre line of the shaft. There was already a hole through the stern post and tube chocks, and it was now essential to determine the centre of this hole on the after side of the stern post.

Vertical and horizontal marks would have been left on the face of the stern post after the pilot hole had been cut through, and a wooden bridge would be fastened on the post across the aperture to form the horizontal line, after which the vertical mark would be carried down in the plumb to this bridge. We would now have determined the centre line of shaft at a position which will ultimately be that of the extreme after end of the stern tube. A very small cut would now be made in the horizontal piece; this would be dead centre.

The next operation would be to erect a bridge inboard high enough to accommodate the centre line and far enough forward not to be in the way of work on the engine bed. This could be done by fastening two uprights, one on either side of the kelson, strong and firmly fixed, as in that position they could be vulnerable. A crosshead would be levelled across the two posts and fastened, after which a piano wire was stretched from the centre cut at the after end of the tube aperture and adjusted to the height required to bring the wire dead centre, and also the prescribed height of the fore end of the future crank shaft. This line is dead centre of the engine crankshaft.

When this operation is complete it becomes possible to start the fitting of the engine bed itself into the ship. It was very necessary to keep a constant

86

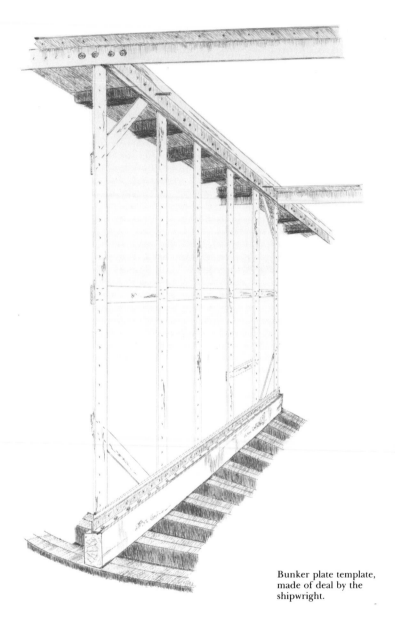

Bunker plate template, made of deal by the shipwright.

tension on the centre wire so that there was never any alteration at all in its function as the proposed centre line of shaft.

With the centre line fixed, work on the bed would begin. I seem to remember some cross bearers; everything was arranged so as not to foul any part of the engine bed, that is, the engine frame itself. The engine bed bearers would be of good selected pieces of oak nine inches by nine inches, and of a length to suit the engine that was to be fitted. These would ultimately be fitted down parallel and in exact relation to the piano wire that we have stretched, both vertically and horizontally, but would be left half an inch lower than the true measurement. That is to say they would be half an inch lower than the bedplate flange, this arrangement allowing for any adjustment that it might be found necessary to make.

The engine itself would be lowered and then adjusted on packings so that the shaft coupling fitted with a maximum tolerance of three-thousandths of an inch; it would be hard to get one thousandth in when finished, however. The remaining space between engine bed plate and wooden bed was taken up by fitted packings on both sides of the engine.

After the two pieces of engine bed had been brought aboard the ship and prepared for fitting, they would be set up and levelled athwartships, at the proper distances from the centre line, according to the measurement required. A measurement would then be taken for seating these down, and this measurement would become standard to measure up from the individual timbers on which the bed was to rest and fit; this would be called taking a mark at it, using rule and pencil. All edges of the frames would be marked up on to the timber where it was to be cut.

When all was marked the timber would be rolled upwards and cutting commenced, using handsaw, chisel and adze. When everything marked had been cut, the timber would be rolled home into position as far as was possible; it was most unlikely that a piece of timber of that size would fit first time, it was almost sure to be a bit tight, or full as it was called, at some spot or other.

It would be hammered down, and when it refused to go further would be scrutinised for any obstacles in the way of a fit; these obstacles would be noted and if necessary a further mark taken, after which the piece would be rolled up again for trimming or a little cutting here and there.

When finally fitted both bearers would be hove down into position by means of cramps used over a piece of timber across the bearers and down under the kelsons. Boring for the fastening could now be started, the holes

Preparation for the engine bed, showing the piano wire used to fix the centre line of the engine crankshaft.

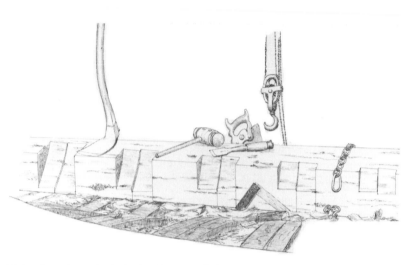

Fitting down the engine bed; trimming out to fit down on to bearers and frames. It was often a tight fit, as seen in the lower illustration.

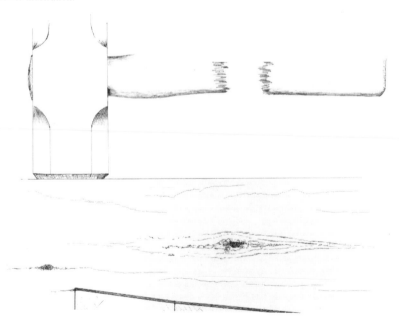

being staggered in the timber from port to starboard say about two-and-a-half inches.

With the holes bored one in each timber and plumb, templates would be made for the bolts, the length of the bolt being just short of the top of the engine bed. The templates would be taken into the blacksmiths' shop and the holding down bolts made up. While the blacksmith was making the bolts, the shipwright would be letting the plate washers into the top of the bearers; these washers would take the nuts of the bolts.

Care would have to be taken when setting out these fastenings, and an engine bedplate template would be used to make sure that they would clear the engine holding-down bolts.

With the engine bed firmly fixed by means of the holding bolts, and the fastenings completed on the outside of the hull, preparations could be made for erection of the boring bar used to cut the shaft tube hole to its final size.

Boring for the shaft tube

The fitter who used to do this job at John Chambers at the time of which I am writing was a Mr Freddy "Nibs" Page, who was very skilled at this kind of work. In fact, he was the only fitter that I ever knew to do this job on wooden vessels both at Chambers and at Richards, and as a consequence of this he was very expert at it.

He always seemed very casual about the job, but he knew exactly what he was doing. In all the time that I knew him I can never remember him being questioned about his work. A very helpful kind of chap, a bachelor, and quite a character, he was never flurried. He was well known and well liked on the yards that I have mentioned.

He had one little vice, however. If overtime was being worked on Saturdays, then one would not see much of "Nibs" after lunch. He would go along to the *Windsor Castle* while at Richards or to the *Station Hotel* while at Chambers, and forget that there was ever such a thing as a shaft tube until Monday morning, when once again Freddy would be up and about and raring to go. As I say, Saturday lunch, or dinner time as it was to us, would always see the last of him for the weekend—unless there was a wartime emergency.

The fitter and shipwright on the job would set the boring bar up on the centre line of the shaft, with the bearings for the after end of the bar coach-screwed to the after side of the stern post, in their exact position in relation to the line, and the fore end bearings rigged up on a strong bridge over the deadwood and secured in position.

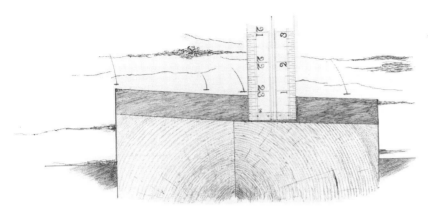

Housing down, "taking a mark" for the final fitting down of the engine bed to agree with the centre line of shaft. The illustration on the right shows the engine bed bolts being pulled down.

I seem to remember that the bar was about eight feet long by about two inches in diameter, smooth and with a keyway cut in it for its whole length. By the side of the bar and supported by bearings at each end was a smaller bar with a thread cut on it for the whole of its length which served to pull the cutting block along the main bar when this was put in motion.

The movement of the cutters along the main bar was effected by means of a starwheel at the outboard end of the bar. When the whole thing was rotated by means of a flywheel and handle this starwheel caught on a projecting pin, and in passing caused the threaded bar to rotate a quarter of a turn. The cutters would be pulled along the keyway outboard to inboard, but I seem to remember that they could be made to cut in any direction if necessary.

The cutters themselves would gradually be extended outwards until the correct diameter was arrived at, with the final two cuts being very fine, leaving the hole ready for the tube to be drawn into it.

The boring mechanism was very primitive but nonetheless effective. Later on when at the end of the war a steel shipyard was brought into being by Chambers and a compressed air plant installed for the purpose of rivetting and caulking, a compressed air pipe was laid to the wood yard, and a little vertical single cylinder steam engine was adapted by Freddy to operate the boring mechanism through a belt drive. This was very successful, and from then on the hard manual work was taken out of the job. Freddy did the same thing at Richards later when he went to work there some time after Chambers had been closed by Shipbuilders Securities Ltd.

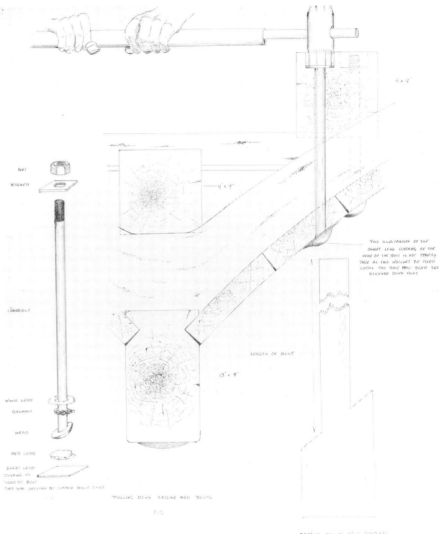

Boring for the stern tube. In the illustration above I have tried to give some idea of what the boring bar looked like. The cutters moved along on a key way, propelled by a slow threaded bar which was knocked around by a star wheel, one point of which came into contact with a pin at every revolution of the bar, see illustration on right.

With the hole at its correct diameter, the tube was inserted and pulled home into position by means of a drawbar, after which it would be secured. It would have been a reasonably tight fit.

I will speak about the cage in which the tail shaft will run at a later stage, as other construction work is in progress.

Rails

Two shipwrights and two apprentices were generally detailed off to work on the rails on each side of the vessel, while the two shipwrights who had constructed the stern would work on the taffrail and cavil.

The sheer batten would be hung in hutchiks for the third time to determine the sheer round the vessel. It would be hung to the underside of rail height from the covering board, and while no extra spring would be given for'ad, partly to keep the bulwark components at a constant width, as I have said earlier aft a little would or could be given; the bulwark round the stern was cut out of vertical boards, as we shall see later. Extra sheer for'ad was obtained by cutting the bow rail with its own individual sheer. When fastened on top of the rail later, not only did this enhance the vessel's appearance but it also gave the forerail quite a bit of extra strength.

The sheer batten used round the stern was smaller and much more pliable than those used on the ship's side, and when set up formed a continuous sheer line right round the vessel. While there were dimensions given from the covering board, it was largely a matter of bringing experience to bear and finishing up with a sheer line that would really please the eye.

After the leading hand on the job had looked the line in and looked it over generally, the foreman shipwright would again be asked to come and look the sheer in. This would be done from every vantage point, mostly from ladders resting on the side of the shop or on pillars. The foreman would be contorting his body to focus his eye on the batten from every angle, sometimes even looking at it from between his legs. It was a bit difficult in the shop, but any defect would be plainly visible once the ship was afloat.

When looking the sheer in the foreman would indicate his requirements with movements of his hands. A shipwright on the stage would move about fore and aft, keeping below the sheer line so as not to obstruct the foreman's view, according to whether it was a beckoning gesture or one of thrusting away; arriving at the spot indicated, he would tap the batten either up or down as required. It probably would not need a great deal done to it; we

must bear in mind that all these men were experienced at this sort of work.

At last he would be satisfied with the job, indicating that he was by a movement of both hands horizontally at breast level, crossing one over the other and giving them a sharp outward wave. This would mean that the line was now approved and could be pencilled.

At this point the sheer would really look something, a beautiful curve.

With the sheer finally approved the thwartship line for the underside of rail would be marked by simply pulling a chalk line across the vessel on opposite stanchions, on the same side of the stanchions in each case, and marking it.

The batten would now be removed and laid on the brackets affixed to the centre columns of the shop for this purpose. Work would next be started on cutting the stanchions in readiness for the rail, the top of the stanchions being cut off at one-and-a-quarter inches above the sheer line.

Round the stern the situation would not be quite the same as that along the vessel's side, as it was customary to give the rail a slight cant inboard aft. To do this a pliable batten would be hung on the inside of the stanchions, slightly lower than the outer mark in the centre of the ship, and allowed to find its own fairness between the centre and the already existing line on the quarters.

After this line had been approved the side lines could be drawn between

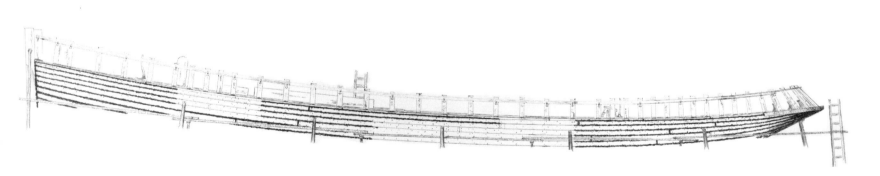

Setting out the rails. The sheer batten is hung in hutchiks at under side of rail height, an inch and a quarter being allowed above this for the top of the tenons.

91

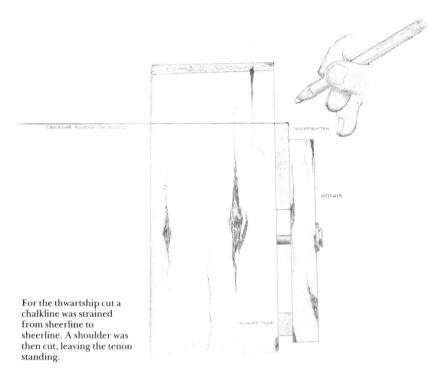

CHALKLINE ACROSS THE VESSEL

SHEER BATTEN

HUTCHIN

DISTANCE PIECE

For the thwartship cut a chalkline was strained from sheerline to sheerline. A shoulder was then cut, leaving the tenon standing.

leave the tenon standing. When this was satisfactory a small arris would be chiselled round the top corners of the tenon. This would be repeated on all stanchions and knightheads.

On completion of this part of the job the shipwrights would make a mould for the fore part of the rail on one side. This would be fitted to the apron, being birdmouthed on the after corner, and the tenons would be marked individually on the under side of the mould, after which these would be cut out and the mould fitted. This mould would be made from three pieces of board, with just the outside curve cut.

The fore piece of rail might extend, say, a quarter of the length of the vessel. The after scarph would be cut so that it laid centrally on a stanchion, with the splay on it running inboard to outboard from for'ad to aft.

The mould would be taken out of the shop and the search for a suitable piece of plank begun. This would have to have some curvature on it and be sufficiently wide to get a seven-inch rail from it, and would have to be two-and-a-half inches thick. Once a piece had been found in the planking area it would be taken into the mill and the outside curve cut on a circular saw. It might be found necessary to cut the inside curve on the bandsaw, or perhaps both cuts would be made on the frame saw. When cut it would be taken into the shop to be faired and the top side and edges planed.

A half-inch bead would be put on the bottom corner of the inside face, and the mortices chiselled out. After marking them off it would first be necessary to bore a series of one-inch holes down to the required depth, one-and-a-quarter inches finally, by means of a brace and one-inch twist bit; this would reduce considerably the amount of chiselling to be done. After boring, the mortice would be carefully cut out and cleaned up, and a little arris would be chiselled on the leading edges.

On Chambers 420 class a filling was placed immediately beneath the outside edge of the rail. This was a piece of four-inch by two-and-a-half-inch oak; the outside edge would be planed fair with the rail and a bead planed on the bottom outside corner, while the inside corner would have a little chamfer put on it. The ends of this filling were dovetailed into the top outside corner of the stanchion.

While the search for the rail itself, cutting it, and preparing it was going on, some of the apprentices would have been cutting the dovetails in the stanchions; these were from off to nothing at the top to half an inch cut back at the bottom of the filling.

With the rail prepared, the first piece would be hove on board by tackle and fitted down into place, while the mould would be modified to suit the other side of the ship. To pull the rail down tight for fastening either a piece of timber would be G-screwed to the side of the stanchions or a cleat nailed

the inner and outer lines and as before these stanchions would be cut at one and a quarter inches above these marks. To find the tenon line a batten one and a quarter inches wide would be laid on top of the stanchions for the whole length of the ship, faired and secured into position by means of nails on each side of the batten, with a finer batten round the stern because of the sharper curve.

When all the tenons were marked work would proceed on the cutting of them, the mark on the top of the stanchion being extended down the side to the shoulder line. Cutting the shoulders was achieved by securing two little battens one on each side of the stanchion at the cutting line; these would act as a guide for the saw, with the shipwright sawing on the line and up to the vertical tenon line, after which a quick tap on a chisel at the tenon line would

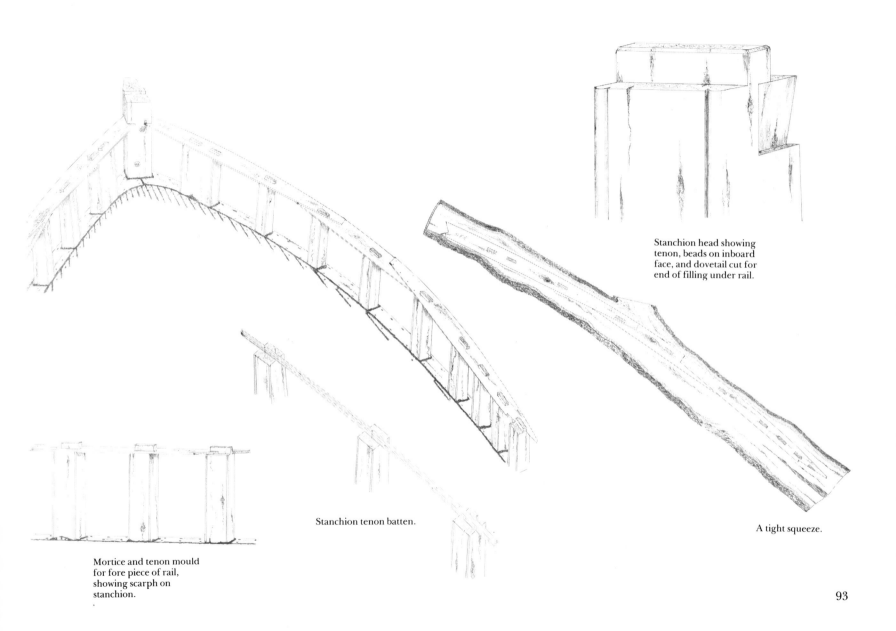

Stanchion head showing
tenon, beads on inboard
face, and dovetail cut for
end of filling under rail.

Stanchion tenon batten.

A tight squeeze.

Mortice and tenon mould
for fore piece of rail,
showing scarph on
stanchion.

93

on, after which a pair of G-screws would be put on and the rail hove down. The leading hand would mark the fastening off, the bolt in each stanchion being centred either for'ad or aft alternately, a nine or ten-inch by half-inch galvanised pilot-pointed bolt being used. Driving the bolts at an angle like this was said on our yard, and I believe generally in the port of Lowestoft, to be driving them on the sosh. The holes would be bored and reamed, and the bolt driven and punched to just below the surface of the rail; being driven at an angle would help to prevent the rail being lifted when rubbing against other vessels in port. The fastenings were in effect dovetailed.

The G-screws could now be removed and preparations made for the next piece. The second piece of rail and indeed the third piece would be used on the side of the vessel, which while not straight was not of sufficient curvature to warrant a mould being made for it. If the piece was virtually straight it could be pulled to the line of stanchions with comparative ease.

To prepare for cutting the shipwright would make a scarph mould to the after end of the first piece, incorporating the scarph stanchion and the following two stanchions, and cutting the mortices in and from the after mortice in the mould; the other stanchions would be marked on a batten which would be laid on top of the stanchions, that is just the fore and after ends of the tenons. The piece would be allowed to extend aft as far as

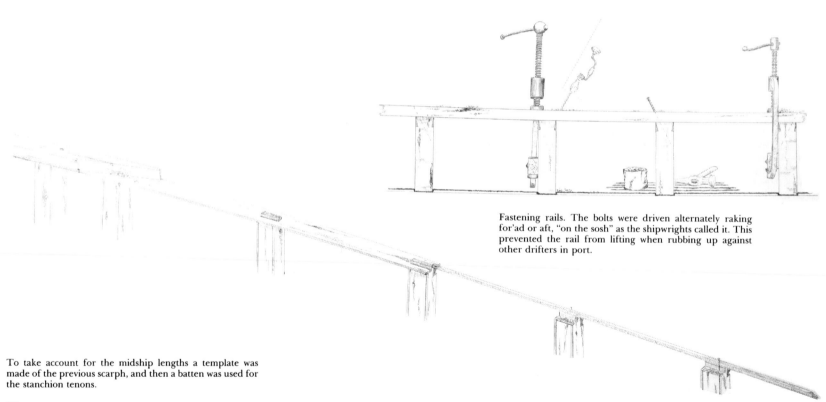

Fastening rails. The bolts were driven alternately raking for'ad or aft, "on the sosh" as the shipwrights called it. This prevented the rail from lifting when rubbing up against other drifters in port.

To take account for the midship lengths a template was made of the previous scarph, and then a batten was used for the stanchion tenons.

94

Taffrail tenon

Taffrail mould centre
piece

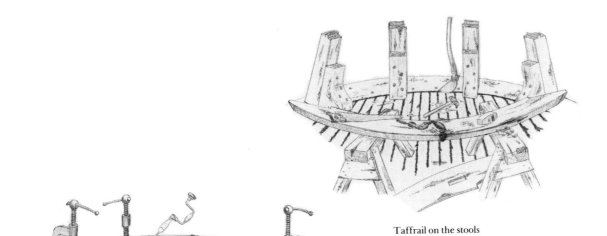

Taffrail on the stools

Fastening off

Taffrail and quarter rail

possible, when the same procedure would be repeated up to where the fore end of the quarter rail would come.

The scarph, while of the same shape as the keel scarph, was not proportionately as long, and the end joggles or snibs would be cut with an angle leading aft from top to bottom. The scarph would be eighteen inches long, with the fore end of the scarph inboard.

To fasten the scarph two galvanised flat points would be used at the joggles or butts, while two half-inch through bolts would complete the fastening, the fore bolt being driven from inboard and the after bolt from outboard. In each case these would be cut off and clenched on a galvanised washer which was let in to a fraction below flush. The usual down bolt was driven into the stanchion.

This work would be proceeding on both sides of the ship at the same time.

Meanwhile, work would be proceeding on the taffrail on much the same lines as that on the rails. A mould would be made for the centre piece, which would have the curvature of the stern and the bevel of the stanchions cut on it; the mortices would also be cut in it.

There was one difference between the taffrail and the rail; it would not be scarphed to its neighbour, the quarter rail, but each would be cut to have a keypiece fitted between them, the keypiece being the means of coupling them together. The through bolts were all driven from outboard, with flat points at the joggle or snib. The inside of the taffrail would be cut square on the bandsaw and this face would be planed and the usual half-inch bead formed on the bottom inside edge. The taffrail was cut much wider in the centre than the rail, after which it was allowed to taper gradually off to rail width through the quarter rails.

The same method of fastening was used for the taffrail as for the rails, with one exception, as we shall see.

Fillings

The fillings which were fitted tight up under the rail and between each pair of stanchions were of oak measuring four inches by two-and-a-half inches, planed on the inside edge and at the bottom, with a chamfer on the bottom inside corner.

They would be measured, cut to the dovetail, and then driven home tight, after which the outside edge would have to be cut to the shape of the rail, planed and with a bead on the bottom outside corner, as I have indicated. After fitting, the outside ends would be fastened to the stanchion with galvanised flat points, while along under the rail, to which the filling would be pulled up tightly by G-screws, holes would be bored for five or six

96

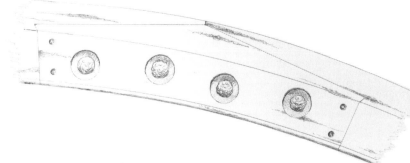

Taffrail and quarter rail key piece

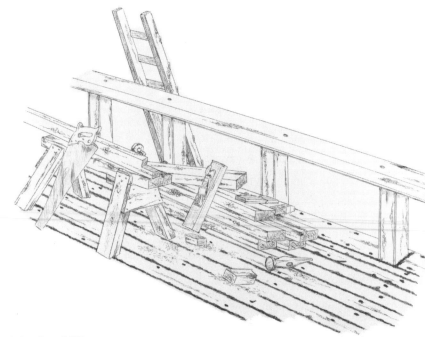

Fitting the rail fillings

il scarph

galvanised flat points which would be driven flush from underneath the rail.

This would occur for the whole length of the ship from for'ad to where the vertical bulwark round the stern would begin; here a different arrangement was made, as follows: one-and-a-half-inch redwood fillings were nailed up to the rail at one-and-a-quarter inches from the outside edge of the rail, all the nailing being done with galvanised flat points.

Bow rails

With the rail fillings complete, work would be started on the bow rails. An effort would be made to find a piece of oak wide enough and long enough and with enough shape, clear of sap and bad places, to cut both the bow rails out of one piece. The rail would need to be six inches deep at the apron, tapering down to one inch at the after end.

stening the fillings

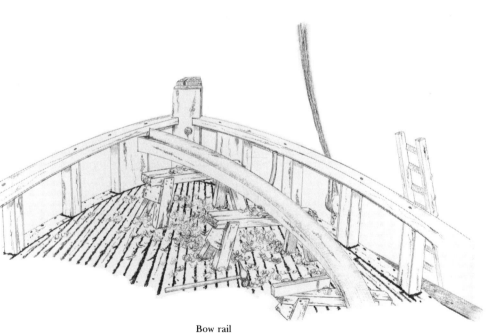

Bow rail

A mould would be made for each piece and the wood would be cut most probably on the bandsaw, after which the taper would be cut. When in the shop the two pieces would be planed up and a convex top shaped by the shipwrights on the job, using adze and plane. The round on the top would not be made too apparent.

When finished, the piece would be bird mouthed at the apron, fitted and then hove down tightly to the rail with G-screws. When held securely the

outside of the rail on the apron would be fastened, using two spikes in each piece, punched down to just below flush.

Now all would be ready to start the fastening in the rails, using purpose-made bolts which would be staggered, one in the rail and one through rail and filling. Provision was made for dowelling when boring, and when the bolts were in, the heads would be white leaded and dowelled down, then cleaned off, leaving the whole job looking quite smart at this stage. The rail, stanchions and coaming would be given a coat of battleship grey priming paint.

Cutting the stem head

At this point it would be decided to cut the stem head. This job entailed cutting both stem and apron, and if an apprentice was detailed off for the job the foreman shipwright would come along to decide on the rake of the stem head itself. When this was decided upon it was customary to tack two battens on the sides of stem and apron at the marks, and these battens would give guidance to the sawyer when cutting the head off.

The shipwright or apprentice would sharpen his saw for the job, and after the pieces were sawn off planing of the stem head would take place, after which a very small arris would be put round the whole.

When completed, as with the bow rail, a coat of primer would be applied, and this would help to prevent the freshly cut wood from opening.

The hawse box

The hawse box of oak would be prepared in the joiners' shop. It would be long enough to reach from the after end of the stem to the centre of the first stanchion, embracing the knighthead, and wide enough to take the hawse pipe, streak, and the scroll, and the name above the streak. It would be parallel from the stem to the after side of the name, beyond which it would be tapered down in a graceful curve to the width of the washstrake, and with a half-inch bead planed on the top outside edge.

With the streak or hollow planed in, a shipwright would collect it for the ship, cut it, fit it, and fasten it with galvanised flat points.

It was now possible either to fit the hawse pipe or at least to mark it out for cutting. When marking one had to remember to leave enough room for the hawse pipe flange above the covering board. To do this a guide hole would be bored through knighthead and hawse box, ater which the aperture itself could be set out by bending a piece of three-eighths-inch steel rod to the

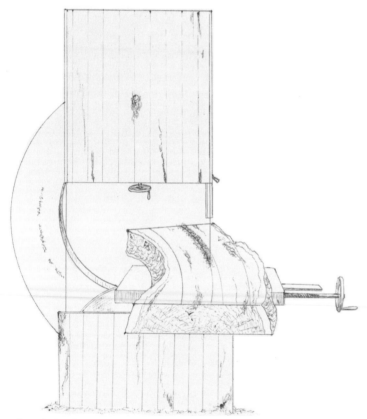

Bow rail on the bandsaw

radius of the barrel of the hawse pipe, and then filing a point on the end of the hook and to the outside edge of it. It was then a very simple matter to mark the elipse both on the inside and outside of the work. There were usually one or two of these rods of different radii hanging around in the shop.

With the hawse pipe set out, an auger would be used to bore a series of holes through knighthead and hawse box, round the perimeter, using a guide rod through the pilot hole. After this it was a simple matter to cut the core from the wood by means of a socket gouge. After the core had been removed the hole would be cleared of ragged wood by means of gouge and round-bottomed planes.

As it was not possible to buy a plane with an iron short enough to pass

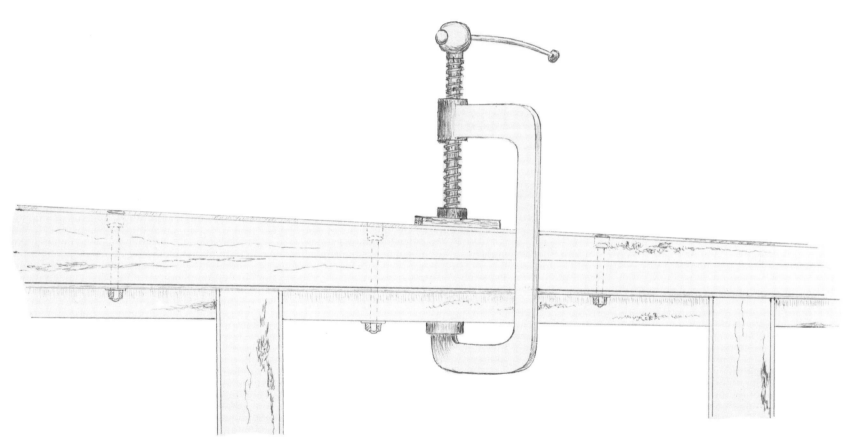

Bolts staggered in bow rail, bringing one in rail and one in fillings. The heads were dowelled.

Tizzard or tizzot bolt

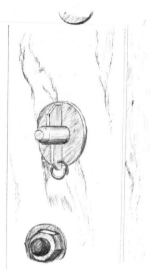

Forelock in after end of
tizzard bolt on apron

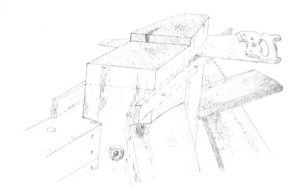

Cutting stem head

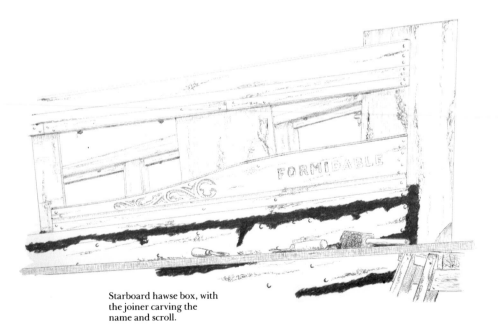

Starboard hawse box, with
the joiner carving the
name and scroll.

Boring for the hawsepipe.
The centre guide rod is
shown.

through the hole, a plane or planes would have to be made for the job, or borrowed from somebody else. If a plane was made for the job a broken-off chisel could usually be used as a plane iron.

In my illustration you will see the two gouges and the planes that Mr Bob Snelling, a Lowestoft shipwright, used when fitting the hawse pipes in the Lowestoft drifter *Pacemaker* in 1911 while serving his apprenticeship at Sam Richards. Mr Snelling made the planes for the job, using old worn chisels that somebody gave him as irons.

It would be necessary to fit the hawsepipe reasonably well as it was made of cast iron, and it could be cracked on an uneven bearing when fastening it. This was an extremely rare occurrence, however; these things were pretty tough, as were all drifters' fittings.

The pipe would be fitted by trial and error, that is to say, the shipwright would offer it up to the job a few times as it neared the final fitting, and any small mark left on the wood by the pipe would be noted and eased off if the projection stood in the way of the pipe fitting.

When it was home snugly it could be fastened, finally being painted post office red.

Tampion

With the hawse pipe fitted, the tampion, which would have been made in the block shop by the block and spar maker, would be fitted. The bole might possibly have been made up of a piece of redwood or pitchpine, with the cap of English elm or beech.

An eyebolt would be fitted in the centre of the inboard end to accommodate a forelock which would hold the tampion in position in the hawse pipe. With the nail head holes puttied up, the whole would be given a coat of primer, followed by an undercoat of blue and finally a coat of blue gloss paint.

Most of the paints used on these ships at that time were simple oil bound paints, sometimes made up by the firm of ship's painters themselves. To get the gloss, I believe, varnish was used as an ingredient.

Name and scroll

With the hawse pipe fitted, it was now possible to set out and carve the name and scroll. The groove for the streak would have been planed into the board in the joiners' shop; concave in shape, it had a width usually of one inch.

Mr George Knights, the foreman joiner on No. 3 yard, generally used to do this job for'ad while Mr William "Chuddy" Tills would carve the vessel's name and port of registry aft, after having fitted the stern bulwark or "starn palins" as Chuddy would say. Although Mr Knights had carving tools he would use an ordinary gouge for the job, as the section of the name and scroll was a simple half-round.

Chambers' vessels' names were in block letters on a straight line both for'ad and aft, with the name on the hawse box about two inches above the streak. The scroll started just aftside of the hawsepipe, beginning with a C for Chambers and tapering off in a graceful design.

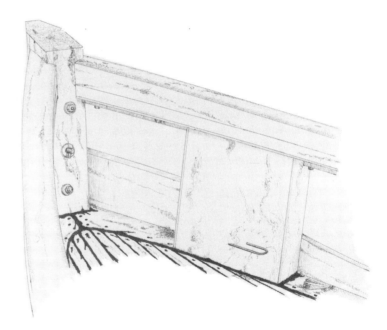

The method of setting out the ellipse for the hawse pipe. A piece of round iron was bent to hook shape, the short end pointed and set to the radius of the barrel, the long end inserted into a pilot hole.

All the yards in East Anglia had their own scroll identification. Richards' scroll had three berries at the ends of branches with leaves, while on Colby's of Oulton Board acorns and oak leaves were the motif, the acorns being at the end of the branches.

Mr Knights would make a first-class job of the scroll. He was not only a first-class tradesman but also a first-class man, liked by all and respected by all, another member of a wonderful team to my way of thinking. I am not romancing; at my age one is able to speak from experience, surely.

With the name and scroll complete, a coat of grey primer was applied; this would prevent the wood from opening.

Tizzard bolt

While we are for'ad let us now put the tizzard bolt in, but first I will give you some idea of the function of this bolt as well as its construction.

Made by the shipsmith in the blacksmiths' shop, it consisted of a black iron bolt with an eye formed at its outer end in which a loose link was placed. The loose link was made so that it could drop down and hang in a vertical fore-and-aft slot so as to be just below flush in the stemband.

The bolt itself was made long enough to project through the after end of the apron, at about half the distance between covering board and stem head. The extra length on the inboard end allowed for a slot for a forelock, which came against a washer on the apron, the whole thing being in the centre of stem and apron.

While the bolt was not a loose fit in the hole, the hole in the stem and apron was large enough to allow for the bolt to be removed easily in case of emergency, and it would be greased when in use in case it had to be slipped quickly, hence the forelock. When made the bolt would be dipped in bitumastic while it was hot, the bitumastic being a presevative for the black iron.

The function of this bolt was to allow a big bass rope tizzard to be hooked into it after being secured to the messenger rope along the bottom of the nets several fathoms from the ship. The purpose of the tizzard was to act as a spring between ship and nets when the ship was ranging about in bad weather.

Earlier drifters had had a tizzard bolt in the stem that was fixed and did not fold away under the stem band, and as a consequence could do damage to other vessels, or be bent over and become unuseable or even broken off. The *Formidable* type of tizzard bolt came into being about 1910.

An apprentice was usually detailed off to do this job, which would be done before the top piece of stem band was put on.

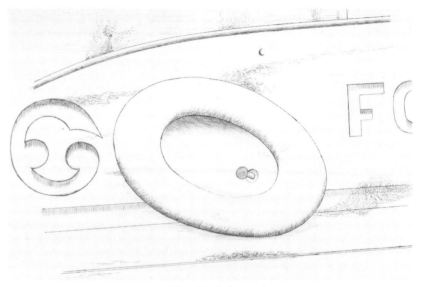

Fastening the hawse pipe with one countersunk head bolt on the inboard end and another outboard.

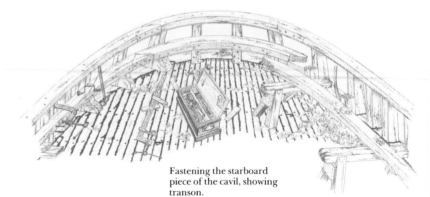

Fastening the starboard piece of the cavil, showing transon.

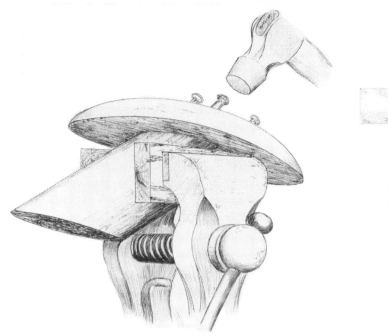

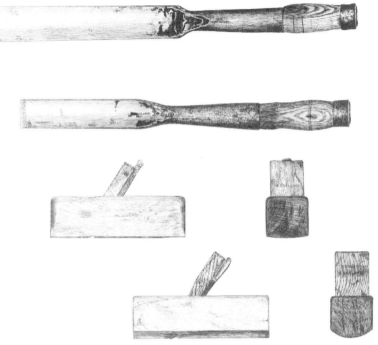

Making the tampion or plug for the hawse pipe. On right are some of the tools used for making the hawse pipe. After the perimeter of the aperture had been bored with an auger the core had to be removed by gouge and the cut planed smooth. The particular planes shown were made by Mr Bob Snelling in 1911 while serving his apprenticeship at Samuel Richards' yard, Lowestoft, and were first used on the drifter *Peacemaker* in that year. The plane irons were improvised from old chisel blades as the ordinary plane iron would be too long to give freedom of movement in use.

Cavil, pin rail and fender rail

We will now have a look aft to see what the shipwrights who are working on the stern are doing. We find that they are on the cavil.

To do this job they will have lined out the top of the stern stanchion knees ready for cutting off; these will form a seating for the centre piece of cavil or transon.

A mould would be made for the centre piece, and as with the taffrail the piece would be left at its widest in the centre; the whole cavil would be four inches thick. The after edge would be cut bevelled to fit the stanchions, while the inside edge would be square. As with the taffrail the centre piece would be coupled up with those on the quarters by means of a key piece; where

these pieces butted end on it would be cut square, as with the butt ends in the key piece itself.

A small arris would be planed on to the edges of the timber, which in itself was P.A.R., with the extreme ends of the cavil bitt-shaped. Double fastenings would be put in the stanchions with two half-inch bolts driven from the inside round the centre of the stern, and possibly one bolt as the wood became of less width. The stanchions being close together in this area made the whole structure stronger. The bolts would be pilot-pointed and a washer would be let in flush on the outside, the bolt cut off and clenched over it.

At this period the mizzen shrouds were carried down to the cavil, but in the standard drifters they were secured on the extreme outside limits of the top of the galley, on to which the deadeye eyebolts were fitted.

On each side of the vessel immediately opposite the tabernacle the stanchions had been closed up for strength, and on the inboard side of these stanchions a pin rail was placed to accommodate the foremast shrouds. The ends of the pin rail were bitt-shaped the same as those on the cavil, and the fastening was reinforced by the use of three lengths of shaped binn iron, with the lower arm of each of these leading down to the stanchion at an angle. This class of vessel was among the very last to have these irons fitted; the arrangement was reminiscent of the old-fashioned chain plates, only used inboard instead of outboard.

Eyebolts for the mizzen and fore shrouds were made up by the blacksmith. Two on each side were put in the cavil and pin rail. Steel belaying pins were used in both these rails for downhauls and in the pin rail for the derrick span and the halyard of the tow foresail, which was sometimes set when on a fairly long run; a cleat was also put on the tabernacle for this purpose alternatively.

Further forward on the knighthead would be a large belaying cleat for the forestay downhaul, while on the two stanchions abaft the knightheads a further belaying rail would be fastened. This was seven inches by two-and-a-half inches, fastened on edge vertically and with bitt ends; it was used to take a quick turn on a mooring rope or the bow fender lashings. This rail was fastened with galvanised spikes.

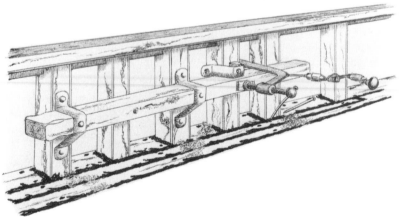

Fastening the port pin rail.

From the end of the cavil for the length of the casing an oak fender rail was fastened on the inside of the stanchions about five inches down from the rail; the size of this rail was three-and-a-half inches by two inches and it was fastened with galvanized flat points which were punched below flush and puttied. The ends of the rail were simply rounded back to flush with either the fore or after side of the stanchions at which they ended.

Between the two thwartship boards was fitted a similar rail, but in this instance it was placed about one-and-three-quarter inches down from the underside of the ship's rail, to accommodate the outboard ends of the mackerel boards, about which I shall write later.

Quarter rubber

Just before the cavil was fitted a quarter rubber was placed one on each side of the vessel. This was also of oak and was fitted horizontally, reaching over six stanchions. It was fastened so that the fastenings, which were through bolts except at the extreme ends, would come just below the cavil, so that in the event of a rubber becoming damaged it could be replaced without any disturbance to the cavil.

The size of the timber would be about five-and-a-half inches by four inches. Its purpose was to fend off other vessels and to protect the bulwarks, while at the same time strengthening the stanchions in this vital area at the point where the wedging pressure would build up at times in the struggle to get up to the market. The pressure here was terrific at times at the peak of the autumn herring fishing, when a large number of vessels would be trying to get up to the market at the same time.

At the time *Formidable* was built quite a lot of redwood was being used on local yards, together with Douglas fir and Oregon pine, for such things as bulwarks, rooming off boards, stanchions and components of that sort. It was, however, becoming increasingly difficult to use one kind of timber only for one type of job, because of importation difficulties, so we were beginning to lean more heavily on home-grown timbers, poplar for instance. I seem to remember, though, that the war was almost at an end before the real effects of these circumstances was felt.

"Starn palins"

To start the bulwark we will go aft to where "Chuddy" would be preparing to start work. The stern bulwark would be made up of deal cut four inches by one-and-a-half inches P.A.R. and with a half-inch bead on one outside corner, each board being finished in the same manner. The wood was

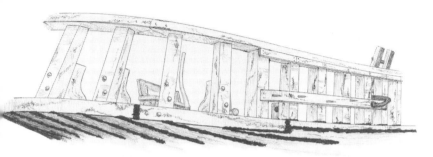

Fastening off the starboard quarter rubber. This was done before the cavil was fitted as the fastenings came just below the cavil.

The joiner constructing the "starn palins". Steam drifters built of wood at Lowestoft and Oulton Broad at this period had a tug stern, with only one or two exceptions.

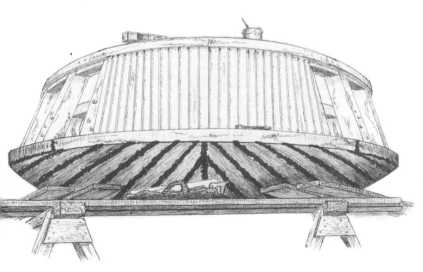

primed with grey priming paint, having first been knotted by a painter.

"Chuddy" would have rigged a stage on stools on top of the original stage to enable him to reach the work, and, starting in the centre, would be getting the fillings cut off, painted and nailed in position. Following this he would start the bulwark, also in the centre, and work his way round the stern to where the vertical boards were to stop on the quarter; this point would determine the angle of the ends of the side bulwark, which would follow. A special bearer would be fitted to take the ends of the side bulwark from underside of rail to covering board.

All the cutting of the vertical boards would be on bevels, of course, and these ends would be painted before nailing in position using galvanised flat points. This was the only piece of bulwark that the joiners worked up, although they did prepare all bulwark for use in the joiners' shop after it left the mill.

To gain experience an apprentice joiner, Jack Moyse, might possibly have been sent with "Chuddy", he would work away from the centre on the other quarter. Jack, a pleasant, friendly boy, started his apprenticeship on the same day that I did; he became quite a good joiner and later became a master builder, that is house builder and repairer; he did not have the same love of ships that I did.

With the bulwark fastened work could be started by "Chuddy" in cutting the streak, name, port of registry and scroll ends in, and this he used to do with good effect.

I think that the work at this stage must have excited him quite a bit, as he might disappear at dinner time in the same way that "Nibs" the fitter did, only in his case it was to *The Lady of the Lake*. He'd come back the next morning, usually holding his head and reporting that he had seen pink elephants during the night or some such thing. In fact I think he saw them during the day, as every now and again one would hear him squeal. "Here they come agin! Here they come agin!" What a character he was!

In my illustration of the bulwark I have shown a section of the various components making up the whole on the vessel's side.

The wash strakes were lifted from the covering board I think it was five-eighths of an inch or possibly three-quarters. It could not be lifted more than this, as more would allow herrings to be washed through in the event of a little water coming on deck. The wash strake had a one-inch groove running along the middle of it and a half-inch bead along the top outer edge.

Above the wash strake was the halfround, as we called it. This was a much wider board and, like the bullnose, would be prepared in the mill on the planing and spindle machines.

105

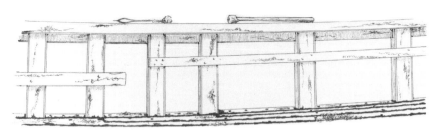

The fender rail.

Shipwrights would work these up on the ship after they had been finished off in the joiners' shop, with the wash strake being fastened off by means of countersunk head dump bolts staggered in each stanchion. The half round would be fastened by four staggered flat points, the halfround having first been set down tight to the wash strake.

The bullnose would next be worked and set tight up under the rail fillings, where it would be fastened with two galvanised flat points in each stanchion.

It now remained for the shutter to be worked. This would be taken account of at each stanchion, a board would be set out for width and taken into the mill to be cut, then back to the joiners' shop to have the edges shot and a bead put on both the outside corners, after which the shipwrights would pick it up, take it aboard and drive it home into position and fasten it.

With the job finished up to this point, it now remained for the nails to be punched, stopped and puttied over, after which the whole of the work would be rubbed down and the whole job given a second coat of primer.

I expect that you have noticed that I have mentioned shipwrights and joiners on this job. It was in fact where the line of demarcation was very apparent between the two trades; this allowed the joiner to prepare the wood, while the shipwrights worked it up and fastened it on the ship, except for the "starn palins", or stern bulwark. I'm not quite sure what happened on other yards, but this is how it was on ours, by agreement with and between the unions.

Wash ports

Just at the fore side of the fore thwartship board a wash port would be fitted on each side of the ship to help to clear any water from the fore deck.

These wash ports consisted of a grating of black iron made up in the blacksmiths' shop of a flat bar top and bottom twisted at the ends to accommodate the fastening, and with a series of round bars shouldered in between and rivetted over on the outside of the flats to hold them in place. The completed grating would be dipped in bitumastic while warm, after which it would be fitted and fastened by the shipwright.

It was very simple but effective, about eighteen inches in length and the width of the wash strake.

Rudder trunk

I should really have written about the rudder trunk before we laid the deck, but I have tried to space my subject out in relation to its position in my series of drawings. In addition in my search for authentic information

The name, port of registry, scroll and streak, cut in by the joiner.

106

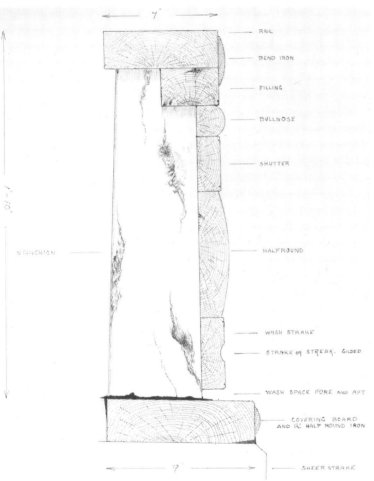

RAIL

BEND IRON

FILLING

BULLNOSE

SHUTTER

HALFROUND

STANCHION

WASH STRAKE

STRAKE OR STREAK. GILDED

WASH SPACE FORE AND AFT

COVERING BOARD
AND 1½" HALF ROUND IRON

SHEER STRAKE

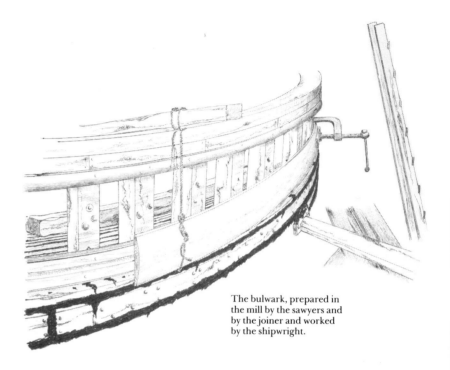

The bulwark, prepared in
the mill by the sawyers and
by the joiner and worked
by the shipwright.

The wash port grating in
the wash strake. There was
one at the foreside of the
foremost thwartship board
and another opposite the
galley.

regarding the various component parts of the ship, and this took time, I could find no shipwright other than my old friend Mr Percy Jillings who had actually made and fitted one of these rudder trunks, and so I am almost entirely dependent on what he told me.

I can remember him making and fitting one or more rudder trunks. Shipwrights tend to become specialists in certain jobs when working on one yard, after they have done those jobs once or twice successfully.

The rudderstock, three-and-a-quarter inches in diameter, was of wrought iron and the rudder trunk was square in section, made so that an aperture three-and-a-half inches square was left at the bottom end of it. That at the upper end was four-and-a-half inches, the one-inch taper being made up by allowing the trunk to expand a half-inch all round, and the finished shape was wedging.

Percy told me that it was made of three-inch selected deal, but I think that it may well have been pitchpine, more water resistant than deal. The joints were tarred and teak splines driven tightly were used as stopwaters; these were also secured. The whole structure was fastened by half-inch galvanised through bolts driven flush, cut off and clenched flush.

Bullens Shop and the leanto. The prototype wood standard drifter was laid off on a floor in the leanto, after which all ship's lifeboats and other small boats for Chambers' vessels were built on the floor by Mr Fred Rouse and Mr Alf Hammond until the closure of the yard in 1931.

Preparations were made very carefully to receive the rudder trunk in the stern timbers and the carlins above. It was made of good length and when ready was driven down tight top and bottom, after which it would be cut off flush under the counter, while at the upper end it would be cut flush at the carlin; before the deck was laid over it a watertight joint would be made and the trunk would be secured. Later a hole would be cut through the deck in the centre of the top aperture for the stock, while the lower end would be caulked round in the ordinary way and left square.

Flat iron straps in stern

I seem to remember two flat iron straps being used in these vessels as a reinforcement in the stern. These were fitted on a beam across the fore side of the stern post and carried down to a frame and floor situated across the stern timbers, but as I am vague about these I will not attempt to describe them further even though I have attempted to illustrate them.

Cleaning out and concreting

During the construction of the vessel and after planking up she would become cluttered up with debris, chips and shavings, and it would be the job of the saw mill people, possibly, of an evening to clean her out. Some of the young boys would sometimes clean out the smaller stuff, and stages and things of that sort would be removed by the shipwrights.

She would be cleaned out extra well on one occasion, though, when preparations were being made to concrete the bottom of the vessel. This job would be done by the saw mill staff on a Saturday afternoon when all other work had ceased, and running into the Sunday.

A banker board would be placed at a convenient position on the ground and a quantity of ballast sufficient to do the job would be laid close to the board; sufficient cement would be brought in, and two or three barrels stood on end would be filled with water. The ballast, cement, and water would be mixed by hand on the board by two men using shovels, while overhead a gin block would have been fixed with a rope downhaul and hook through it.

The concrete when mixed would be hove aboard in buckets and passed down into the hold by a man on deck, while two men would handle it below, one of whom would undertake to trowel the concrete up. The concrete would be put between every frame, starting from for'ad, though it did not really matter where a start was a made.

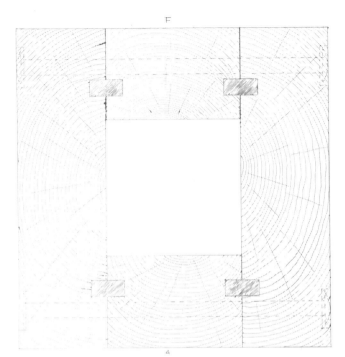

Section through rudder trunk at its upper end. The rudder trunk was tapered, as it was driven down tight into position. Having been left longer than the length required, it would be cut off at both ends when tight.

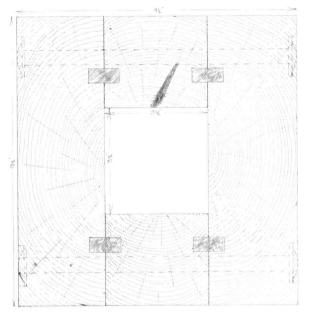

Section through rudder trunk at its lower end. Made of selected timber, it had tight-fitting teak stopwater splines as tongues, and tarred joints. Fastenings, shown in broken lines, were set in flush to allow the rudder trunk to be driven down tight.

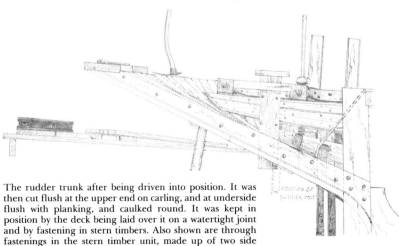

The rudder trunk after being driven into position. It was then cut flush at the upper end on carling, and at underside flush with planking, and caulked round. It was kept in position by the deck being laid over it on a watertight joint and by fastening in stern timbers. Also shown are through fastenings in the stern timber unit, made up of two side pieces and a central piece.

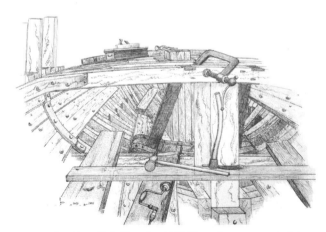

Looking aft. In Chambers' 420 Class a three-quarter-inch by four-inch or five-inch flat hanger was used to help support the counter from a beam seated in the forepart of the sternpost. I have drawn this to the best of my recollection.

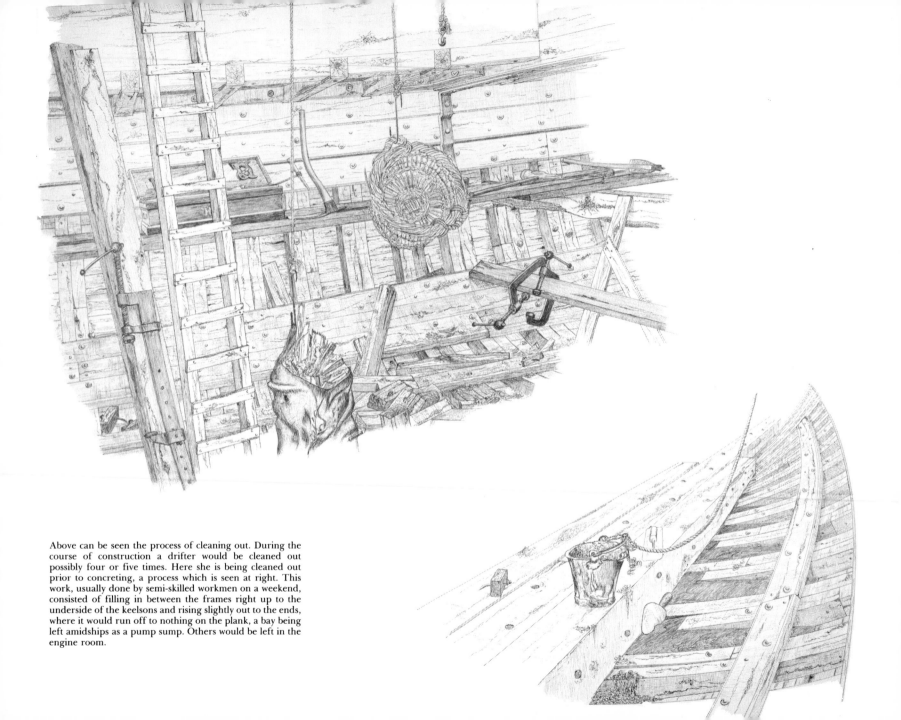

Above can be seen the process of cleaning out. During the course of construction a drifter would be cleaned out possibly four or five times. Here she is being cleaned out prior to concreting, a process which is seen at right. This work, usually done by semi-skilled workmen on a weekend, consisted of filling in between the frames right up to the underside of the keelsons and rising slightly out to the ends, where it would run off to nothing on the plank, a bay being left amidships as a pump sump. Others would be left in the engine room.

One space would be left out amidships, just the fore side of the wheel house, while another would be left at the after end of the engine; these would be pump sumps.

The concrete would be filled tight up under the kelson and side kelsons, and allowed to taper off to nothing on the ship's side. Close to the kelson this would act as a waterway, while also acting as ballast which would keep the vessel stiff and upright on launching.

Coal bunkers

Work would next proceed on the bunkers and things of that nature. A sheathing of one-and-a-quarter-inch oak would be put over the ordinary ceiling in the way of the bunkers, with the two timbers being given a coat of tar in between them; this ceiling was fastened with galvanised flat points.

Some time ago we took the bunker plate template, or mould as we called it, into the blacksmiths' shop, and the plates would by now have been made up to this, allowing one plate to overlap its neighbour. The bolt holes have been drilled and the door aperture cut out of the aftermost plate on each side of the ship; around this aperture a built-up groove would have been formed, and into this the plate forming the door of the bunker would have been placed in position.

After the steel yard came into being all holes, or should I say, all holes wherever possible, were punched.

The plates would be taken into the shop and help given to get them on board the ship, after which two or three senior apprentices would erect them, using chain blocks hanging from a spar in the roof and over the job. The plates would be hove up into position, a podger put into a hole to guide the plate into position, and it was then a simple job to bolt each plate. With drilled holes it might be necessary to use a drift here and there, bearing in mind that a drill might end up a little off-centre, especially if it got off to a bad start. The plates would be bolted as the job proceeded with half-inch hexagon-headed bolts, with the nuts outside the bunker.

Two templates would be made for the angles that would be placed on the ship's side at the fore and after ends of the bunker. After the angle was made up these templates would be used to mark out the outside edges of the bunker end plates. With the angles made up, fitted, drilled, covered with bitumastic, then coach screwed to the vessel's side, it was an easy matter to erect and bolt these plates up, after which an angle would be cut, fitted and also bolted up and down the vertical corners of the bunker. Then it just remained for the blacksmith to fit the doors and attach the loose chain and

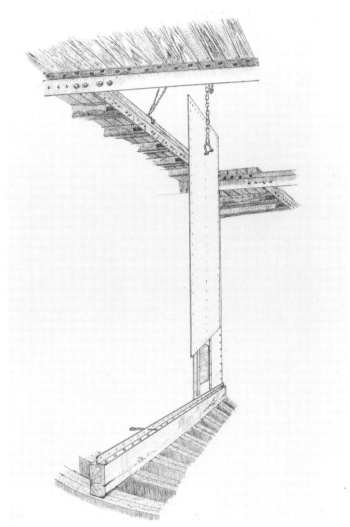

Bunker plates, prepared by the blacksmith and hung by the shipwright, were made of three-eighths-inch steel on English elm bearers.

111

hook by which the driver or fireman would hang the door, leaving whatever aperture they required.

When all was finished, a horizontal but not very wide floor to the bunker would be laid. It was placed as low as possible because of the loss of carrying capacity if it was made wider, and was just wide enough for anybody to stand to trim the coal. Substantial bearers and timber were used, remembering that sometimes the first lumps of coal might drop directly on to the floor say from a railway truck twenty or more feet above, depending on the state of the tide. The floor would be of two-inch oak boards.

For a distance of about six feet from the after end of the bunker, however, the floor would be built up flush with the bottom of the door; this would allow the fireman to slide his shovel wherever he wanted without any fear of it coming up against any obstructions.

With the bunker space complete, it now remained to fit the coal bunker rings and covers. These were made by the firm in their own foundry at Oulton Broad, the bunker rings that we used being a standard size and shape, and of a very heavy cast iron section, the lid or cover itself being fitted with two locking projections which were made to slide into contact with and under two purpose-made projections on the inside of the bunker rings. These were made so that when bunkering was finished a coating of grease could be put on the underside and side of the lid; not only would the lid be locked when twisted home but it would also have become reasonably watertight.

Before the fitting of the bunker rings could be accomplished, however, a doubling of one-inch by seven-inch oak would have to be put on the deck in the way of them. To do this the deck would be cleaned of surplus pitch and any high spots would be trimmed off, after which the areas to be covered would be properly set out; the deck would be given a coating of good thick coal tar. A rectangle of tarred felt would now be cut to size and lightly tacked over the area, using copper tacks, and after this was done the fitting of the doubling would be started.

Six seven-inch boards would be set out, using three on each side of the centre line of the hole. The outside edge of the two outside boards would be half rounded, with the extreme ends of all the boards also half rounded.

After the underside of the boards had been tarred they would be laid and set up tight one to the other, bored and nailed with three-inch galvanised flat points, which were punched to just below the surface. The felt would be cut off cleanly round the wood and that was the job finished.

With the doubling completed, work would be begun on fitting the bunker rings themselves. To do this the centre of the ring would be established and the outer circle of the flange marked by driving a nail through a batten at a

112

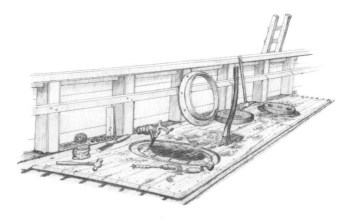

Coal bunker rings being fitted. To protect the deck an oak doubling was fastened over tarred felt. After the circle had been scribed the chisel and adze would be used to reduce the thickness of the combined deck and doubling, then a hole would be bored and the circle cut out with a turnsaw, the ring fitted and bolted down on white lead and an oakum grummit.

Fastening an inch-and-a-quarter oak doubling over the deal ceiling in the coal bunker. In the way of the bunker the three-quarter-inch ventilating space in the ceiling would be filled in.

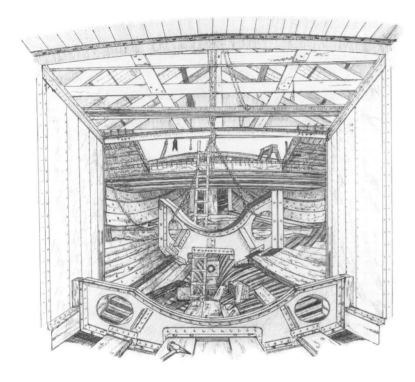

distance equalling the radius to the outer edge of the flange. With this line scribed the shipwright would begin to chisel down to the thickness of the flange; very soon by means of the chisel and adze the thickness of the wood would be reduced, after which the mark would be scribed for the outer edge of the ring itself, at which point further chiselling and more trimming with the adze would be necessary. Very soon it would be possible to bore a hole on the perimeter of the ring line to allow the shipwright to start sawing the circle out with a turn saw.

After the circle had been cut out a small chamfer would be cut round the bottom edge of the hole. And after the trimmed work had been scrutinised and any faults put right, it would be possible to put down the white lead, and then a grummet of oakum on which the flange of the bunker ring would sit.

With the ring having been dropped into place, the shipwright would bore for the fastenings and the bolts would be driven down with grummets of spunyarn under the heads. Washer and nut would be put on and the bolts screwed down tightly from below. As the screwing down operation took place one would usually see white lead spewing out from under the various components; this was a good sign, showing that all was well and that all interstices were filled.

Boiler cradles

With the bunker plates in position it would be possible to put the boiler cradles in.

A template would be made for each of the two cradles across the kelsons and between the bunker plates. The templates would be taken over to the engineering shops, if I remember rightly, where the cradles were made up. When completed these would be given two coats of bitumastic, after which they would be taken across to the ship and hove on board.

The cradles fitted over the kelsons and two side stringers situated between kelson and bunker. Fastening was by coach screws in the kelsons, but if just clear of a timber when over the side stringer bolts would be used, while at the extreme ends the vertical angles would be bolted to the bunker plates. Usually it would be necessary, depending on who was doing the job, to start the holes with a round-nose chisel, set up a drill post and drill further holes with a ratchet drill.

I still have my round-nosed chisel, with which I have started quite a number of series of holes, for instance when fitting a water tank on top of a standard drifter galley. The contents of this tank would be used to flush a toilet that was built into the galley structure. I fitted several of these tanks.

To revert to the round-nosed chisel, one simply dug a hole through the

The for'ad boiler cradle in position and the after one being lowered into the boiler space. This illustration gives some idea of the appearance of the roof of the shop in which the *Formidable* was built. Below are round nosed chisels and a steel drift.

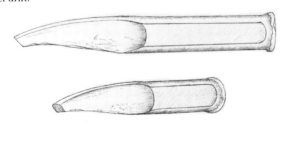

113

Tie irons, made up by the blacksmith in collaboration with the shipwright, were used to supplement the bolting of the sternpost to the keel. Tie iron bolts were driven alternately head and point, then cut off and clinched.

plate with it, rounding it nicely afterwards with a drift, and then went on from there with drill post and ratchet, forcing the drill through the hole by means of pressure put on the ratchet pillar, which was threaded and with a hexagonal sleeve on it, on which we would use a spanner, giving a part turn when necessary.

Usually the apprentices who were on the bunker plates would fasten the boiler cradles, or there might be a shipwright and an apprentice on the job.

Following this one boiler stop would be fastened down to the kelson, with a further one to be put on after the boiler was in.

Tie irons

While boiler cradles were being fitted, such things as tie irons could be fitted and fastened, that for the stem being just a curved three-and-a-half-inch by half-inch iron with three holes in the stem forefoot and a further three in the keel, three bolts being driven from port and three from starboard. These were half-inch galvanised pilot-pointed bolts, cut off and clenched up on the tie iron. Aft two tie irons, oval in shape, would be fitted to the heel of the stern post and keel.

These irons would have been made by the blacksmith and while still warm dipped in bitumastic. The irons would be offered up so that a mark could be taken of them, after which the shipwright would chisel wood out to the depth required. Holes would then be bored through the wood, these being seven-sixteenth holes, after which the irons would be offered up for marking and drilling, four holes in each half in the case of those fitted aft. The bottom of the cut would be given a liberal coat of tar before the irons were finally put in and fastened off.

At the same time that the tie irons were fitted, two one-and-three-eighth-inch holes would be bored through the keel close to them; these holes would be used for the launching pins, one for'ad and one aft. They were bored about two feet from the end of the keel, if I remember rightly, and each of them would be reinforced by having a plate washer let in round it; these were oblong in shape and were well fastened.

Stern tube

The stern tube would be fitted by "Nibs" and the shipwright who was on the job when boring out was done. The tube would be pulled home into place by means of a long threaded draw bar; when safely housed it would be secured.

114

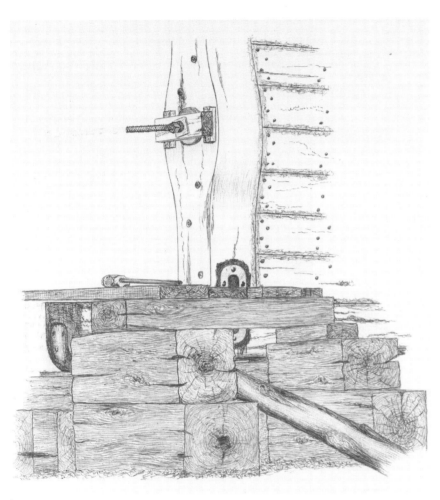

Drawing in the stern tube using a threaded bar.

In the meantime the shipwright would have made up the "cage" in which the bearing on the shaft was to run. This cage, made up in a separate tube which would be fitted into the shaft tube, consisted of a number of lignum vitae splines about one inch thick fitted round the inside of the cage tube and with the last one expanded in shape slightly. This expansion was used to set all the splines up tightly together when it was driven in.

When completed the cage would be put on the lathe in the firm's engineering shop to be bored out exactly to the size required, with "Nibs" in charge of it. In between the splines the shipwright would have planed

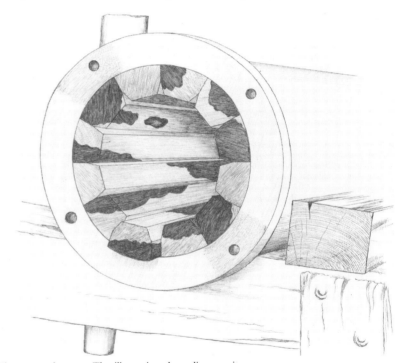

The stern tube cage. The illustration shows lignum vitae splines being fitted and the key spline, slightly tapered, being driven home tight. These splines were bored out to fit the sleeve which had been pressed on to the tail shaft. The V-joints provided for sea water lubrication.

115

sufficient off the inside edges to have left a V joint, and through this V between each pair of splines sea water would percolate, lubricating the shaft itself at its outboard end. The bearing was about two feet six inches long, if I remember rightly.

The sleeve on the shaft was of brass or white metal and was put on the shaft hot, after having been bored out on a lathe. This was a tricky job as the sleeve had to be just right to slide home over the shaft to just where it belonged, the shaft being set up at an angle for this purpose; it was anticipated that it would go no further, although a means of preventing it from doing so was put on the shaft. Once on the shaft, it would be allowed to cool off and shrink itself on tightly.

With the cage in the tube, the shaft would now be put in. On the inboard end of the tube was a gland known as the stuffing box packed with a graphite-covered packing; this prevented water from entering the ship. When the engine was running the gland was allowed to leak a tiny bit, and by this means the "driver" knew that the tube was filled with water.

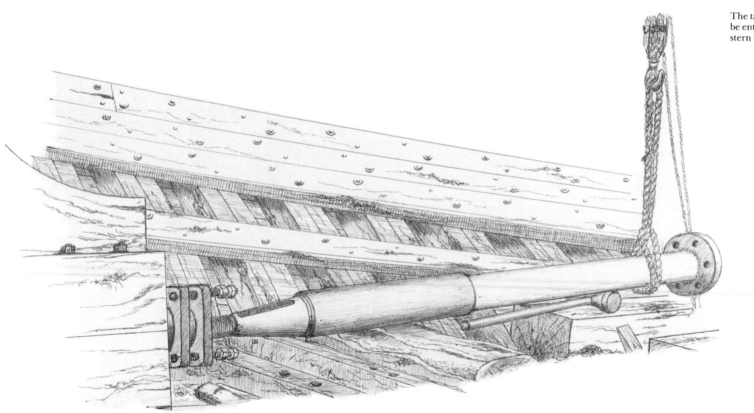

The tail shaft about to be entered into the stern tube.

116

Rudder

I suppose that the rudder stocks of the *Formidable* and *Implacable* were the last two to be hand forged at the Oulton Broad yard of John Chambers. So far as I can remember those for the standard drifters were forged in the North of England, at Darlington, I seem to remember.

The diameter of the stock, which was of wrought iron, was three-and-a-quarter inches. After being cut to length it would be set out so that the position of the straps could be marked on the post by means of a centre punch, used by the smith in charge of the job. The post would be swelled, or jumped up as it was termed, where the three straps were to come; each of these areas would be laid on the forge and heated in turn. When hot enough the bar would be struck at each end by two strikers, four in all, using a hammer each. These men would be driving 1-2, 1-2, 1-2, thereby swelling the bar to the amount that the foreman required. When the straps were welded on later there would be a certain amount of shrinkage on the bar, and the swelling compensated for this.

The bars would be cut to length when all three swellings were complete, after which the toe could be formed. After heating it would be put in the swage on the anvil, the smith using a withe swage which the striker would hit with his hammer. The stock would be on a chain hanging from the forge gantry and one or two other strikers would be rolling the bar over as the toe was being formed. It was impossible to make the toe anything other than the size required as the top and bottom swages would meet. The toe would no doubt have become a little lengthened in the shaping of it, but this was soon rectified by cutting it off to the length required.

To make the straps, which will have to be welded on to the stock, three blocks of iron called "stumps" would be cut off to length. As these would have to be split and shaped, they would be made hot and two holes would be punched through them at what would become the ends of the split that was to be made; these ensured that the split in the iron would not run further. Splitting would now take place using hammer and withe chisel after heating once more. The smith would then shape the stumps into the form that I have shown in my illustration, with a tapered end in readiness to receive the seat of the strap itself.

The straps were made of four-inch flat iron by three-quarter-inch minimum, and the stump ends of these were beaten to a taper in the same way that the stump itself was.

When all was ready the two pieces would be heated to a white heat and very quickly the tapered ends would be laid one on the other and encroaching on each other to allow for a diminishing size during the welding

Making the rudder stock. A three-and-a-quarter-inch diameter iron bar is being heated at one end in the blacksmith's forge in order to shape the two-inch diameter toe. Prior to this operation the post would have been swelled or jumped up in the strap positions to allow for shrinking and drawing out when welding.

process. The strikers would start to hammer the two pieces together at an extremely fast tempo, bearing in mind that the two pieces of iron had to be literally beaten one into the other during the short time that the iron was hot enough to do this.

The blacksmith, after the first rush was over, would indicate to the striker where he wanted him to hit the iron by touching it momentarily with his own

The head of the rudder stock is squared to a depth sufficient to take the yoke, which was usually shrunk on after the vessel was afloat, and the tiller on top of that. A slot was made to take a forelock in the tiller. Below is the toe being formed.

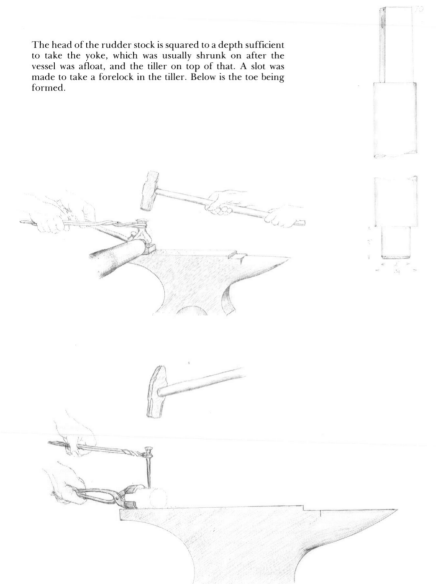

hammer. The two of them would be working at top speed, the striker being relieved by another who was standing by for this purpose, as the work was being done with a twelve-pound hammer. At Chambers' Lowestoft yard fourteen-pound hammers were used.

The last few blows would be used in trimming the weld up, after which the strap would be measured, marked off, then cut off to its required length and rounded at the ends, with an arris being hammered on in the meantime as the work progressed. The opposite end of the strap would now be treated in the same manner, after which the iron would be heated again at the throat and the two ends turned up to be parallel with each other. The bolt holes for the rudder blade itself would then be drilled.

Next would come the biggest operation of all, the welding of the straps to the stock, this was called "fire" welding. Pretty well all hands in the blacksmiths' shop would be on this job, as the job would now be so heavy and there would have to be enough men to keep the job going, with no slowing up of any part of it. Once again the stock would be slung from the gantry and a portable hand-hold would be clamped on it by a bolted collar to make it easy to turn the job first one way and then the other so that the strikers would hit the iron exactly where required.

Four strikers would stand by for this so that they could relieve each other when tiring. The stock would be on the first forge, while the strap would be

Making the straps. A piece of three-inch bar is cut and two holes are punched in it. It is then split and shaped to the stock and to receive the remaining length of strap, which is welded on.

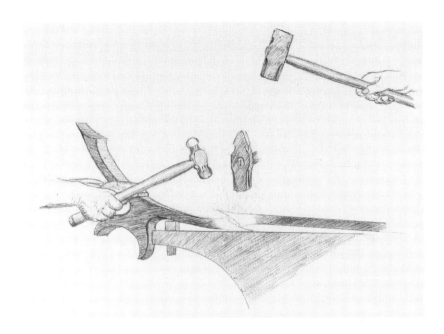

on the next one, and at a given signal the one would be put on the other and the beating begin, care being taken to keep the straps square with the stock and with the second and third ones in line with the first. All this work had to be done at top speed; I have known accidents to happen, but also to be ignored.

On one occasion at Chambers' Lowestoft yard some hot scale went into the foreman blacksmith's shoe, but he kept on with the job until it was finished even though smoke was coming from his shoe. He was laid up for several weeks afterwards. On another occasion a blacksmith's fingers got in the way of a hammer when on a rudder job, but he saw the job out before receiving attention.

With the completion of the straps the square at the rudder head for the yoke would be completed, after the stock had been cut to length.

During the beating process the stock at the strap position would have been

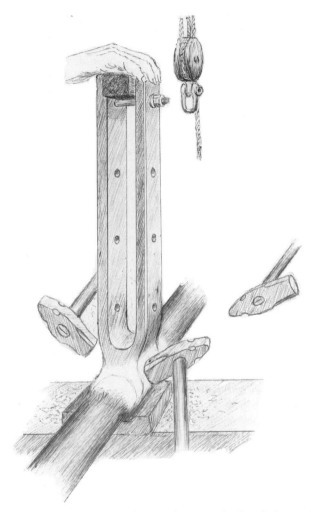

The extension to the straps was a length of inch-and-a-quarter by three-inch wrought iron which was welded to the base piece. The two parts of the scarph were laid together and hammered by the strikers using a very fast tempo, the blacksmith controlling the iron and indicating the position of the next blow with his ball pein hammer. The two pieces having first been heated to a white heat, the fibres of one piece were driven into the pores of the other, welding the two together, as seen at top left. When welding on the straps the rudder stock would be rolled from side to side, as seen above, a tackle being used to assist this operation.

worked backed to its original size. With the completion of the rudder stock, work would be started on the rudder yoke, and for this purpose a big piece of square iron would be cut off, put on the forge to be heated, jumped up, flattened and expanded. A hole would be pierced and later squared to fit the rudder stock, after which the two ends would be heated and shaped for welding on the two arms of the yoke. These two arms would have eyes formed in the ends, and would have been tapered before being prepared to be welded to the boss. The eyes will eventually take the shackle pins of the steering chains.

With the completion of the yoke, the blacksmith would start to prepare for the tiller, the preparation being the same except for the fact that the boss would be smaller and that only one welding arm would be needed; on to this would be "laid on", as it was called, a piece of round iron to form the rest of the tiller. This would be formed into a graceful upward curve, levelling off

towards the top end, on which a knob would be formed. This knob at some time or other would be used to ensure that a bolt rope did not slip off the tiller, as for instance at the very first time of use, on launching, when the tiller would be secured amidships by the bolt rope.

The blacksmith would have formed the "toe iron" which had a central keep formed, and on each side of which straps were formed to the shape of the after end of the keel; the outside of these came flush with the outer skin of the keel. Holes would have been drilled in this iron opposite each other, after which the iron would be warmed and dipped in bitumastic.

The shipwright would fit the toe iron, using a chisel for the job, and when all was ready a good coating of tar would be given to the wood, whereupon the iron would be driven home tight and fastened off, the bolts being driven alternately from port and starboard; they would be cut off and clenched.

At this point the shipwright will take over again to make up the rudder

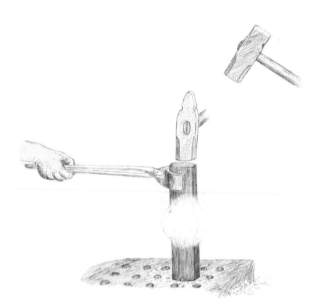

A piece of iron being jumped up to form the boss of the rudder yoke. After shaping and holing, the arms of drawn-out two-inch by three-and-a-half inch iron would be welded on.

The blacksmith jumping up a piece of iron for the tiller boss.

The tiller boss ready for the shaft to be welded on.

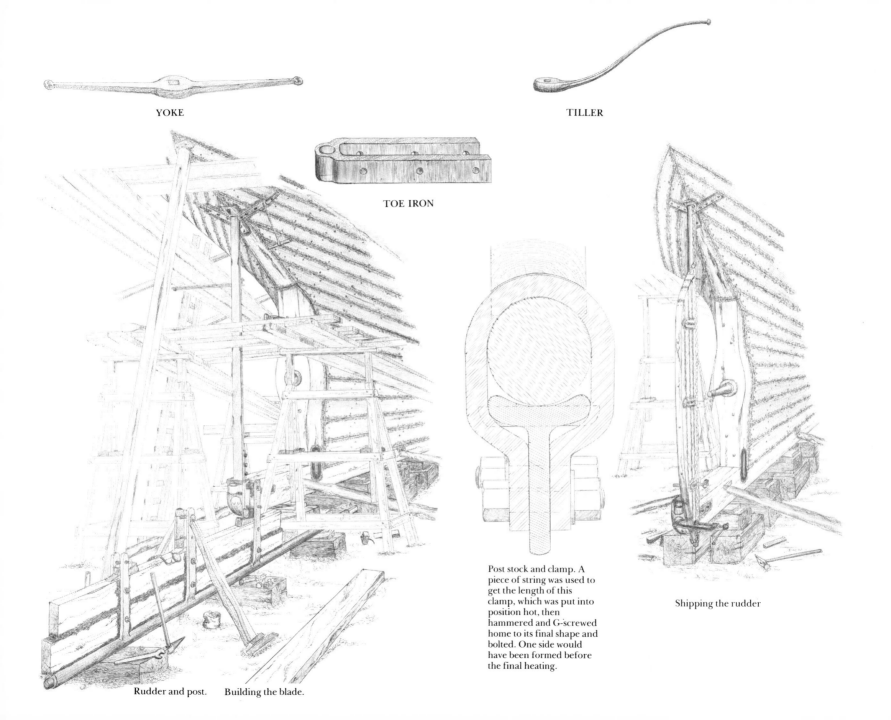

YOKE

TILLER

TOE IRON

Rudder and post.   Building the blade.

Post stock and clamp. A piece of string was used to get the length of this clamp, which was put into position hot, then hammered and G-screwed home to its final shape and bolted. One side would have been formed before the final heating.

Shipping the rudder

itself, on which oak will be used having first been sided to fit between the straps, which will have been set in a plumb position with the rudder stock resting on bearers on the shop floor. The rudder would be built up of timber lying around the planking area, probably short lengths of topside, bilge, or stringer, and it would most likely be built of four pieces. Each one of these would be fitted tightly between the straps, having been given a coating of tar everywhere it touched iron. As each plank was fitted the shipwright would bore it off and bolt the piece, using hexagon-headed black iron bolts which would have been given a coat of bitumastic by dipping. Each plank would be set down tightly to the previous one before fastening.

When all was fastened the finished shape of the rudder would be lined out, after which it would be rounded off, using saw, adze and plane. The rudder could be made to look very nice when it was being finally shaped and rounded up, after which it would be given two coats of tar.

Rudder post

The rudder post was made up of heavy T-bar with the top and bottom ends flanged in a fore and aft direction, these flanges being drilled for bolting.

At the location of the rudder clamp and gudgeon the edges of the angle would be set back a little to allow the clamp to fit more snugly, after which the post could be hove up into position using a chain passed down through the rudder trunk and hooked to a chain secured to a spar on the roof trusses.

The post would have been prepared from a mould made by the shipwright for the use of the blacksmith. It would of course usually fit first time, as the shipwright would have kept in close consultation with the blacksmith while it was being made.

After the post was erected two further straps would be made from a shipwright's mould for the head of the post, and two more for fitting on the keel, the first two being shaped so that one fitted on each side of the post under the stern. When all were completely fastened the whole would be quite a substantial job.

With the rudder post in position, the rudder could be shipped. This would entail using the chain blocks again, securing a chain or wire right round the rudder and stopping it back with a small wire to the square at the head of the rudder stock, which would help to guide the stock into the rudder trunk which, being square, left enough room for the chain. It might be necessary to dig out a little soil below to allow the rudder to enter without trouble.

A pair of G-screws near the toe of the rudder would serve to keep the chain secure and also to give the shipwright below a handhold in the event of him needing to move the rudder at all sideways. With the rudder in position the clamps, or bands as the blacksmiths preferred to call them, could now be made; a stage would be rigged for the blacksmiths to get the measurement and put them on. Two holes would have already been drilled in the rudder post at each position, and the blacksmith would take the measurements, usually using a little piece of trawl twine to get the length, and make a little sketch of the band in which the position of the bolt holes would be shown, one near the throat of the bar and the other one staggered from it.

The band would now be made up completely from four inches by half-inch flat iron, with holes drilled for three-quarter-inch bolts. A slot cut in the wood at the stock was left for this band to pass through. After it was completed it would be reheated and offered up, and at this point a man would be stationed on the stage in readiness to receive each band from a striker who would run from the blacksmiths' shop with it after it had been reheated for the last time.

The blacksmith on the stage would take it from the striker with tongs, push it through the slot and start to hammer it home right away, then get a pair of G-screws on it. A long threaded bolt would be put through it to heave it home. He would finally bolt it and allow it to cool off, all this work being done at top speed before the iron cooled off too much.

With the rudder in position it now remained to secure the lignum vitae bush at the rudder head.

Two three by three-inch angle irons which would have slots cut in them to allow for half inch forelocks would be bolted down through deck and carlin to accommodate the two pieces of lignum vitae which would encircle the rudder stock. These were slotted so that they would not be able to escape from the angles and forelocks, the forelocks being wedge shaped to allow any wear in the wooden bush to be taken up.

The pieces of lignum vitae would be fitted round the stock end with a half an inch of space allowed between the two pieces; this space would allow for any wear in the circle, which might enable the rudder to slap about, to be closed. The forelocks had a series of half-inch holes in them which allowed for a bolt to be put through to prevent them from slipping back after setting up.

Some time later, shortly before the vessel was listed in readiness for launching, the tiller would be shipped so that the rudder could be secured in a fore and aft position by means of bolt ropes fastened to the cavil.

A forelock was passed through the stock above the tiller to prevent it lifting off.

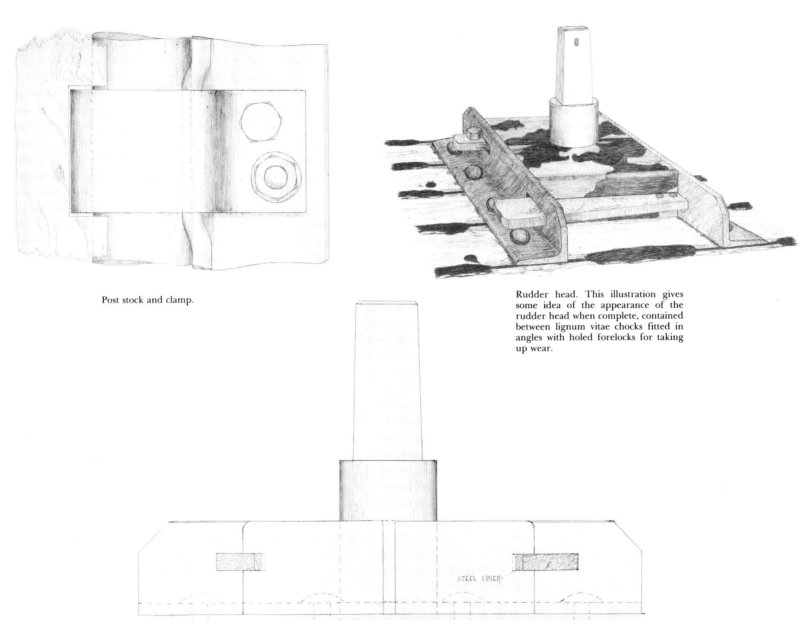

Post stock and clamp.

Rudder head. This illustration gives some idea of the appearance of the rudder head when complete, contained between lignum vitae chocks fitted in angles with holed forelocks for taking up wear.

STEEL LINER

Section showing gap and forelocks.

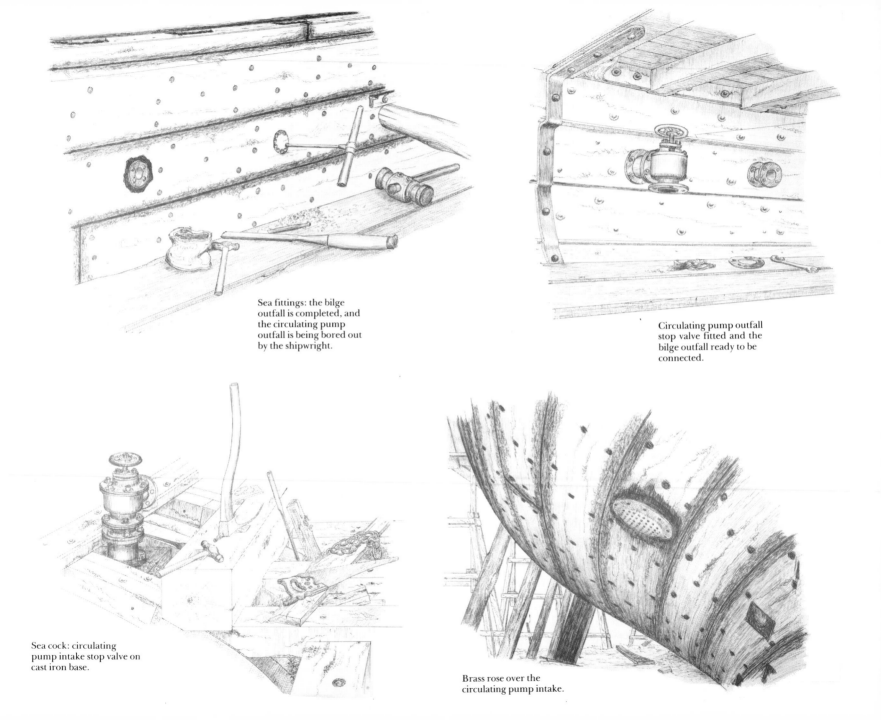

Sea fittings: the bilge
outfall is completed, and
the circulating pump
outfall is being bored out
by the shipwright.

Circulating pump outfall
stop valve fitted and the
bilge outfall ready to be
connected.

Sea cock: circulating
pump intake stop valve on
cast iron base.

Brass rose over the
circulating pump intake.

Sea fittings

One shipwright and an apprentice would usually be detailed off to instal the sea fittings. Work would most probably be started on the condenser circulating pump intake valve stand, situated on the port side of the vessel between the engine bed and bilge stringers and towards the after end of the engine bed. A timber bed to bring the flange up level, and to reinforce the plank that would have to be cut, would first be fitted down on the inside of the ship's bottom. The joint between plank and chock would be made watertight, though a pipe would be fitted through to the outer face of the plank. After fitting the bed, boring out could be started.

All joints between metal and wood were bedded down on white lead and tarred felt. Spunyard grummets would be put round the bolts under heads and washers, after which the whole fitting would be hove down tight.

During wartime the cast iron fittings that were fitted directly to the hull of a fishing craft were found to be very vulnerable when a mine or depth charge exploded in the near vicinity of the vessel. To counteract a tendency for them to crack the valves were later mounted on welded steel pylons placed directly on the hull of the vessel. A brass rose would be fitted at the seaward end of the aperture to ensure that no debris was taken into the system while the engine was running.

The condenser outfall and the bilge suction outfall would also be fitted at about this time. These two pipes were fitted in the top stringer immediately below the shelf, and were fitted with screw down stop valves to which the pipe from engine or pump would be fitted.

To fit the pipes the shipwright would bore the core of the hole round with an auger, after which he would clean it out with a socket gouge in the ordinary way, fitting the pipe as he went along. The flanges would be let in flush, then bedded down on white lead with a spunyarn grummet, while spunyarn grummets would also be placed under the heads of the holding down bolts.

Binn irons

With the intake and outfall pipes installed it would be possible to put the binn irons on. The hull would be given two coats of coal tar and a coat of black varnish on the strakes which would accommodate the binn irons, while the irons themselves would be given a coat of bitumastic. Generally the tarring was done by the men from the saw mill during the weekends and evenings.

Three binns were put round the 420 class, one on each of the three top strakes, each one starting at the hooding ends of the planks. Aft the top iron ran until it curled under the quarter, stopping when it became of no further use, while the one on the strake below that stopped about two feet short of the top one. The bottom iron stopped the same distance short of the second, so that all three finished symmetrically.

A further iron was put round the rail, right round this time, while a short one was put on each quarter rubber, with the ends of these turned home towards the bulwark. All these were fastened with countersunk head bolts just under four inches long.

Around the outboard edge of the covering board a one-and-a-half-inch convex iron was placed, fastened by means of nettlefold brads.

Bollards and fairleads

It would now be opportune to fit the bollards, of which there were two on each bow. These were let in flush, that is, the base plate lay flush with the top of the rail, and then were secured with six countersunk head bolts each.

To seat the bollards the shipwright would mark them out and then bore holes with a big twist bit to the depth of the base, after which he would chisel the wood out neatly; when the bollard fitted he would give the area a coat of paint, put the bollard in and fasten it off, pulling the holding down bolts down tightly by means of nuts and washers on the underside of the rail.

Two fairleads were fitted in the quarter rail in a like manner.

A large towing bollard would be fitted on the fore deck in the centre and about midway between tabernacle and apron. This was put down on tarred felt and fastened by bolting through beams and carlins.

Two smaller bollards were also fitted on deck, one on each quarter.

Molgogger holes and molgogger

The molgogger holes, of which there were four each side, spread out on each bow so that a choice of position could be made when in use, extended from about a foot from the apron to abreast of the main hatch coaming heading; all were equally spaced.

The holes would be bored large enough to allow the molgogger to swivel freely. After boring the hole, a steel washer with a hole drilled to take the shank would be let into the bowrail flush and screwed down in position, using four screws, one in each corner of the washer. A cast iron cup was fitted to and screwed down on to the covering board for the molgogger shank to stand in; this cup was flanged and had holes in each of the four corners for galvanised screws. The fittings were made so that the molgogger could be quickly removed, while at the same time it would be held strongly and securely. I have no doubt at all that the methods used, while of the very simplest, were also the most efficient, as were most of the working parts of a Lowestoft drifter at that time.

You may be wondering what a "molgogger" is. It was a portable fairlead over which the messenger rope, that is, the rope that ran along the bottom of

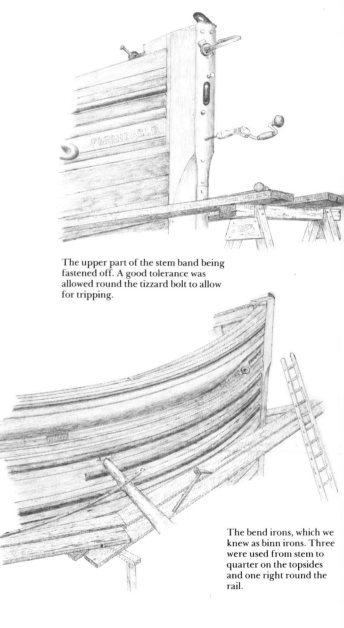

The upper part of the stem band being fastened off. A good tolerance was allowed round the tizzard bolt to allow for tripping.

The molgogger in position.

The bend irons, which we knew as binn irons. Three were used from stem to quarter on the topsides and one right round the rail.

126

Black iron countersunk
head bolt, as used to fasten
bend irons.

By now the hull would have had two
coats of coal tar, while the bulwarks
would have had one coat of priming and
one undercoat inside and out.

Fitting fairleads and boring molgogger holes. I have
indicated how the inside face of the stanchions was grained
about a week in advance of the actual painting of them. The
rail was painted black, in some cases with a red bead, and the
inside of the bulwark and the fore and aft faces of the
stanchions and knightheads were green, while the inside
face of the stanchions was grained, as were the cavil and pin
rail.

the fleet of nets and to which each net was secured at each end by a seizing,
was passed when being hauled, the seizing having been cast off by that
member of the crew known as the castoff just before reaching the molgogger
itself. There were four vertical rollers and a horizontal roller in the
molgogger.

As the warp was hauled over one roller and was contained between four
vertical rollers it was virtually impossible for it to be chafed during the
hauling operation. After leaving the capstan the warp was led to the rope
room over another roller and below; this roller was generally of a softer
wood, possibly spruce, due to the fact that the warp moved about more and
so spread the wear.

In bad weather the molgogger would be secured, that is, held down, by
means of a lanyard which was spliced into an eye on the frame; this lanyard
would be carried down on the inside of the vessel's rail and secured round
the shank below.

Stem band

At about this time the stem band would be prepared and fastened. The
length which turned under the forefoot would have been made up from a
piece of sand band, and starting from there would be gradually reduced in
width and shaped to conform with the shape of the stem itself, running up
the stem at the width required.

The stem head band would be made from a mould provided by the
shipwright doing the job. This mould would give the blacksmith the shape of
the stem head, including the shape of the top of the bading, and a slot cut in
it would indicate the position and size of the loose link of the tizzard bolt. A
good tolerance would be allowed for the link so that it could be tripped
easily.

An eye would be formed at the head of the band to accommodate the
fixed hook of the bottom block of the forestay downhaul. The blacksmith
would give the eye a tilt aft to conform with the general direction of the
forestay itself.

When finished the band would be drilled to the shipwright's requirements, for countersunk head bolts as in the sand band, after which it would
receive two coats of bitumastic; the stem itself would have been coated with
tar and black varnish in readiness to receive it. It just remains for it to be
taken into the shop, to be offered up on to the ship, then secured by means
of G-screws and fastened, well and truly.

Up till about this time many drifters, including the sailing boats, would
have whiskers fastened on each side of the stem and carried back on to the

127

covering board. I would think that the overall length of these would be two feet six inches, by two inches sided. They would be fastened with galvanised flat points, and when fastened a length of one-and-a-half-inch convex iron would be shaped to a mould made by the shipwright, then drilled for nettlefold brads, painted with bitumastic and secured in position by the man on the job.

These were used a great deal as a means of getting on board or ashore when the vessel might be laying head on. I do not remember *Formidable* having them, but my friend and fellow apprentice Mr Fred Woolnough has assured me that she did. These were discontinued with the advent of the standard drifter.

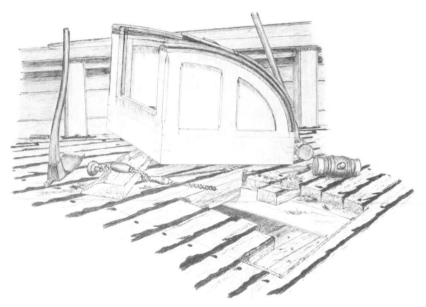

The fo'c'sle hoodway, made by the joiner and fitted by the shipwright, who is cutting away the deck to seat the hoodway on to the carlins and beams.

Fo'c'sle hoodway

Among the various works going on at this moment would be the fitting down of the fo'c'sle hoodway, which would have been made in the joiners' shop. This would have been made perfectly by any one of the several joiners employed on the shop; I have already named them with the exception of Jimmy Wilson and "Banker" Roope. I always thought that any one of these men and the boy Jack Moyse would be hard to beat at his job.

The hoodway itself would have an oak coaming; all the rest of the framework would be of selected oak, including the hatch runners, while the panels in the sides would be of Oregon pine. The hatch cover itself would most probably be of redwood tongued and grooved boards.

The completed hoodway would be made watertight as far as possible and given two coats of grey primer. It would also be fitted with a good substantial hasp and staple, both galvanised. The treads at the top of the washboard and steps would be of good section purpose-made galvanised iron, fastened by means of brass screws.

The shipwright who was to fit down the hoodway would get it on board and mark out the deck for cutting, which he would do firstly by boring a series of holes close up to the inside of the line, after which he would cut the square out using chisel and adze. When the cutout was ready the hoodway could be dropped into position and held down by means of G-screws. The holes for the fastenings would then be bored upwards through carlin or beam, with the bolts being driven upwards from below. It would then be caulked round and payed up.

Rooming off

Rooming off was a comparatively easy job for a shipwright from the physical ability point of view as it was one of the few more or less light jobs in the trade. It resembled carpentry, and one was able to stand and look down on the job most times; as a consequence it was a most sought after job, a relief from the contortions that most of the shipwrighting jobs on the ship called for.

The stanchions and boards were all of soft wood, the stanchions most probably being of Scots pine, we called it fir as quite a number of these trees grew locally, while the pound boards would be of imported deal.

To set the stanchions out the shipwright would drop a plumbbob at each end of the inside face of the fore and after coamings, and a line would be struck on the timbers in between the two spots to give the fore-and-aft line. It was to an offset from this line that the toe plate for the stanchions would

be fixed, room enough on the plate being allowed to accommodate the stanchion. The plate would be spiked down to the timbers, after which stanchions would be set out, each stanchion being immediately below the half-beam above (allowance being made for the declivity on which the ship lay); when the half-beams were set out on the coaming this was done with rooming off in mind, and so a stanchion would automatically come into its proper place.

With these lines set out, a cleat would be fixed round the proposed toe of the stanchion. This same principle applied to the stanchion's head, with a shoulder being cut at the back of the stanchion to stop it from falling forward, the shoulder backing on to the coaming. The stanchions, which were six inches by six inches square, would have been cut in the saw mill, most probably on the rack bench. They would be put through the planing machine and spindle machine, by which the grooves for the pound boards would be spindled out.

When jobs of this sort were done the machine, which would be revolving at a pretty high rate, would keep up a continuous hum or drone, and there would be fine shavings and dust all round the machine and in the air. No masks were worn in those days, although goggles sometimes were.

When fitted in the ship, each stanchion would be finished off with a small arris on each corner.

The side stanchions came under the coaming and were fixed. Three other fixed stanchions were erected on the kelson, one in the centre of the fore main hatch beam and one in the centre of each of the after beams, while on the centre line of the hatch itself were fitted portable half stanchions, that is, half the height of the hold including the depth of the coaming. These stanchions would have portable bearers called "perks" fitted on top of them athwartships, the ends of the perks being tenoned to fit into the main groove of the opposite stanchions. In the centre of the underside of the perk would be a mortice cut to fit over a tenon at the top of the stanchions, the effect of which was to stabilize the stanchion.

The perks would later be completely covered with loose boards lying in a fore-and-aft direction. The purpose of these was to carry a whole fleet of nets. In the illustration "Longitudinal Section" you will see the nets on the perks.

The bottoms of the wings, as the fish pounds were called, were built up several inches at the stanchions. Small floors were laid and fastened in these,

Fish pounds being built. The stanchions were grooved on the spindle machine in the sawmill, and wherever possible the pound boards were in standard lengths. The rope hanging down has in its end a timber hitch topped with a half hitch, which was mostly used to handle timber.

running off to nothing on the ship's rise of floor, so a small area was level in the pound for the fisherman to work on when discharging the catch, that is when he had worked his way down. This also made a good base to the pound for cleaning purposes, as except for the waterway the whole of the hold was ceilinged out.

Pound boards were usually cut on the band saw, with a slightly rounded end to make it easy to lift the boards from the stanchion. Efforts would have been made to keep the boards to a standard length, but this was not always possible, and each board was numbered in accordance with its own particular group in any given position. On the ship's side and bulkheads, cleats would be nailed to form grooves for the boards, galvanised flat points being used as fastenings. Here again boards would have to be numbered because of the varying lengths and bevels.

When building up a "wing" the key board at the top would pass through an aperture cut on the stanchion for this purpose, and this board would be kept in position by means of a wooden button on the board below.

When the hold was completed by the shipwright the whole would be given a coat of white "petrifying" paint.

Main hatches

With the fitting out of the hold completed, the shipwrights would set about making the "fore and afters" or beams and hatches.

A score or recess would be cut on the inside faces at the top and in the centre of the coaming headings, and into this score would be fitted the fore and afters, one for the main hatch and the other in the "after well". These timbers would be six inches by six inches, with a little bevel on each edge of the top, planed to the same bevel as that of the coaming heading; in the centre of the top and for its whole length would be fastened a piece of elm, most probably cut two-and-a-half inches by two-and-a-half inches and fastened with galvanised flat points, to take the ends of the hatches themselves.

On the bottom corners a half-inch chamfer would be planed, and about four inches from the end and in the centre a hole would be bored horizontally to take a lanyard of two-inch rope, knotted at each end probably with a wall and crown, and left hanging about one foot on each side; by means of this rope the beams could be lifted out. They were made so that they would fit no matter which way they were turned.

The hatches themselves were made of imported deal or redwood, of two pieces of nine by two-and-a-half inch planed all round stuff, the two pieces

being bolted together by two lengths of mild steel rod, driven to just under flush at each end.

The hatch would then be cut and fitted. Two hand hold holes would be chiselled out sufficiently large to allow a hand to reach round in them, a piece of one-and-a-quarter-inch convex iron would be fitted across the diameter of the cut-out, let in flush and screwed down into position by means of a galvanised screw at each end. This iron would be given a coat of bitumastic before fitting. When finished the coamings and hatches would be given a grey undercoat primer, then a blue undercoat, followed by two top coats of blue.

There was no need to number the hatches as the sizes would have been worked out so that they fitted anywhere.

In the deck beside the coamings two self-locking fish rings would be fitted. These were similar to bunker rings, but smaller, flush with the rim and galvanised. They were fitted down into an elm chock or pad on the deck which would be about two inches thick to allow the ring to finish flush with the deck gratings which have to be fitted; these chocks would be fitted down on tarred felt and white lead, and it was through these that the herrings would be scudded down into the wings.

Thwartship boards

The thwartship boards were built up of two pieces of three by nine-inch deal, plus a piece cut to the deck camber and fastened on the bottom edge.

The shipwrights would fair the edges of the deals that were to be fitted together, after which these would be laid flat and given a coat of paint along those edges. They would then be cramped together and holes would be bored at intervals of about two feet to take lengths of half-inch steel rod which would be driven flush. The cambered pieces would be nailed along the bottom of the lower board using galvanised flat points.

Small V-shaped cut-outs would be made at intervals along the bottom edge of the board to release any water that might be trapped on the deck at the base of the board. When the boards were made up they would be cut off for length across the ship, one at the fore end of the hatch and the other at the after end. They would be cut to come in line with a stanchion, if possible, if not other provision would have to be made; cleats would be nailed on the stanchions, one on each side of the board, to contain it.

A coat of primer would be given, after which a length of binn iron with rounded ends would be fastened along the top of the board using nettlefold brads. When finished the boards would be painted blue.

The thwartship boards not only contained herrings when hauling, and nets when cleaned, but also formed a very effective breakwater to stop water from rushing aft.

Deck gratings

Between the thwartship boards were fitted deck gratings two inches deep, with one-and-a-quarter-inch bearers and three-quarter-inch planed splines.

The gratings fitted tight to the thwartship boards and from bulwark to coamings, with the splines running fore and aft with half-inch spacing between them. The splines, two inches in width, were nailed to the bearers using galvanised wire nails, which were punched and turned over on the underside.

When the nets were cleaned they would lay on these gratings, which also kept herrings and mackerel up from the deck and prevented the herrings from passing through the wash space between washstrake and covering board. The gratings were untreated, but gradually became stained by the catch and impregnated with herring oil.

Mackerel boards

One further job needed to be done to complete the work in relation to the catch, and that was to fit mackerel boards. These were made up from one-and-a-half-inch by seven-inch deal, planed all round and fitted from just under the rail to the fillings and to the hatch coaming.

The outboard end of these rested on a rail which ran fore and aft, and which was fastened to the inside face of the stanchions. This rail also acted as a fender rail when the boards were not in use. The inboard end of the boards rested on a portable two-inch by eight-inch bearer which would be shipped temporarily by the side of the coamings into prearranged cleats on the thwartship boards.

To ship the boards the outboard end would be tucked under the rail while the inboard ends rested on the portable bearer. When in place the boards would be held down in position by another board lying flat and running fore and aft over the top of the boards at the coaming end of them, and cleated to the thwartship boards.

The purpose of the mackerel boards was to contain the catch of mackerel on deck, so as to save a lot of handling and help to preserve the appearance

Making up the thwartship boards, whose purpose was to contain the herrings when hauling and the nets when they had been cleaned.

131

The fitter shipping the propeller.

of the fish, as this mattered a great deal in those days. If that catch was very heavy, the nets would be left stowed in the hold and cleaned when the vessel arrived in port, by pulling them up on to a quay or on to another vessel lying alongside.

These boards also carried the nets from side roller to coaming when hauling. As a fleet of mackerel nets was much more bulky than a fleet of herring nets, the perks were lowered to the bottom of the hold. When fishing for mackerel the boats would usually be fishing from Newlyn and would have to have their hatches and tarpaulins on when going to sea and be battened down, whereas herring nets in the North Sea would often stand a foot to two feet above the coaming.

When I was a boy the older and smaller steam drifters used to fish for mackerel from Lowestoft during May and June, accompanied by several sailing drifters.

Shipping the propeller

Shipping the propeller was one of the jobs which made it quite apparent that the ship was almost ready for launching. Because of this the whole project took on a new air of excitement, although the men on the job would be the last to admit this; I do not suppose that most of them even noticed anything, but nevertheless the difference was there.

I suppose that underlying this excitement was the fact that the change from the inanimate to the animate was now becoming more and more apparent. Only a few weeks earlier we had been handling individual pieces of timber, just pieces of wood, pieces of trees; now we had an almost living vessel on our hands, one that would travel many thousands of miles on her own under the guidance of one man, a floating workshop that would help to feed and nourish us. To me at any rate there was something in this shipbuilding business, and there still is.

The propeller would be brought across from the firm's foundry, where it had been cast in a mould made up of blacksand, the mould being black lead polished. After it had cooled it would be trimmed and cleaned up generally and then taken into the fitters' shop to be machined out to the correct size and shape for the shaft. The hole for this would have been made at the casting stage by the use of a core, made of straw, horse manure and sand from a mould made by a pattern maker just outside the core oven in which it was baked.

What a sight the foundry was on a dark winter afternoon, with the flames, sparks and glow from the furnace reaching up into the sky.

132

When machined out and ready the propeller would be loaded on a low bogey and taken right under the stern of the vessel. It would take several men to pull the bogey and manoeuvre it if there was not a horse available. A set of worm-geared pulley blocks would have been hung over each quarter of the ship and these would be hooked into two sling chains on two blades of the propeller.

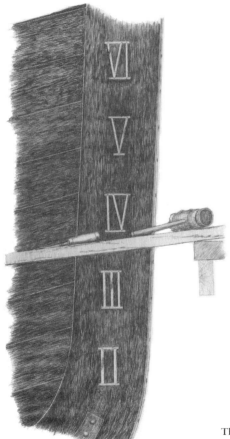

The shipwright cutting the draught marks in the stem.

"Nibs" would be in charge of the job, with a fitter's mate as his assistant. Should he need any other help he had only to ask Mr Jenner, the foreman, or Mr Coleman, and one of the yard labourers would be detailed off to go to work with him.

The chain blocks, which were old-fashioned, were a nuisance as the angle at which they were used made the pulley chain inclined to ride off the wheel. Nevertheless they were all we had at the time. Not very long after that the new improved enclosed blocks became available and things became easier. Even with our blocks it was possible to place the propeller exactly in position, it would be slid on to the shaft, and the nut put on and tightened up by "Nibs" himself, with the help of his mate.

The nut would then be covered with a sand and cement compo which would be brought to a hemispherical shape. Later still, when the ship's bottom was given a coating of anti-fouling paint, the propeller would be painted white.

When the ship was launched the propeller was allowed to revolve as the vessel slid into the water.

Water line and draught marks

To fix the water line the sheer batten would be hung round the ship for the fourth and last time. On this occasion it would be hung in improvised hutchiks, fastened with wire nails in order not to leave a large hole in the plank at this stage.

A dimension would be given to the shipwright in charge for for'ad, up under the stern and amidships, the midships measurement being set out on the vessel's side, using a straight edge and spirit level under the keel, with the dimension taken on a vertical batten from the straight edge to the ship's side. With the batten hung in the hutchiks the rest of the fairing would be done by eye in the same way that the sheer itself was looked in.

When all was ready either the foreman or Mr Coleman would be asked to come and look the water line in. After it had been finally approved, it would be raced in with a race knife, leaving a permanent mark on the vessel's side.

The draught marks would usually be cut in by the same two shipwrights who cut in the water line. There would be stages to rig and manoeuvre, as with the water line.

They would set the marks out in Roman numerals and cut them in V-section by chisel. To mark them off correctly the dimensions would be taken from the keel, using a vertical batten, straight edge, and a spirit level for those under the stern.

Painting the ship's exterior

Below the water line two coats of a reddish-brown anti-fouling composition would be applied over the coal tar already on. This work would be done by the sawmill hands as overtime, using tar brushes, except for the water line itself where paint brushes were used. Above that up to the covering board black varnish was the medium used.

I have already said that the bulwark was given a coat of black gloss paint. Now the streak, scrolls and name would be finished in gold leaf, not forgetting the port of registry. How marvellous the gold on black looked when freshly done. I think that all who were connected with the vessel were proud of her when nearing completion, and pleased that she had been given that luxury.

The port registry letters and the vessel's number, which were painted four times on the bulwark and picked out twice in metal on the funnel, were painted white, and with hawse pipes red, tampions blue, and rail bollards and fairleads in post office red she began to look quite smart.

Some vessels were given a grained casing, set out in panels, and when done by an expert this looked a very fine sight. Other vessels had their casings painted a dull brownish red.

Cabin and fo'c'sle

For a week or so now work would have been in progress on the cabin. The floor bearers would have been fitted; at the fore end of the cabin they were two-inch by seven-inch imported deal, while right aft they would be reduced to two-inch by six-inch. The floor itself was a good T and G board, with a hatch fitted in it to enable the driver to get to the stern tube stuffing box.

The engine room bulkhead, fastened to the foremost bearer, was of a good quality imported T and G deal.

At that time materials such as Formica had not been invented and although all the woodwork was good, it had one very great drawback: the grooves in this type of construction were breeding places for insects and the like, and most of these vessels were plagued with them to a certain extent, although great efforts including fumigation were made at times to get rid of

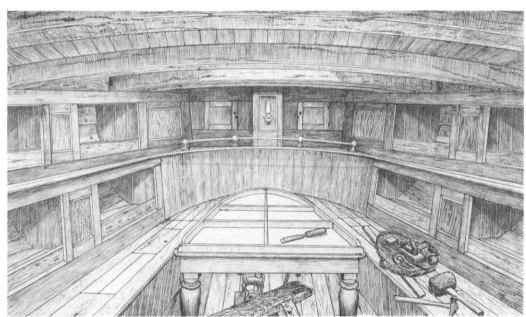

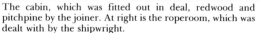

The cabin, which was fitted out in deal, redwood and pitchpine by the joiner. At right is the roperoom, which was dealt with by the shipwright.

For the water line three pitching spots were given, one on the stem, one up under the stern and one amidships, where a straight edge was set up tight to the sand band and levelled; a spline with the height on it was then used to transfer the measurement from the straight edge to the ship's side. The batten was faired by eye between these spots, as seen on the right where it is hung in hutchiks; the line was scrieved in with a race knife after having been inspected by the foreman.

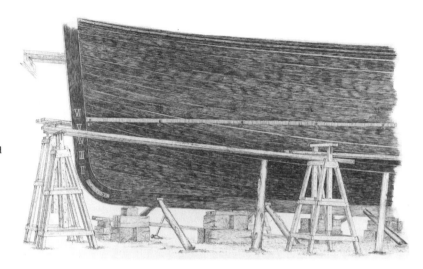

them. Some vessels sunk in collision still had some of these pests living when they were raised; probably they had survived in an air pocket.

Two by two-inch deal was used for studwork for the seat lockers, bunks and any other similar structure. The T and G facing boards to the seat lockers and round aft would be of pitch pine, while the various panels and locker doors would be of Oregon pine; the tops of the seat lockers would be of T and G deal, as were the bunk bottoms and bulkheads.

The faces or fronts of the bunks would be raking outwards from bottom to top, while the top bunks would be set back outboard about six inches, leaving a ledge which would be made up of pitch pine with a rounded nosing. Portable boards would be cut in as hatches along the centre of the seat lockers; these would have a thumb hole bored in them for lifting purposes, as a good bit of material that was not often used would be stowed in them, sea boots as well at times.

A bread locker on the fore bulkhead would be used as a store for most of the dry foodstuffs, while if I remember rightly the meat would be kept in a basket along with the potatoes and green vegetables in the small boat. If the vessel was going to be at sea for a few nights, some meat would be laid on the salt carried in one of the foremost wings of the hold, and this would help to preserve it. In smacks it would be laid on ice in the fish room, as they would generally be at sea for at least a week.

Round the after end of the cabin a brass rail would be fitted, held in four-inch high stanchions. This would contain gear that might be laid on this ledge, and would also serve as a hand hold for anybody going to the after lockers. The stern post would be panelled, while on each side of this would be fitted lockers with panelled doors.

The whole of this work in the ship would be done by "Chuddy", "Banker" Roope and the apprentice Jack Moyse, although as much as possible would be prepared in the joiners' shop.

A small coal-fired stove would be fitted at the fore end of the cabin close to the bulkhead. Behind the stove itself and the funnel, the bulkhead would be lined with sheet asbestos, covered with sheet iron fastened with galvanised felt nails. Near the stove was fitted a mirror and beneath this was a little brass-fronted mantelpiece with raised sides, and on some ships with a brass rail which would hold shaving brushes, etc., when necessary.

The seat lockers would in some vessels be fitted with cushioned seats, a luxury that smacks never had. In the deck above the cabin a steel skylight would be fitted and fastened by the shipwright, using coach screws to fasten it. This skylight of steel plate was of the pitched roof type with a rounded top or apex, and fitted with four fixed portlights, two on each side, while a mushroom ventilator was fitted in the fore end on the top. The mushroom, of the screw down type, could be opened or closed from below if necessary.

135

Access to the cabin was through the galley. Steps were made for the fore end of the cabin and fitted.

When all was completed, the woodwork would be varnished except for the deck head, bunk interiors, lockers, etc., which would all be painted with white petrifying paint. The skylight would also be painted white on the inside, and granulated cork would be scattered over this surface while the paint was still wet; what remained on the surface after the paint had dried helped to combat condensation.

The cabin table would be set square with the centre line, with its widest part at the fore end; it would taper aft and be rounded. The table was fitted with portable fiddles.

Fo'c'sle

After finishing the cabin "Chuddy" would move forward to the fo'c'sle, which would not be quite as elaborate as the cabin and would be constructed completely in deal.

The floor bearers were of the same material and the same size as those in the cabin. The seat lockers were of the same pattern except that there was a slight difference in the general layout, as the ship would be narrower for'ad; no cushions would be fitted in the fo'c'sle. Loose boards were left in the centre of the seat locker tops, as in the cabin, in order to be able to store gear in them.

The studwork was the same as far as construction was concerned and the bunks would recede off the plumb line vertically, partly following the shape of the vessel, but there was no ledge between the two tiers, the vessel being more wall-sided for'ad.

A locker was built right in the eyes of the ship. In some vessels this was large enough to stow the tow rope and also the tizzard, where they would keep dry because of the fire in the fo'c'sle. A locker situated at the after end of the fo'c'sle would be fitted out as the lamp locker. The cladding of the whole work was in T and G boards. A small stove was fitted at the after end close to the bulkhead, and as with the one in the cabin was backed with asbestos and sheet iron. A funnel "scoot" was fitted through the deck close to the hoodway, and on this the funnel was shipped, in some vessels being supported by metal stays.

These things would be fitted by an apprentice, who would also fit a melon-shaped radial deck light; the flange of this would be let in and bedded down on white lead, while a brass flange would fit over this to hold it down, fastened with brass screws. The deck on the underside would be splayed back to allow the maximum amount of light to enter the fo'c'sle.

Portable steps were fitted at the after end ofthe fo'c'sle under the hoodway and close to a locker bulkhead, thus giving a man a chance to keep his footing when mounting or descending them by leaning on the bulkhead as much as possible.

When the woodwork was completed the painter would come along and treat it with knotting, after which it would be given a coat of grey primer, undercoated, and then given a gloss coat; most probably this would be of a light brown colour, while the beams clear of the bunks would most probably be painted the same colour. The deck head, locker and bunk interiors would be painted with white petrifying paint.

The fo'c'sle, fitted out in deal by the joiner.

Toilet and food storage

I am sorry to have to mention these two subjects in one breath, as it were, but in some small way they are intertwined. I will start from the beginning and hope that explanation will be forthcoming.

In drifters such as the *Formidable* there were no toilet facilities whatever. I expect that she and *Implacable* were among the very last built in East Anglia without these, as in the standard drifters which followed the galley structure was built large enough to accommodate a closet; a water tank was fitted on top of the galley to provide the water for this.

In the *Formidable* a tub would be used, and at that time this would have been a bowl, or bowel to give it its proper name, with the head knocked out of it. This was in fact a small barrel thirteen inches high by ten inches across the head and twelve-and-a-half inches diameter in the middle, used to support the nets of a sailing drifter. This served the purpose for the ten men in the crew of a drifter.

In order to use it water would have to be drawn in a bucket from the sea and emptied into the tub first. Drawing this water could be very hazardous, particularly if the vessel was under way; several men and boys lost their lives doing this.

For some reason or other there seemed to be greater thought given to the boys in smacks than in drifters. I can only think that this must have been because the boys in smacks were more in the eyes of the crew than those in the drifters, partly because in a drifter the cook was obscured from view because of the casing itself. But no man in either would let a very young or small boy draw water by this means if he could help it. When he was able to draw water in this way, a lad would be warned never on any account to take a round turn on his hand with the bucket rope, but to let the rope lie in his hand while gripping it, tip the bucket quickly and draw it immediately. He would have to use the bucket quite a bit when he did get used to it, as there was washing vegetables, peeling potatoes, and washing up to be done with seawater. Unless every care was taken ten men would soon use the small amount of fresh water that was carried.

I think that on several occasions when the cook was a small lad straight from school, and he had not been briefed properly on what he should do and what implements he should use, he has been seen using the tub for potatoes; quite a natural mistake, I suppose, but one that would soon be put right.

Nearly everything was done by means of galvanised buckets in the way of cleaning things; they were also used for washing oneself and for washing clothing. There was usually an enamelled bowl for making up dough or pudding material, while enamelled plates, or platters as they were called, and enamelled mugs served to eat and drink from. An enamelled jug of generous proportions in which tea was carried along the deck to where the men were at work was known as the "Gorger"; I may add that this was a well-used implement. I believe that all this enamelled ware was responsible for some cases of appendicitis caused by chipped enamel, and there was certainly plenty of that.

Eating utensils were very simple. On starting his seagoing career a boy would normally be told to take knife, fork and spoon. These might be of a well-worn variety; on occasions an ordinary jack-knife, or shut-knife as we called it, would be used. Whatever the boy took with him would be his own, and nobody else would use them. When a meal was finished they would usually receive a quick wipe and be tucked away into the bottom of his bunk until required for the next meal.

If one required a bath when away from home, then the R.N.M.D.S.F. mission or Y.M.C.A. were available when in port, but as there were not many baths in either establishment most of the washing down was done on the engine room footplate close to the boiler when in port, using a bucket. On the side of the boiler about level with the furnaces was a valve to which was attached a length of copper pipe; one would stand the bucket so that the pipe entered the water, turn the valve on, and the steam would heat a bucketful of water in a matter of seconds.

Launching

I think that preparation for launching a ship and the launching itself from No. 3 yard at Oulton Broad was one of the most exciting jobs that I have ever experienced.

You will see by my plan of the yard as it was at the time about which I am writing that the "big shop" in which *Formidable* was built, in the west berth, was some distance from the water. We would in fact have to pull the vessel some two hundred feet towards the river in order to launch her. When the "big shop" was built for Mr H. Reynolds, who first opened the yard, excavation was made into a steep riverside bank for it. It was built by the shipyard workers themselves, and in planning the shop three birds were killed with one stone. First the excavation had to be made for the building and berths; secondly the excavated material was brought forward on to the foreshore, some of the mud being excavated to make way for it, and after this had settled down it was trimmed to the required declivity, to provide space for two more building berths; thirdly these operations brought the yard out close to the river channel and so made it unnecessary to dredge the area.

The "crick", as this extended foreshore was called, was contained on both sides by old wherries filled with some of the mud which had been excavated by hand; this held them down and in position. The remains of some of the wherries can be seen to this day, though rather less than when I was a boy.

I can only describe the method by which we launched our ships as by "Hollows and rounds". The ways were simply pieces of old oak or elm let down into the foreshore of the crick flush with the surface, with long stakes of oak driven down beside them and nailed to them, using cleat nails, to prevent them from moving. This was done at intervals of, say, three feet for about twenty-four feet up the yard from the river end of the crick, making about eight or nine of them in all.

A "dead man" made from a piece of old oak keel.

This reinforced area formed a good base for the launching ways at the bottom end, and also provided something to secure the hollows and packings to after being laid, sometimes a couple of tides before the launching itself. Shores would be fastened also to prevent the hollows from moving sideways.

Scattered around the crick here and there were "dead men" which formed an anchorage for anything that needed securing, either for use in launching

A hollow block.

or pulling out. These were made up of a piece of old keel, a piece of oak tree or something of that sort. A hole would be excavated for this timber about six feet deep or a bit more, and a piece of old anchor chain would be shackled round the dead man or carried round the timber and rove through a big link on the other end. The chain would have been cut long enough for a considerable portion of it to be left above ground and easily discernible.

Hollows and rounds

The hollows were lengths of pitchpine from thirty to forty feet long, sixteen inches wide by eight inches deep, on the top surface of which was formed a concave two inches deep and extending to one and a half inches from each edge.

The rounds were thirteen inches wide, eight inches deep and nothing under thirty-three feet long, also of pitch pine, and shaped on one surface with a convex curve to fit the hollow.

Both the hollows and rounds had a ringbolt fitted at each end and on the side for the hook on the horse's trace when fleeting them along. Hollows and rounds were reinforced by horizontal through bolts at intervals of about four feet to ensure that the timber did not split when under stress.

The hollow blocks were made up of short lengths of baulk across one surface of which a hollow about two inches deep would be carried. I will describe how they were used just before we start to launch.

The jacks that we used were certainly old-fashioned, and I would think they were in themselves very old. But they seemed very strong, and were certainly very fast and very handy both for lifting or lowering, either directly or through a foot frame.

Built of iron and wood combined, the jacks had an iron shank, one edge of which was toothed to take a small cog wheel in the frame. The shank had a short forked head, while the foot was at right angles from it, moving up and

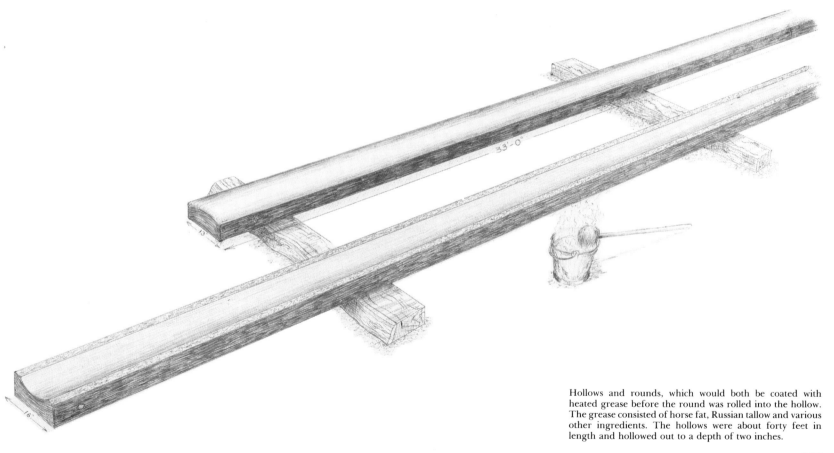

Hollows and rounds, which would both be coated with heated grease before the round was rolled into the hollow. The grease consisted of horse fat, Russian tallow and various other ingredients. The hollows were about forty feet in length and hollowed out to a depth of two inches.

down in a channel left for the purpose in the frame. They were fitted with a double-handed handle, on the spindle of which was a ratchet wheel, into which a pawl would drop to prevent the shank running back under load.

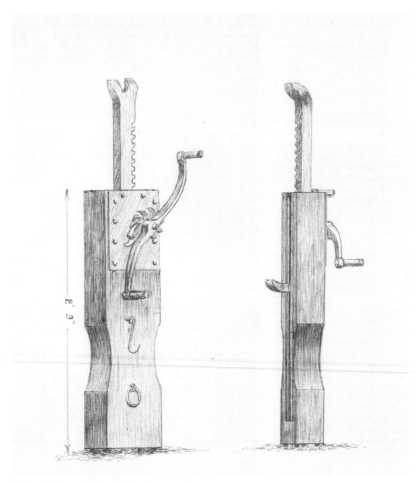

Timber jacks used when listing the vessel.

Crab winch

A very substantial piece of old-fashioned portable equipment built for use with a horse, the crab winch was built up on a strong triangular base, with the post and barrel carved from an oak tree.

The post, the toe of which revolved in a hole in the base, was held in its upright position when in use by three curved pieces of oak, the main one of which extended from above the barrel to the apex of the triangular base; it was this piece which took the thrust of the chain, which would have several turns round the barrel when heaving. The post revolved in an iron collar, half of which was hinged to allow the removal of the barrel, the loose half being kept in position by a forelock or pin.

Supporting the main piece were two other curved pieces of oak one on each side of it and close to the barrel, extending from the main piece down to the base platform. These were fitted to the main piece by a cut resembling a crab claw jaws, and as they resembled the crab in that they curved upwards and to the centre, this is purported to have given rise to the name "crab winch". In my *Comprehensive English Dictionary*, by John Ogilvie, of 1870 the machine is described as a wooden engine with three claws for launching ships and heaving them into dock.

The top end of the post was square in section with a slightly rounded taper towards the top, banded twice to prevent it from splitting. In the post were two square holes at right angles to take the capstan bars, while in the centre of the top of the post was a small ringbolt to which a spline would be secured to keep the horse on course.

Around the barrel of the winch in a vertical position were four iron "whelps" made up from short lengths of binn iron; these helped to prevent the hauling chain wearing the barrel away.

Hauling gear

Two large iron treble-sheave blocks were used for launching; these were fitted with English elm bases or skids. The two blocks that were used were very old; I would think they might have been made just a few years after shipbuilding was started in the harbour at Lowestoft. For the purchase, chain was used, as this would lie flat or stay in small stable heaps on being pulled off the barrel of the winch by the horseman using a small chain hook, unlike wire which would have been a bit unruly and have tended to kink up and so hazard the horse; in addition, the horseman could control the purchase better with a hook.

Before any attempt was made to list the vessel the rudder would be

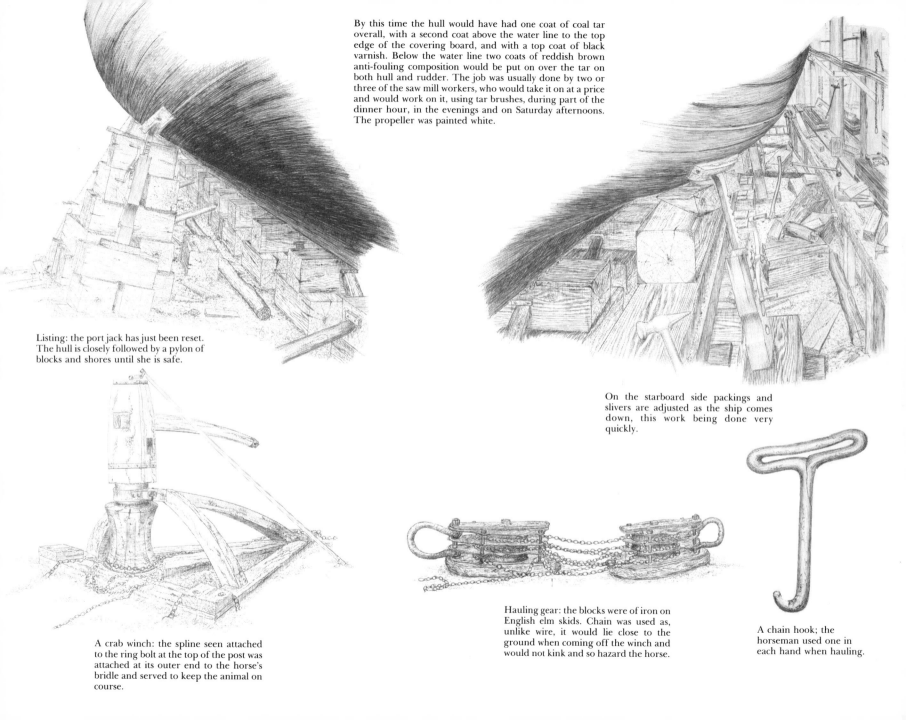

By this time the hull would have had one coat of coal tar overall, with a second coat above the water line to the top edge of the covering board, and with a top coat of black varnish. Below the water line two coats of reddish brown anti-fouling composition would be put on over the tar on both hull and rudder. The job was usually done by two or three of the saw mill workers, who would take it on at a price and would work on it, using tar brushes, during part of the dinner hour, in the evenings and on Saturday afternoons. The propeller was painted white.

Listing: the port jack has just been reset. The hull is closely followed by a pylon of blocks and shores until she is safe.

On the starboard side packings and slivers are adjusted as the ship comes down, this work being done very quickly.

A crab winch: the spline seen attached to the ring bolt at the top of the post was attached at its outer end to the horse's bridle and served to keep the animal on course.

Hauling gear: the blocks were of iron on English elm skids. Chain was used as, unlike wire, it would lie close to the ground when coming off the winch and would not kink and so hazard the horse.

A chain hook; the horseman used one in each hand when hauling.

secured fore and aft by the use of bolt ropes from tiller to cavil, and two angle-iron straps would be bolted on to rudder and rudder post to prevent the rudder from slamming round when the vessel entered the water, or indeed when being listed.

Listing

With the description of the principal implements used in launching on No. 3 yard completed, I will get on with the job itself.

Before any work was started, the whole of the bottom of the shop in the proximity of the ship would be scraped clean of chips, shavings, odd pieces of timber, wedges, etc, so as to leave a clear floor. This rubbish would be used to heat the launching fat.

On No. 3 yard we listed our vessels to starboard, so preparations would be made under the starboard bilge to receive the vessel. Deals would be laid flat, blocks would be placed on them, and on these a hollow would be laid immediately below the hardest part of the vessel's bilge. The hollow would then be packed up to the required height and declivity and also adjusted so as to be parallel with the keel and at a given dimension.

When it was finally in position it would be greased with a mixture of horse fat and Russian tallow obtained from a local factory. In winter some engine oil would be included, the whole being warmed up by one of the boys. A mop would be used to apply the mixture to the hollow.

Preparations would next be made to place the round into the hollow. To do this, blocks would be built up beside the hollow on which to lay the round upside down. The round would first be inspected for cleanliness from the point of view of grit, etc., and when it had passed inspection it would in its turn be greased, after which several of the men on the job would roll it over into the hollow, where it would be temporarily dogged into position to prevent it moving, bearing in mind that we have two greased surfaces lying together. Temporary packings would be built up on the top of the round in readiness to receive the vessel.

Two timber jacks would be set up to lower the vessel away. On the port side a pylon of blocks would be built up to the vessel amidships and two jacks set up in readiness for listing. All topside shores would now be removed, as well as any other obstructions that there might be to listing, except for the bilge shores. The stem and stern post shores would have been removed for some time now, and all stages would also have been taken down.

On the starboard side a clearance would be made round the bilge shores, and shorter shores with packings would be laid handy in case of emergency. Shovels would be laid within easy reach.

142   Tinker and "Hino" Crickmore pulling the *Formidable* out of the shop.

All the available shipwrights and apprentices would be mustered and given their respective stations by the foreman shipwright, although this was another of those jobs in which every man knew what was expected of him, by virtue of his apprenticeship. Pylons and packings would be up tight to the vessel and all hands would be ordered under the bottom, each with his own maul.

We would spread out along the hollow blocks on both sides of them, or perhaps it would be better to say on both ends of them as they were thwartships. After a quick look round, the foreman shipwright would give the signal to "Set Up", and with a whistle to keep us in time, we would swing the mauls in unison and so strike all the slivers together, repeating the process until the vessel was lifted enough to release the keel blocks, which would be pulled out of the way and stacked for future use. The bilge packings would also be tightened up.

Emphasis was put on the port side slivers under the hollow blocks, as this canted the hollow blocks slightly and thus resisted the tendency to sideslip. As an extra precaution shores were set against the end of blocks here and there, and about three were set against the after side of the blocks to put up a resistance to them on the first movement of the vessel. The declivity at this stage was not enough to let the vessel move on her own, but there could be a mild jerk when she first started, particularly if it was in cold wintry weather and the fats had become bound together temporarily.

Before actually listing, a length of hollow would have been laid from the end of the keel on the line and declivity and this would have been packed up ready to receive the ship. A further length of hollow would also be laid on the end of the bilge hollow, and these would extend well out of the shop, the doors of which would now be opened to their fullest extent.

After a quick look round to see that everything was in order, the foreman, who would have been hovering around quite a bit lately, would instruct somebody to remove the ladder from the vessel's side, and with this done he would give the order to start listing. The men on the port jacks would start to heave gently while those on the starboard side would gently lower.

The shores on the port side would very soon fall, while the man and boy on the blocks would follow up with packings until it was no longer necessary to do this. On the starboard side packings would be quickly removed or adjusted and shores would be quickly replaced by shorter ones, the port jacks becoming ineffective as the list increased. I would think that the list would be about fifteen degrees, and I expect it would have taken about a quarter of an hour to accomplish.

Mr Stuart Jackson, who was the senior apprentice on the yard at the time of which I am writing, was telling me shortly before he died a few years ago

144

that this job of listing always frightened him a bit. I must confess that I never thought about it in that light; no doubt I was so impressed by the efficiency of the men around me that I did not dream that the job might get out of hand. All the same, everyone concerned must have felt a little relieved when the ship, weighing about eighty-eight tons, was resting on her bilge. Everything on the job would have had to be done pretty briskly and accurately.

Once the ship was resting on the packings, these could be adjusted and others fitted, some to the shape of the vessel. Unlike launching ships in the upright position, entailing the fitting of poppets and packings, there was almost an air of casualness about launching by hollows and rounds; when safely listed there was not much that could go wrong, providing care was taken over every aspect of the job. As far as the time factor was concerned, the vessel would be made ready to launch in the first day, while if she was to be launched in the upright position I expect that the preparation would have taken several days, almost a week, perhaps. I am referring, of course, to our own method; whatever way she was to be launched, she still had to be moved down the yard some two hundred feet.

The first move

During the time the vessel was in the process of being listed "Hino" would have been preparing to pull her out of the shop. He would have had Tinker pull the crab winch some way down the crick, not far off the line of the launch, and here he would have secured it to a dead man by means of two sling chains of equal length in the form of a bridle, each shackled from the base corners of the winch to the link of the dead man itself.

He would then have had the horse drag the purchase into position on the exact line of the ship's movement and have shackled the bottom block to a chain rigged between dead men to keep it on line. After that he would work with a shipwright in securing the hauling chain to the ship itself.

The foreman would be having another look round while "Hino" was getting the winch ready, letting go the iron retaining collar round the barrel and with some help lowering the barrel to the ground so that three or four turns of the purchase could be laid round the barrel pivot hole. It could then be stood up again and secured, and the capstan bar could be rigged.

The hook on the horse's trace would be slipped into the link provided at the end of the capstan bar, the guide spline would be lashed to the ring on the top of the winch barrel, while the other end of it would be secured to the horse's bridle, and all would be ready.

Not far to go. Work is being completed on the bottom ways below high water mark for tomorrow's tide.

The foreman would give the order "Heave away!" and "Hino", who by now would have squatted under the bar on a short length of block, would just say a quiet "Gee up!" to Tinker and the horse would start to walk round the circle, guided by the spline.

After taking up the slack a little weight would come on the chain, and the ship would start to move, almost imperceptibly at first unless the weather was very cold, then it might be with a little jerk. If the weather was frosty the fire on which the fat was warmed would have been placed so that the warmth from it would be carried down wind towards the scene of operations, and this warmth would help to ease the situation.

In the very first moments the after end of the keel would have entered the centre hollow, which by now would be fully packed up and shored up to keep it in position. The hollow on the end of the first bilge hollow would have been treated likewise, and a further one would be prepared by the shipwrights. These would be shored parallel to each other and from each side to prevent them moving out of line.

When the vessel reached the end of these, others which had been liberated would be fleeted down the yard in readiness to be rigged up again. The declivity would have been increased a little and the hollows and the ground would gradually be converging. By now it would have become necessary to shift the winch to a different position, up the yard and with the bottom block anchored to a dead man well down the yard.

At this stage and with low water, preparation would get under way for placing the bottom ways in position. The mud would have to be cleared away and both keel and bilge hollows would be laid, packed and shored in position. The packings would have to be nailed to the ways, while the hollows themselves would be secured to the ways by using short lengths of angle iron which had been shaped to a right angle and had holes drilled in them. These would be placed in position and coach screwed to hollow and yard way, and if it was expected that there might be an abnormally high tide, a few sandbags might be placed on the extreme ends of the hollows.

It was customary to launch on a full or new moon and so on a spring tide, and if a fairly fresh or strong north-westerly wind was expected great care would have to be taken with everything that would be below high water as the tide would come well up the yard, making it almost impossible to get at any part of the job that might not have been properly secured on the previous low tide.

With the ship nearing the water the final preparations for launching would have been made and all surplus material carried up the yard to well above high water mark. The job would be a bit messy down by the mud, but nobody seemed to mind that. The hauling chain would have been brought forward at this stage ready to attach to the vessel in the morning and the vessel was left to rest over night. There would be a shore up under her stern, the round dogged to the bilge hollow, a chain passed up through the hawse pipe from a dead man and made fast round the deck towing bollard, all to ensure that she could not launch herself.

As soon as work started on the morning of the launch on the final preparations, one of which might be the erection of a very small launching platform, a pole would be erected with flag halyards on which to hoist a burgee with the vessel's name on it. This pole was usually secured to the main hatch coaming in the after well with G-screws, while the toe would be lashed to the kelson via the pump sump. The flag would then be hoisted, and depending on the owners of the vessel a string of flags might be hoisted stretching fore and aft to dress the ship.

A final check would be made on the security of the rudder; it did not matter about the propeller, which could revolve freely.

A length of spunyarn would be tacked along the ends of all slivers and packings which would float when the vessel righted herself as she went off; this would not only prevent a lot of this material from being lost but also make it much easier to retrieve it. Two men or boys would be in the yard boat lying just upstream from the launch, ready to secure all the launching gear that floated and to take it back to the yard.

Check chains would have been laid out on the day before, one part of which would have been hove on board through the hawse pipe or secured to the chain that I mentioned earlier. The chains when laid out would be placed in small heaps up on the crick and would act as a brake when the ship went off and gathered way; in that respect she was not isolated but still connected to the shore.

On this particular morning a mild air of excitement pervaded the yard, and as the launching time drew ever nearer people who were interested in or in any way connected with the launch would begin to collect just outside the big shop; that is, friends and relatives of the owners, builders, crew, workmen and others.

It's strange, but as I am writing this my pulse is quickening a little, as if it was happening now.

The hauling chain is now shipped over the pin which had been brought forward the day before, and thus would be on one side of the vessel only, the port side. "Hino" is all ready and the horse's trace hook is in the crab-winch bar link, and the guide spline has been lashed to winch and bridle.

A bottle of wine has been hung over the bow on a ribbon in readiness for the christening. The sightseers are drawing nearer to the ship, hoping to hear the lady's words.

She's off! As the *Formidable* enters the water the tug *Imperial* is standing by to tow the vessel to the sheerlegs at Lowestoft to receive her engine and boiler.

The paddle tug *Imperial* belonging to the Great Eastern Railway, built in 1879 by Thames Iron Works and the smallest of our three harbour tugs, is standing by off the yard and just below the launching area in readiness to pick the vessel up to tow her to Lowestoft for her boiler and engine as soon as she goes off.

The handling crew are on board the drifter, also a few young members of the various families. The shore which was set up under the stern the evening before is now removed, also any dogs from the ways; by dogs I mean steel holding dogs.

The tide is by now lapping round the after end of the keel.

"Remove the ladder! Stand by!" Then "Heave away!" and for the last time Hino says "Gee up!" Tinker starts and the ship begins to move, faster now than before as she has been given greater declivity. She is beginning to move on her own.

The lady to whom the christening has been entrusted swings the bottle towards the ship with a vigorous thrust, it smashes and she quickly quotes the words always used at launching ceremonies as the vessel glides swiftly away from her.

Now that she is afloat the launching gear comes bobbing to the surface, from where it will be picked up by the people in the yard boat and towed ashore. As the tide falls after the launch and exposes the hollows, etc., these will be liberated, together with any other gear such as shores and packings, pulled up the yard and stowed away or stacked in readiness for the next vessel, the *Implacable*, and then the standard drifters.

The tug has gently come alongside the vessel, put a rope aboard and is making for the sheerlegs at Lowestoft with her in tow.

After a successful launch it was customary to pass drinks round to the men who helped build the ship. They would drink to the good health and prosperity of the shipowners, crew, and the firm; but what happened in the case of *Formidable* I do not recollect, bearing in mind that there was a war on.

And speaking of the war, by this time it had been decided by the Admiralty that there was a real need for steam fishing vessels. There was talk of a different kind of drifter to be built for the Navy, slightly larger than *Formidable* but fitted with standard machinery. A few more men were being taken on, but these had to be fairly elderly men; among them was a dear old chap, one Jack Barnard, who had formerly been master of the very old clinker-built paddle tug *May*, owned by the Great Eastern Railway and employed towing mud barges out to the local dumping ground, the mud having been dredged from the harbour.

Jack became the man who had charge of the ships when afloat and was also made responsible for some items of rigging, he being an old sailorman.

Here was a fine addition to the staff employed on the yard, everybody liked Cap'n Jack, as we called him. We all knew him when he was in the *May*, and used to pull his leg about the methods he had to use to turn her in the harbour; she had no differentials and both paddles would revolve in the same direction, either ahead or astern together, and in order to turn her in the harbour he would have to have the foresail hoisted to help blow her round. This sometimes took a considerable time, much to some onlookers' amusement. She also worked about quite a bit when at sea, and one had to be careful when sitting on the lockers below as she could give you quite a nip.

So now Jack was in charge of the mooring of the vessel on arrival at the sheerlegs about half an hour after leaving the yard.

At this stage one could see whether the caulking had been well done or if anything had not been done quite right, such as a small defect in a plank not remedied in a satisfactory manner. One might see a small weep of water in one or two places, but nothing serious. The valves on the sea fittings would have been tightly screwed down by "Nibs", who would also have attended to the stern gland. Should there be a weep anywhere this would most probably "take up" in a day or so. The vessel will later be put in dry dock before going on sea trials.

On arrival at the sheerlegs the tug cast off and went about her duties, and *Formidable* was moored so that the boiler cradles came centrally beneath the lifting tackle of the sheerlegs; the sheerlegs could not be moved sideways at all.

The boiler, a two-fired single-ended marine boiler by Messrs. Riley, of Stockton-on-Tees, was on a rail lowloader standing under the sheerlegs in readiness, while the engine, casing and funnel were in the harbour yard, to be brought out later. At this point two more men enter the story, Mr Pieter Balder, a Dutchman, and Mr Bob Richardson, a local man from Oulton Broad, both marine engineers.

Pieter, aged twenty-six at the time, had been born at Haarlemmermeer, near Amsterdam; I will go so far as to say that he must have been one of the best marine engineers ever to have worked in the port of Lowestoft. He was a wonderful chap, having served his apprenticeship at Amsterdam on both internal combustion and steam engines. He went to sea as an engineer some time after finishing his apprenticeship, left a ship in 1915 in London and came to Lowestoft shortly afterwards, married and had four sons. After a few years in England he was naturalised and worked in Lowestoft mostly until his death more than thirty years ago. He did outstanding work here, and he is another man that I feel privileged to have worked with.

Bob also was a fine chap and a pleasure to work with. He later went into the Broads holiday business and owned quite a considerable yard.

With the vessel in position, the order would be given to the sheerlegs winchman to heave away. As the hauling wires tightened one would notice the boiler very slowly but surely start to lift off the lowloader.

When the boiler was just clear the order would be given to cant the sheerlegs forward. On would see a toothed wheel at the base of the back or canting leg of the sheerlegs start to revolve, slowly creeping forward on a rack at the side of the track on which the leg moved. And so the thing would start to cant forward over the ship, while at the same time the lowering mechanism would be put into motion.

It would not be very long before the boiler, nearing the cradles, would have to be held so that it landed exactly where required. Then the engine would be brought out on to the quay, and once again slinging would take place. A pair of bridles would be used and spreaders would be put in them so that no pressure would be exerted by the wire slings on the cylinder casing.

Again care would have to be taken to ensure that the engine dropped into its proper place, according to a mark on the engine bed. The engine would also be up on packings very slightly. With the engine safely lowered the next item would be the fore piece of casing, then the funnel, and after that the after piece of casing. These were not placed exactly in position, for various reasons, but once the casing was aboard it could easily be handled up at the yard fitting out quay by our own little manually operated crane.

With the boiler and machinery on board, the vessel was ready to return to the yard except that it was necessary to put one or two tons of coal into the bunkers. A coal boat would come alongside to supply this, and as soon as all was ready the tug would come alongside again, make fast, and get under way for the fitting out quay at the yard.

The weight of boiler and engine in the standard drifters was forty-two tons, while the weight of those in the *Formidable* would be a bit less.

The first job that the fitters would do on starting work on board the ship would be to fit all valves on the boiler, water glass, pressure gauge, and so on; see that the fire bars were all right; damper, fire doors, smokebox, manhole doors, mud doors all screwed up tight; secure the funnel; see that the safety valve was in order; make and fit the blow-off pipe and whistle pipe, and close the valves tight.

The boiler could now be filled with water, having first been checked for position. The chocks could then be made and fitted, preventing the boiler slipping fore or aft. The chocks were made from pieces of very stout plate shaped to the round end lap at the centre of the bottom of the end plate.

Lowering the boiler into the *Formidable*, using the Great Eastern Railway's sheerlegs at Lowestoft. The view is seen from the yard boat as it is sculled back to No 3 yard.

Lowering the compound engine into the vessel as she lies under the sheerlegs. In the background the tug *Lowestoft* is towing two armed smacks to sea, and a minesweeping trawler lies at the South Quay.

Deep enough to reach up on to the end plate from the kelson, the chocks would be placed on the centre line of the ship.

On both sides of the plates and riveted right through were substantial angles shaped to the vertical and bottom edges of the chock, a right angle in fact, although the final shape was triangular. And through the bottom flange of these angles holes had been drilled to take the fastenings which would be driven into the kelson.

Lagging the boiler

The first job to be undertaken when work was restarted at the yard would be to lag the boiler. It would have to be filled with water and the fires would have to be lit to warm it up a little, hence the need for coal at this very early stage. One of the labourers who had had experience in the stokehold would be chosen for the job of starting the fires.

A Mr Harwood, a self-employed bricklayer, used to lag the boilers for the firm. He, by the way, was "Hardo's" father. The man who was chosen to look after the fires would be detailed off to act as labourer to Mr Harwood, while "Hardo", who had not yet started his apprenticeship, would also help.

The lagging was made up of a pink asbestos powder in which there was some fibre, I seem to remember. The powder was delivered in paper sacks and mixed with water in two pieces of barrel which had been sawn in half for the job, and which suited admirably. As the boiler warmed up a little Mr Harwood would mix some of the asbestos into a liquid form in a bucket and have it passed below to him, and using a limewash brush would proceed to work over the area on which he was proposing to start lagging with some of the liquid.

The boiler would be lagged about three-quarters of the way round it; that is to say, about a quarter of the cylindrical shell under the bottom in the vicinity of the furnaces would remain unlagged. Along the bottom edge of the proposed lagging area, provision would have been made to fit two angle bars for the full length of the boiler; these were to contain the edge of the lagging and also served for securing the wire netting reinforcement. Pieter and Bob would fit these.

The job would soon be well under way, with the material being mixed up on the quay, passed on board and down below, where Mr Harwood would seize upon it and proceed to throw it on to the washed area of the boiler by the handful. Very soon this area would begin to look like a pink swallows' nest, albeit a very large one. And so the work would proceed on the cylindrical part of the shell and the fore end.

When the first layer was complete, rolls of wire netting which had been lying on the quay would be taken aboard and placed right over the first layer of lagging from angle iron to angle iron, cutting out and fitting round any valve or such things as the "dome" as they came in the way. The wire netting would not only reinforce the lagging but also form a very substantial key from one layer to the other. When the wire netting layering was complete the lagging throwing would be resumed, but with this difference: instead of

Lagging the boiler.

151

Trowelling the top coat up. The lagging was usually carried down to just above the boiler cradles.

leaving it rough, the lagger would trowel it up as the area grew large enough and before it became too stiff for this to be done, and soon the boiler lagging would be finished.

Two coats of black varnish would then be brushed on. To finish off some vessels would have a sheet of galvanised iron put right round the job and banded, but I cannot remember any drifters having this done.

With the boiler lagging finished work could be started on several other jobs such as bringing the two parts of the casing together and fastening it off. This would be done with the help of the little five-ton crane on the quay. There would most probably be a couple of shipwrights working on board, also one or two apprentices, I expect. To fasten the casing the chequer plate in the way of the boiler and bunkers would have to be bolted up to the underside of the angle along the outside of the bottom edge of the casing. A piece of felt would be inserted between the two, after which half-inch hexagon head bolts would be passed through and screwed up tightly on washers, with the heads of the bolts on deck; grummets would have been put under the heads of these bolts.

The two halves of the casing would then be bolted together right across the casing just to the after side of the funnel. The plates, as with all the butts of the casing, would be secured with a buttstrap and half-inch countersunk bolts. Holes would now be bored up through the deck from the bunker along the edge of the chequer plate after felt and coal tar had been put down, and round head bolts with grummets under the heads would be put

152

in and screwed down tight from below. The fore end of the casing would be bolted right down through the deck and iron beam.

The deck would have been faired in readiness, and felt and white lead would be in readiness all around the perimeter of the casing. Hexagon head bolts would now be used wherever possible, and coach screws where it was not possible to get bolts in. The whole job would not take long to complete.

With the boiler lagged and the casing fastened it would be possible to fit the boiler feed tanks, which would most probably be on a railway wagon. This would be worked down to the crane, after which each tank would in turn be picked up and lowered into the after well, where it would be manoeuvered on to an already prepared platform, one on each side of the centre line and leaving sufficient space in between them for the chain locker and pump well.

Once the tanks were placed they were secured by cleating, etc., and the filling and air pipes, together with the boiler connections, could be fitted. The filling and air pipes would come up through the deck between the wheelhouse and the main hatch after coaming.

I fitted several of these tanks myself when I was an apprentice, and as they were very narrow and with a small manhole, I found them a bit difficult to clamber out of. It was not so bad getting in them, as one had plenty of room to manoeuvre, but getting out was a different matter as one did not have much room in which to contort oneself, bearing in mind that there were angle bar stiffeners in the tank and crossing it.

I remember one of my friends, "Boiler" Tripp, who was a cutter and welder, working under similar circumstances many years later on a vessel in the port using a torch in the tank. Some waste material caught fire, he was unable to clamber out of the tank, and in a very short time he was dead. This was a great tragedy for the port, as he was a very popular man indeed.

When fitting the pipes that went up through the deck one would first have to bore a pilot hole from inside the tank, after which the rest of the job would be a fairly easy matter. In the case of the filling pipe one would cut out the hole in the deck for the pipe, which would be galvanised, and then screw the pipe down into the tank, a job usually done by the fitters, after which one would chisel wood out of the deck to the shape and depth of the flange round the cap, bed the whole down on white lead, and screw it down. The flange and cap would be brass, and brass screws would be used. A very similar operation would be rquired for the air pipe, which was different in that it would end in a swan neck.

In the meantime Pieter or Bob would have fitted the boiler connection, after which, with a final inspection of the interior of the tanks, the manhole cover could be put on.

The freshwater tank for the crew, which would have been put below before the casing was closed in, was carried on brackets in the port after corner of the engine room. In my illustration of the galley you can just make out the pump which was fitted to the tank, as near to the port fore corner of the galley as the stove would allow. The fitting on this tank would have been put there by a plumber, except that the hole through the deck would have been bored by a shipwright to the plumber's requirements. As I have said earlier, not a great deal of water was carried and the tank was not a huge one.

Work could now begin on fitting the engine. An intermediate length of shaft would be fitted first to decide exactly where the engine had to be placed, and the coupling up and lining up would be done from there. There was a maximum tolerance of three thousand parts of an inch, or "three thou tolerance" as it was called, on the shaft coupling.

My job would be to fit packings between the engine bed plate and the engine bearers, the packings being of well seasoned oak, using the saw mill to thickness them and a plane for a final fit.

With the engine lined up, and this included the thrust block, boring for the holding-down bolts could be started. I seem to remember that slots were chiselled in the sides of the bearers and on these the plate washers and nuts

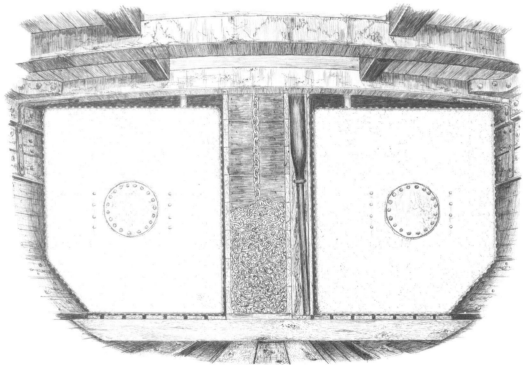

Boiler feed tanks, chain locker and hand pump. The methods of securing these are not shown.

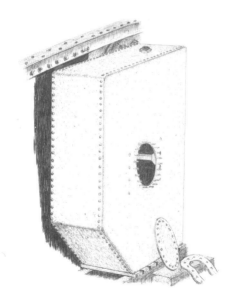

Tanks situated between the back end of the boiler and the after well.

153

were put on the bolts, after which all the bolts would be tightened down, a little at a time on each one, using a piece of pipe on the spanner for the final pull.

After this was done the fitters would get on with the steam pipes, circulating water pipes, and all the rest of the work that goes with the job, including the fittings to the donkey pump on brackets on the port side, just to the after side of the port bunker. The pump would have been brought on board at the same time as the boiler feed tanks, the steering gear and capstan.

The engine room telegraph would be aboard, and this would be hung on its own bracket close to the engine start and stop valve. This is also where the reversing lever was situated, close to the starboard fore pillar of the engine, and all within easy reach of the driver.

Work would next be started on the engine room floor plate bearers. This work was very similar to that done in the cabin, but shipwrights would be doing it in the engine room. After the bearers were completed the chequer plates for the floor would be cut, fitted and laid, using buttstraps at any joints; some angle bars were incorporated here for the engine room floor.

There would be a step down about six to eight inches at the fore part of the engine, on to what I can only term the stokehold footplate, though everything was contained in the one space as the boiler was fired from aft. This step down gave the fireman, as the stoker was called in drifters, ample room to clean out the ashpans beneath the firebars. This ashpan was simply part of a whole cylindrical furnace structure.

There was plenty of room on this footplate to handle the coal from the bunkers, the doors of which were immediately adjacent to it on both sides, to swing a shovel and to use a slice, or to clean the fires. As the ventilators were a little to the after side of the funnel and fairly close to it, the ash bucket would come down from the vent into which it was hoisted when tipping the ashes, almost exactly where it was required.

With the footplates laid, the steel ladder could be fitted at the starboard after end of the engine room. One would have to go through the starboard side of the galley in order to get either up or down the ladder.

The acetylene gas generator with which these vessels were fitted was rigged upon a shelf inside the engine room just at the after end of the starboard bunker. A seat locker would be built below this, extending for the full length of the engine room to the after bulkhead. A stores cupboard or locker would be built from the seat locker at this point, extending to the deckhead and out to the vessel's side.

With all this work completed it would be possible to paint the engine room out. Although the owners would be consulted as to colour scheme, etc.,

154

Left: At the foot of the engine room ladder. The engine in
this case is a triple expansion engine.
Above: The after end of the wheelhouse and the fiddley
hatch.

sometimes the "driver", as the engineer was called, would be asked if he had
any preferences. It was to be his own and the stoker's workshop, perhaps for
some time to come.

Some drivers and firemen took great pride in their engine room and
certainly in the engine; woe betide anybody who for any reason made a mess
down below. Some engine rooms were very tastefully decorated, particularly
in Scottish vessels, where some of the panelling painted on the inside of the
casing was a work of art. I have seen pictures of drifters painted in some
vessels.

I think perhaps that at this point the word "driver" might need a little
explaining. When the very early steam drifters were built in East Anglia
most fishermen were very shy of machinery, and as somebody with a
mechanical turn of mind was needed to look after such new-fangled things
as boilers and engines the owners naturally turned to the traction engine
drivers on the farms. Such men were already called drivers, and they
continued to be called this when they went to sea.

With the coming of diesel, however, the man responsible for machinery
became the Engineer or "Chief".

Wheelhouse

During the time that work has been going on in the engine room other
work has been in progress, one of the jobs being the building of the
wheelhouse cab. This was built in the joiners' shop, and in our ships was
usually of pitchpine and deal.

Built by Mr George Knights and one or two of his fellow workers, the
finished product was usually a really beautiful job with a smart cambered
roof with rounded fore corners. The vessel's name, together with a short
piece of scroll at each end of it, in gold leaf on a black background with
rounded ends was carried in the centre of the fore top rail, and as this was
varnished pitchpine it looked really fine.

Immediately above the name and on the roof in the centre was the
"mitchboard" or mast and derrick crutch, made of English elm with
gracefully rounded parts, and varnished. Vessels built on No. 3 yard had
mitchboards made in one piece, but the mitchboards of our No. 1 yard
vessels were built up of four pieces.

The studwork of the cab was made so that it slipped into the casing when
being lowered down on to the ship; it would be fastened down by
coachscrews, screwed up through the angle flange surrounding the
wheelhouse on the outside into the sill, so that no fastening could be seen in
the woodwork.

Tarred felt would have been used between wood and steel under the sill. I
ought to mention that the sill was of English oak, and was finished off with a
bullnose shaped perimeter and varnished.

The roof was built of selected stout T & G boards on cambered oak beams
of a bullnose section, and was covered with sail canvas painted white with a
gloss finish. Close to the edge of the roof were varnished pitchpine anti-drip
splines, left with open corners at the after end of the wheelhouse. These
helped to set the wheelhouse off.

155

Just to the fore side of the wheel a hole was cut in the roof for the compass, which was housed in a roof top binnacle, eventually to be painted post office red.

Railway carriage type sliding windows were used, manipulated by the use of leather straps as in a carriage. There were three of these windows across the fore part, with two smaller angled fixed windows in the corners, two other opening windows each side, and three more across the after end of the wheelhouse, with one fixed window in the top part of the door, which was in the starboard after corner.

Work in the wheelhouse would be carried on with the fastening down of the steering gear, which was bolted down to the casing top, and with the fitting of the steering chains, which were passed round the barrel of the gear itself and under the sheaves, and then left hanging out of the slots provided for them in the two fore corners at or just above the casing level. The two chain sheaves would be fitted in the corners and the chain rove round them.

After this the engine room telegraph would be fitted, being put down on a base which would be fastened right down through the casing top, with a hole cut in the steel plate where the pillar was to stand in the starboard fore corner. Copper spun rivet telegraph chain was used, and sheaves to take this would be arranged under the plate and just above the boiler, where the lead was to be into the engine room. After this was done it was a comparatively easy matter to rig the chains and wires to the engine room itself; this was one of the jobs that Pieter and Bob would be doing.

I seem to remember that the telegraphs that we used were made by Chadburn, while the steering gears were of Chambers' own manufacture.

With the work completed on the floor of the wheelhouse it would be possible to give it two coats of bitumastic, while the surrounding plates would have had two coats of red oxide, possibly to be finished off with a coat of grey primer.

The remaining work in the wheelhouse would consist of putting in the surround, which would be made up of deal T & G boards with a V-joint, varnished when the job was completed. A seat locker would be fitted across the after end to the door, and floor gratings would be made and laid; these would come about six inches above the casing top and be left untreated.

A chart rack would be fitted up under the deckhead at the after end and two binocular boxes fitted, one in each of the fore corners of the wheelhouse. These would be varnished, with the exception of the seat locker tops, on which there might even be a cushioned seat.

Finally the ship's bell with the name engraved on it would be hung on a bracket fixed to the after head rail in the centre and immediately above the fiddley grating.

156

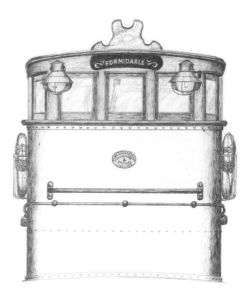

The foreside of the wheelhouse, topped by a mitchboard made of English elm four inches sided. The *Formidable* was one of the last drifters fitted with the sheet horse seen above the handrail.

Looking for'ad inside the wheelhouse, showing the wheel, telegraph, binocular boxes and whistle lanyard.

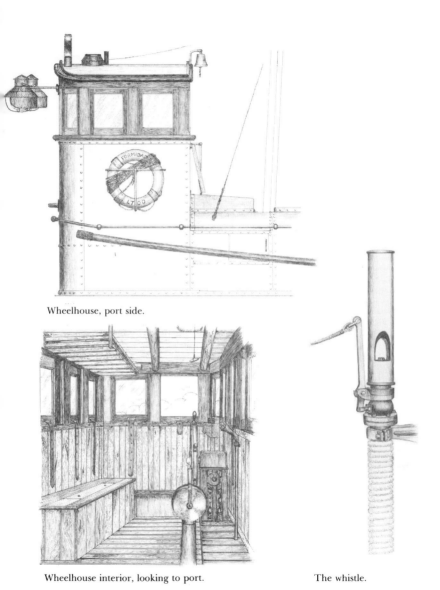

Wheelhouse, port side.

Wheelhouse interior, looking to port.

The whistle.

All that remained was to bore a hole in the roof over which to fix the small curved tube through which the whistle lanyard will pass. This had to be in such a position as to be very easily reached by the helmsman. A voice pipe to the engine room, complete with plug-in whistle, was also fitted to the fore end of the wheelhouse.

Most of the work in the wheelhouse was done by the joiners.

Rudder yoke

Before the steering chains could be connected it was necessary to shrink on the rudder yoke. The first thing was for the blacksmith to make sure that the rudder was exactly fore and aft.

The yoke would be put on the nearest blacksmith's fire, with the boss in the fire itself, and the fire would be blown up. While it was heating pieces of old plating would be laid round the rudder stock on the deck of the vessel, and buckets with lanyards on the handles for drawing water were placed nearby, together with a hammer.

When the iron was hot enough, and it needed to be red hot, the blacksmith and his striker would snatch it up by the extreme ends, which would be wrapped in rag as they could get very warm. They would run with it as fast as they could down to the ship, it would be quickly lowered on board, rushed aft and put on the square at the top of the stock; it would then be tapped down lightly on to the shoulder prepared for it, at which point the water from the buckets would be poured over it until it had become cool enough for the blacksmith to be satisfied that it was well and truly shrunk on. After that the plates which had been laid down to protect the deck and pitch from the heat could be removed and carried ashore.

The steering rod tubes of about three-and-a-half inches in diameter were fastened to the sides of the casing. They would extend some five or six feet beyond the after end of the galley at about three inches from the deck, to which they were fastened on brackets. The steering rods would now be inserted and connected to the chain coming off the steering gear, while the after ends would be connected to the eyes at the end of the yoke by means of a length of chain travelling on a horizontal sheave bolted to the deck. To prevent the chain chafing the deck a substantial piece of oak doubling would have been fastened to the deck by the shipwright.

All the steering arrangments have now been dealt with except the steering wheel. Built up of teak, iron and brass, the wheel would be large enough for two men to handle, three feet six inches in overall diameter. It was brass banded on both sides, and the spokes were fitted into a cast iron nave, over which was fitted a brass cover.

One other job to be done was the fitting of the fiddley grating and cover. The hatch, situated just to the after side of the wheelhouse, enabled the boiler cleaners to get down on to the boiler and through the manhole when it was necessary to clean the boiler; that is to say, chip and brush off any scale that might be adhering to the tubes and shell of the boiler, an operation which would usually take place between the end of the autumn herring voyage and the time the drifters would be getting ready to start the next year's voyages.

Side light irons and boards

The side light irons were manufactured by the blacksmith from round mild steel bars of sufficient diameter, so that when extended and carrying the board and sidelight they would not sag. Two angle irons placed one at a distance above the other supported the whole fitting, these angles being bolted to the side of the galley just below the round of the roof and towards the fore end. They would be drilled to take the side light irons.

The irons themselves would have a shoulder fashioned on them sufficiently high to rest on the top angle. About six inches above the top angle the bar would be bent at a right angle, and another right angle turned upwards at a distance along the bar suitable to allow the side light board to be directly over the rail of the vessel when extended, in which position they would be held by a long hook secured to the top angle iron and to an eye in the after side of the extended bar, usually the fore one. When not in use the side light boards would be swung inboard and hooked back to the galley.

The boards themselves would have been made in the joiners' shop to Board of Trade requirements. Two narrow plates with an eye formed at right angles to them at each end would be bolted on at the back of the boards; these plates would be shipped over the end of the upturned bar when shipping the boards. On the back or main board at the after end and facing outboard a steel tongue would be screwed on which to secure the side light; there was an aperture in the back board to enable the man putting the sidelights out to secure the lamp by screwing a thumbscrew on the lamp itself tightly.

The side light irons would be finished in black varnish or a similar bright black paint, while the boards themselves would be painted port, red, starboard, green, with the backs and ends white.

On the galley roof would be fitted a small skylight, and two funnel scoots would be fitted, one for the cabin and the other for the galley cooking stove. Some vessels also had a ventilator to the cabin.

A square would be cut out at the after end of the roof and this would have an angle coaming, large enough for the mizzen mast and the mast partners which would be fitted round it.

A wicket style door was fitted; this enabled the cook to close the bottom half only if there was much water coming on deck. A sliding door was fitted in the starboard side of the casing opposite the dome to give the driver or fireman access to the main steam valve. The safety valve could be reached from the fiddley hatch.

Two circular ports would be fixed in the galley, one on each side and towards the fore end. Handrails were fitted at the bottom edge of the rounded plate of the casing structure on both sides.

A sheet horse iron would be fitted on the foreside of the wheelhouse. It would sometimes be made use of when a tow foresail was set, as it was at times on long passages and with a favourable wind.

Small cast iron steps were fitted on the side of the casing just to the afterside of the wheelhouse to give access to the door, while a brass hand rail would be fitted vertically from the casing top to the underside of the sill, where it was curved home to the steel plate.

On the foreside of the cab and fastened to the head rail would be fitted two acetylene gas working lamps on the end of swivelling brass tubes about two feet in length. The lamps had a very considerable brass hat and chimney over them, fitted with an anti-glare shield fixed round the after side to shield the lookout man's eyes. A glass bowl was suspended beneath each cover to protect the burner, and each bowl had a crossed brassware guard hanging around and beneath it. The gas was channelled to the burners through a tube from the generator in the engine room.

Four funnel stay lugs would be bolted to the casing, two for'ad and two after side of the funnel, while four corresponding lugs would be positioned on the funnel itself. The two stays leading down from the lugs on the fore side of the funnel would lead to the two corresponding lugs on the casing, while the stays from the after lugs would cross over, that is, the stay from the port lug on the funnel would lead down to the starboard lug on the casing, while the reverse would be the case on the other side; this arrangement helped to steady the funnel better as it allowed a greater span. Each stay, which would usually be painted white, was fitted with a thimble through which was a rope seizing securing the stay to the lower lug.

An ash bucket ring was fitted to the after side of the funnel to contain the ash bucket when it was not in use. Just to the after side of this and towards the port side of the casing a small grindstone would be fixed, so placed as to be within easy reach of the crew.

On the deck across the after end of the galley and for its full width was secured a grating about five inches high by three feet in width. The oak or elm bearers of the grating laid thwartships and the deal bars fore and aft; the bearers were fitted down to the deck.

In some ships the bearers would be painted blue while the top would be left untreated, while in others it might be all blue. This was one of the few jobs where tradition did not say either one way or the other.

Further aft another grating was to be found; this one was over the quadrant, or I should say yoke. This grating was built in an angle iron frame which stood on steel stanchions usually about eighteen inches high fastened

The capstan.

to the deck. The frame would usually be finished in black varnish. The planks forming the grating would be of deal four inches by one-and-a-half inches planed, and when fitted and bolted down would be left with an inch or one-and-a-half-inch space between them. In some ships these might be painted blue, while in others they might be white; some ships never had them at all.

On this grating the after boat chocks, which would be tumblers, would be located. To the foreside of this and close to the cabin skylight would be located a swivelling boat chock with a circular cast iron pillar about two feet high, flanged at the base for bolt holes to be used when fastening to the deck; this was fitted down on tarred felt and white lead. The pillar would be hollow, to take the shank on the underside of a cast iron channel. The channel, which would be four inches wide, would be slightly raised from the centre towards each end. The for'ad boat chocks would be fixed in this channel. If the boat was to be launched it was usual to lift the stern round on to the rail.

In the space between the two chocks the spare propellor would be lashed down on deck.

At this stage we have not a great many more shipwrighting jobs to be done; they were to fit the rope room hatch, construct the chain locker, and in this same area fit the cast iron deck pump, not forgetting the capstan, which I will deal with first.

The capstan for *Formidable* was, as were the great majority of steam drifter's capstans, made by Elliott and Garroods, of Beccles, near Lowestoft; to give it its full title, it was the "Beccles" patent steam capstan. At the time *Formidable* was built there were over 5,500 of these in use; they were of twenty-one different sizes. One of the remarkable things about them was the amount of power they could exert with such a small engine; I would think that they must have been the ultimate in that sort of machine. Steam was provided by means of a pipe from the dome on the boiler passing out to the ship's side, at underside of shelf, then for'ad to the rope room, where it turned from the side of the vessel and was taken over towards the capstan, then turned up through the deck, continuing on up through the spindle of the capstan, which revolved round it, to the engine and gears on top under the casing.

The exhaust from the cylinders returned by the same route but by a slightly larger diameter pipe to the waste steam pipe on the fore side of the funnel. Whenever the capstan was running a soft plume of steam would be visible above the steam pipe on the funnel.

The capstan was situated on the starboard side of and a little towards the foreside of the tabernacle. The base was built up of either two or three pieces

159

of elm, depending on what was available, to about rail height, with the top of it allowed to fall aft a little. Holes were left through the centre of these pieces to accommodate the steam pipes. The base was cut circular and was not very much wider than the base plate of the capstan itself. The bottom piece would be put down on tarred felt and white lead.

Account would be taken of the holes in the base plate of the capstan, the position of which would be transferred to the timber, after which the bolt holes would be bored through carlins and beams. The capstan would be offered on to the job and bolted down, the fitting out crane being used for this purpose.

When complete the base would be painted blue, the chocks green. There were eight chocks, four of wood, usually elm, bolted to the spindle and fitted with brass whelps, and four others of iron, which were held to the spindle by lugs and pins and prevented from moving about by two projections on each side of them, and touching the elm chock on either side. The iron chocks would be painted either blue or black. Around the bottom of the chocks was fixed an iron band which prevented the messenger rope from getting beneath the chocks and so becoming damaged.

Four pawls inside the outer perimeter of the capstan would drop into a rack provided for them with a click, click, click. The cast iron circular plate at the head of the capstan would be painted green, while the casing was painted post office red. The little drum or warping end would be painted black, as would the start and stop valve wheel which projected above the casing.

A few feet aft of the capstan and towards the centre line of the vessel was located the rope room hatch. This hatch or coaming was of cast iron and circular in shape, about one foot six inches in height, with the top edge rolling inwards, the aperture being two feet in diameter. From the top, the structure expanded outwards about one inch towards the bottom, and round the bottom was a flat outward flange in which holes had been left in the casing for holding down bolts.

Putting the hatch down was a fairly simple matter, in that one would first cut the circle through the deck, to a line which had been determined by the carlins already in position beneath the deck. The circle would be cut out, firstly by chiselling round the inside of a line scribed immediately above that of the carlin, most probably using a piece of batten in which one would drive two nails to the radii of the bottom of the hatch, at the inside measurement, of course. One would chisel wood out all round on the inside of the mark to reduce the thickness of the deck, or one would trim it down with the adze, to make it easier to saw round using a turn saw. The shipwright would then clean the cut round on the inside and put a chamfer round the bottom edge of the carlin cut to do away with chafe on the messenger rope.

160

The capstan chocks, which were bedded down on tarred felt and white lead. The holes passing through the chocks accommodated the steam and exhaust pipes which passed through the capstan spindle to the engine above.

The deck round the hole would next be prepared to receive the hatch, after which the hatch itself would be bedded down on tarred felt and white lead, then bolted through deck and carlin, or deck and beam, depending on the position of the holes in the flange, a matter to which the shipwright would devote some thought.

A hatch cover would next be made, if possible in one piece, elm usually. A circular band of quarter steel plate would be screwed round it, using galvanised screws. This band would finish at least two-and-a-half inches deeper than the hatch itself to form a good surround, so as to prevent the hatch moving. A locking bar would be put over the top of the hatch. This coaming and cover would be painted blue.

Two further jobs remain, fitting out the chain locker and fitting the cast iron deck pump.

In my illustration of the boiler feed tanks, which also includes the chain locker and deck pump, you are looking aft. The feed tanks themselves were placed equidistant from the centre line of the vessel, and you will see that the chain locker occupies by far the larger part of the space between them, leaving about a foot of space for the pump, and that largely air space.

Now there was a reason for this: normally the nets were shot from the starboard side of the vessel, and so a drifter with the greater part of the cable lying to starboard, plus the weight of several members of the crew working to starboard, would have a slight list to starboard. This would have the effect of keeping the nets further away from the propeller than they might otherwise have been. Of course, the chain lockers were not in this position in all vessels, but they were in the 420 class and in a good proportion of the drifters of that time.

Towards the end of the nineteenth century and in the early part of this one there was a great deal of religious fervour among fishermen, particularly the herring fishermen, and many of our local boat owners were Church and Chapel members. A great number of them were members of the Sailors' and Fishermen's Bethel at Lowestoft, and many of these men used to interpret the Bible literally in connection with their vessels. In St John, Chapter 21, verse 6, they read: "And He said unto them, Cast the net on the right side of the ship, and ye shall find." And so whenever possible they always shot their own nets on the starboard side.

I myself never worked on one of the chain lockers, but I can imagine it was very strongly built of oak. I do seem to remember that the side nearest to you as you look at the drawing was made up of loose boards in the same way that the fish pounds were, so that should there be any reason to get at the chain one was able to do this.

In the deck above the locker was the chain pipe, of cast iron, fitted with a cover. When fitting the pipe the angle at which it was to be set would have to be given consideration, after which the shipwright would cut the hole in the deck and then make all the usual arrangements to bed the cover down and fasten it off. It was altogether a fairly straightforward job, all built up from a strong base which primarily rested on the kelson.

The pump box, if I remember rightly, was about one foot square and built up from two-inch deal. The pump itself, like the chain pipe, was situated in the space between the after end of the coaming and the fore side of the wheelhouse; the top flange was let down to the deck but not let into the deck except for the boxes that were cast on the flange, namely the box which accommodated the cover hinge and the box which was formed in the casting to accommodate the handle standard or shank of the pump handle.

As Chambers made their own pumps I would think that the *Formidable*'s

would have been one of their own manufacture, with, I expect, a five-inch diameter barrel, tapering off and with a flange at the bottom on which to bolt the suction pipe of two-and-a-half inches or three inches diameter. The pump boxes would be of wood and made up in our own block and spar shop.

The sump into which the suction pipe went was the bay between two frames that was left open when we were putting the concrete into the bottom and forming the waterways.

There now remains the pump to be fixed to the freshwater tank located in the port after end of the engine room; and one can just see the pump in my illustration of the galley. This would be a brass pantry pump, bolted to the galley side and with a rocking lever handle; it would have a barrel about one foot long and about two-and-three-quarters inches in diameter, and it would be fitted with a tap. The barrel would be tinned inside. A plumber would fit

The galley.

this pump up and connect it to the tank. The filler pipe for this tank was just outside the galley and had a brass flange and cover flush with the deck.

In the after end of the galley on the port side was a steel coal bunker fitted with a wooden cover which would act as a worktop for the cook.

At this stage Mr Harwood would be called in again to concrete the deck of the galley, after which he would tile it out, using black and white tiles in a draughtboard pattern.

With the tiling completed it would be possible to fit the cooking range, which would have been about thirty inches wide, coal-fired, with the oven on the left-hand side. It would be fitted with a polished steel rail on iron pillars, the steel rail being slotted to take steel fiddles to steady the working utensils. Above the stove a rack would be hung on which to store the equipment.

A bulkhead lamp fitted with a paraffin oil burner would be the means of lighting the galley and would most probably be hung originally to a piece of wood secured to the galley structure. Although no doubt this will all seem to be rather primitive, it appeared to be pretty snug on occasions.

The galley might be painted out in a light brown and white or some such colours.

Mast, spar and block making

The last two tradesmen to be introduced into my story are Mr William Warford, a mast, spar and blockmaker, whose father was the celebrated Pakefield lifeboat coxswain, and Mr John Godfrey, whom I have left till the very last as we regarded him as the father of the yard; at the time of which I am writing he was certainly the oldest man there. Mr Godfrey was also a mast, spar and blockmaker, but owing to the fact that some time during his working life his spar axe had glanced off the wood and had damaged one of his legs, he would usually be working at the lathe or bench making blocks, deadeyes, parells, cleats and things of that nature. Mr Warford would insist that he himself did the chopping.

Here were two excellent craftsmen, to my way of thinking. That must have been to the Admiralty's way of thinking as well, as when the yard belonged to H. Reynolds, who specialised in Admiralty craft, and also after it was sold to John Chambers, letters would be received from the Chief Constructor's Department commending the firm on the high standard of its work in relation to spars, blocks, oars, etc., as well as to the boatbuilding.

Reynolds specialised in cutters, gigs, whalers and all kinds of small craft for the Admiralty.

Mr Godfrey must have been near seventy when the *Formidable* was built.

He was a very well-read and wise man, quiet and inoffensive, and one to whom people would often turn for advice. Mr Warford, who had worked in France for a few years, was about fifty.

In my illustration of mast and spar making I have dealt with the mizzen mast, which had an overall length of twenty-nine feet. The mast didn't go through the deck, but was stepped in the galley, there being two squares left on it for this purpose. The heel dropped into an angle bar step prepared for it in the deck as part of the galley structure while the upper housing came in line with the deckhead of the galley.

After the baulk for the mast was chosen Tinker would pull it up to the block and spar shop slung under the gill. After being unloaded, it would be taken in and placed on very low stools or blocks to be examined once again for faults and the general run of the grain. When work was decided upon great care would have to be taken to keep the pith and heart wood in the centre of the proposed spar: if there was any doubt about the soundness of the spar from the point of view of quick-changing colours, which could indicate the beginnings of rot, it would be necessary to cut pieces from each end as far as the length of the mast would allow to make sure that the spar was free from such defects. Rind gall was another condition which had to be looked out for.

After it had been decided that this was indeed the baulk to be used, it would be examined for shape; if there was a slight bend in it, it would be best to let the bend lay for'ad, as the mizzen mast raked forward. The centre line would be drawn on the hollow side first, and from this the diameters and radii would be set out; mast and spar makers used a special rule for this.

After setting out, a continuous line for each side could be drawn. With the two side lines drawn and allowances made for variations such as the galley housing, chopping would be started after the baulk had been secured by a steel dog to prevent it from jumping about. The spar maker would chop spots at intervals along the side of the spar using a spar axe, checking either by plumb bob or square, depending on the circumstances, as he worked his way along. The spar axe blade had a depth of about twelve inches and a width of about seven.

After the spots had been completed, and using the lines as a guide, the rest of the wood for the length of the spar would be hewn off both sides, after which it would be rolled over for chopping the other two sides. In the case of the mizzen mast quite a length was left square towards the heel; later a length between the heel and the galley deckhead will be set out to be eight sided, this being the finished shape in the galley. The part of the spar to be rounded will have to be eight-sided first, then sixteen-siding will be carried out, for which further lines will be drawn. The trimming for this will be done

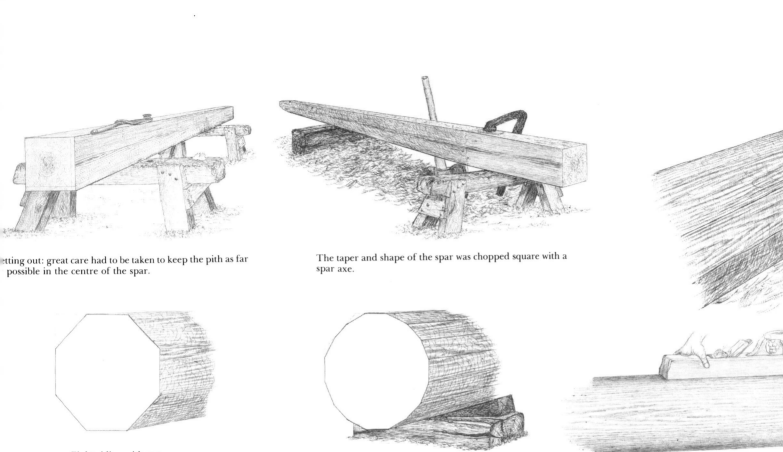

tting out: great care had to be taken to keep the pith as far
possible in the centre of the spar.

The taper and shape of the spar was chopped square with a
spar axe.

Eight-siding with an axe.

Eight-siding with axe.

Sixteen-siding with adze; a draw knife was used in places,
and on smaller spars.

Planing up; calipers would be used to check the diameter.

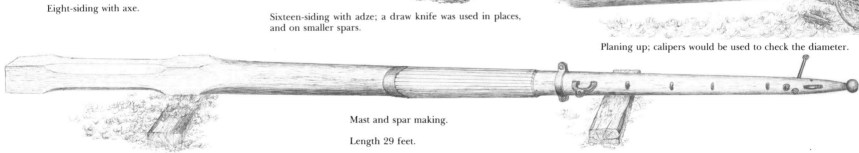

Mast and spar making.

Length 29 feet.

163

FORMIDABLE

Length BP 80 feet   Length OA 88 feet

by adze and drawknife until at last the spar will be ready for planing, during which operation calipers will be used at times. In Chambers' vessels the truck was spherical.

A shoulder was formed on the taper of the mast to carry the band for the mizzen shrouds. Just above this band was a bracket for the mizzen throat halyard block. In my drawing of the blacksmiths' forge you can see this bracket standing on the floor in front of the water trough, and you will see the two bolts which pass through the mast. Above the bracket were three eyebolts which carried the mizzen peak halyards. Another eyebolt above these carried the topping lift. Above these eyebolts and set at an angle slightly to port, projecting from the fore side of the mast was the mizzen masthead lamp bracket, square in section, and tapered slightly. It was made substantial enough not to require any support. Above the bracket in the centre of the fore part of the mast was the "Tommy Hunter" eyebolt, with the eye standing in the vertical position. The "Tommy Hunter", the mizzen mast stay, could be used for heaving the small boat inboard. Above this eyebolt a sheave was let into the mast, standing fore and aft.

A little below the throat halyard bracket the mast was splined round for about a third of its circumference with ash splines in the way of the mizzen gaff jaws; these were allowed to have enough length downwards to allow for reefing. The bottom edges were splayed down to the mast, and this splayed area was covered with a sheet of copper plate secured with copper tacks, allowing the gaff tumbler to slide over it when being hoisted. A gooseneck would be fitted just above the mast partners, at the galley top.

All the ironwork in and around the mast would have been dipped in bitumastic by the blacksmith while it was still warm. Finally the mast would be varnished (or oiled in some places) and the truck finished with golf leaf, quite a good combination to me.

With the foremast the procedure was the same, but there was a difference in the shape of it in that the heel of the mast was left square in order to fit the tabernacle and to assist in the lowering of it. Through the tabernacle and mast were two holes, one above the other; the top one accommodated the pin which acted as the fulcrum on which the mast was raised and lowered, while the lower one took a retaining pin. Around the holes an iron plate washer was let in flush and screwed home by means of galvanised screws. This also applied to the tabernacle.

Higher up the mast a band lwas put on in the same way as that on the mizzen mast, and this accommodated one shroud on each side. Above that was an eyebolt on each side to take a burton which went to the pin rail with the shroud; locally this was known as a "Spanish burton". About three feet from the masthead on the fore side was the eyebolt for the forestay.

The pole end of the mast, as it was known locally, had the same rounding taper as the mizzen mast and also finished with a tenon for the truck, which was spherical and the same as that on the mizzen mast. A small iron band was fastened round the mast at the seating of the truck. These trucks would have been turned up by Mr Godfrey.

Many drifters at about this time did not have foremast lamp brackets but relied solely on the mizzen masthead light; older type vessels had them, however, and so did drifters of a later date.

When the nets were shot another masthead lamp was hoisted on the "Tommy Hunter". This light indicated in which direction the nets were lying. Both these lamps were all-round white lights, with dioptric lenses.

You can see the halyards for this lamp in my illustration "Leaving Penzance".

About two feet from the fore masthead a sheave was inserted into the mast in a fore and aft direction to serve for the derrick and also for setting the tow foresail.

After the masts would come the mizzen boom and gaff, followed by the derrick, net rollers and rope room roller.

Blocks also had to be made. There were thirty-two in constant use, ranging in size from the single-sheaved lamp halyard blocks to the two treble-sheave blocks of the forestay. There were twelve deadeyes of lignum vitae, eight on the mizzen shrouds and four on the foremast, two to each shroud.

The mizzen boom might be of Norwegian spruce or some similar timber. It would be made up in much the same way as the mast, except that in making these smaller spars the drawknife was used more frequently. In lining the boom out the greatest diameter was about one third of the way in from the outer end of the boom, from where it would slowly taper towards the outer and inner ends.

Both ends would be banded, while for the mizzen sheet a horse iron extending about halfway round the boom was fitted on the underside of it. The purpose of this was to allow the mizzen sheet block and two tackles, one on each side of the sheet block, to be accommodated on it, as when shooting her nets the mizzen could be set thwartships, and it needed the tackles to manipulate it and to keep it in position. At the outer end of the boom a vertical sheave was inserted for a chain and tackle outhaul for the mizzen, complete with a traveller, to haul the sail in or out when reefing. To protect the boom from undue chafing from the traveller three or four small half-round chafing irons about four feet long were fastened to the boom. A cleat was also fastened to the inboard end of the boom on which to belay the outhaul.

165

A plan view of the *Formidable*, with half the deck left off to reveal the arrangements below.

The mizzen gaff would be of similar timber but not of such a large diameter as the boom, and would be finished with a long straight taper. Gaff jaws of oak were fitted, with a tumbler between them. Stirrups of wire, served up with spunyarn and afterwards tarred with coal tar, were fitted for the peak halyards and ash cleats were provided to act as stops for these. An iron eyebolt was provided for the throat halyards.

All the iron work would have been dipped in bitumastic while the iron was warm after making up.

Derrick

The derrick, which was about twenty-nine feet in length, was most probably of Norwegian spruce four-and-a-half inches in diameter at the heel and three inches at the head, with a long straight taper. It was banded at each end and oiled in some cases, painted in others.

The head band had two eyes on it, the top one for the lift while the bottom eye carried the gin block. The heel band was a simple plain band. A hinged gooseneck allowed the derrick to be raised or lowered with ease. An ash chock was provided as a stop for the lower leg of the derrick span, while another would be fitted at about ten feet from the heel of the derrick, where a preventer would sometimes be secured to stop the derrick swinging too far round when landing herrings and perhaps fouling the derrick of the ship lying alongside.

To make the derrick and any of these smaller spars and rollers the spar maker would depend largely on the drawknife and plane. Some spar makers in order to overcome a hard knot would shatter the outer portion of the knot by giving it a few sharp blows with a hammer, which would make it easier to plane. Some knots could gap a very sharp plane.

Net roller

The net rollers, which would be either spruce or larch, were about four-and-a-half inches in diameter and were banded at each end. The roller used above the coaming was made to the length of the coaming, that on the rail was somewhat longer.

A pin was driven in the centre of each of the butt ends, the roller revolving on the pins as the nets were pulled over it by the men standing in the hatchway. The pins fitted in an eye at the top of a short stanchion, stood up in a socket prepared for it at the ends of the hatch. The rail roller was also carried by means of a centre pin at each end in the eye of a stanchion, standing about one foot above the rail. The section of the roller stanchions was square, and a shoulder formed on them rested on a washer round the socket in the rail or coaming in which they stood.

Rope room roller

The rope room roller was a smaller version of the ones I have just mentioned. It stood just to the fore side of the rope room hatch and was angled to suit capstan and hatch. It was about two feet six inches long. In some vessels the stanchions which supported it were allowed to extend above the roller itself to form spindles on which a three-inch by six-inch roller of lignum vitae would be placed vertically to prevent the messenger rope from being thrown off it due to some violent motion of the ship.

Blocks

Mr Godfrey, the blockmaker, would make up two sets of blocks for each vessel, the larger ones being of English elm and some of the small ones of ash.

The blockmaker would assemble the shells of the blocks at the bench, using copper nails driven through the whole width of the blocks, cut off and clinched on the cheek. When enough were assembled, they would be taken into the sawmill for the bandsawyer to cut them to shape, and he would follow the line drawn on them by the blockmaker from his mould.

On their return the blockmaker would shape them and round them off, using a rasp, spokeshave, sandpaper or sandpapering machine, after which they would have a lovely finish. Next he would insert any ironwork that there was to go in them, then the sheaves and pins which would have been bored for earlier. The ironwork would have been dipped in bitumastic after being made up.

The finished block would be dipped in copal varnish or perhaps oiled. When hung up in their rows they would look a marvellous sight to my eyes.

The deadeyes, of which there were twelve in the 420 class drifters, would next be made of lignum vitae. Circular in shape, they would be turned up on the lathe.

Rigging

The rigging of a drifter was of two kinds, standing and running, the standing rigging being the shrouds, forestay and "Tommy Hunter".

The standing rigging was made of galvanised mild steel, in the case of all except the forestay served up with spunyarn, which in turn would be dipped in coal tar when finished. The forestay was "white leaded" as it was known locally; that is to say, it would simply be smeared with white lead, using a piece of sacking for the job.

Riggers employed by such firms as the Steam Drifters Stores, the Gourock Ropework Company or R. J. Pryce and Company, a local firm, would set the rigging up. Hemp would be used with the deadeyes, the rope itself being tarred with coal tar as a preservative. Stockholm tar was used years ago, but it was found that of the two coal tar was less injurious to the rope.

The running rigging, that is, the halyards, sheets, falls and purchases, was normally of manilla and remained untreated.

The funnel stays were of wire with a manilla seizing in the lower thimble to secure the stay to the lug provided on the casing; these stays were usually painted white.

The mizzen of cotton canvas was nine cloths wide, made with one set of reef points in it. This sail would most probably have been made by the Steam Drifters Stores, although the larger drifter-owning firms might have their own sailmaker, as did most of the smack owners. The sail would be dressed with a mixture of herring oil and soot, making it almost black. The mast hoops were of ash. The wire topping lift, in some cases served up with spunyarn and tarred, would in many cases have a quantity of "baggy-wrinkle" served round it in order to prevent chafing of the sail. In many ships a small line was attached to the topping lift and led away to a brass thimble secured to the shroud and then down to where it could be secured; this would hold the topping lift away from the sail to prevent chafing.

The tow foresail, a large triangular sail hoisted on the foremast when on long passages, was usually tanned red as a smack's sail would be, as it would not be subjected to smoke the way the mizzen was. The tow foresail was only regarded as an auxiliary.

Some drifters would have a green canvas cover made for the fore side of the wheelhouse when the vessel was new and the casing was grained. This might be used at sea for a time when working, or when landing in port, but in due course it would be forgotten.

The stem fender would be "hitched coir" made on a wire rope with a thimble at the head and at each end. When in use it would be lowered by the head thimble and held in position by the end thimbles, the rope from the head thimble being made fast on the forestay belaying cleat, while those from the end thimbles would be made fast on the bow rail bollards on each side of the ship. The cork fenders were of hitched coir, cork stuffed and lowered on a fender rope.

On each side of the wheelhouse and placed so as to be clear of the sill was located a polished brass lifebelt rack for a regulation sized lifebelt, namely thirty inches overall diameter. The lifebelt would be painted white with the vessel's name and number usually painted on it in black. A lifeline would be attached to the lifebelt permanently and this would be coiled and carried on the rack.

The whistle lanyard was of a flexible galvanised steel wire leading from the whistle valve lever down through the small curved tube on the wheelhouse top. It was finished off with a toggle at a suitable position for the helmsman to be able to grasp it. The toggle would be left low enough for any member of the crew to grasp it.

Captain Jack, assisted by one or two other men who were going to be crew members, would be busy reeving off halyards and the various purchases, so that by this time there would be plenty of paper stuff, as the rope ends were called, lying around mixed with spunyarn and twine. The vessel is beginning to look shipshape.

The small boat has been put on board. She is of English elm planks on oak timbers, and varnished as were many of the small boats when they were first built. I always believe that this was a good thing, as often the inside of the boat would be covered by the simple expedient of putting the plug in the bottom of the boat, then pouring a quantity of copal varnish in her, after which she would be rolled about, tipped up even, causing the varnish to penetrate every nook and cranny in her. It would penetrate between planks and timbers, for instance, where no brush could ever reach. After a few minutes she would be put in the most convenient position for the varnish to drain out of her into a can, via the plug hole. When the interior had dried out the outer skin of the boat would be varnished in the usual way by brushing.

The day of days has dawned! Early this morning the boiler fires have been lighted and the two fitters are busying about, oiling and greasing. One can smell paint starting to burn, and also various things warming up; what a lovely aroma! Burning paint, Stockholm tar, varnish, oil paint and hot oil, all at one time.

The steam valve on the dome has just been opened, and Pieter is reaching for the main steam valve on the engine.

With a long hiss the engine starts to turn slowly. Bob has been up and looked over the stern to see that all's clear near the propeller, and has called down "all clear" to Pieter, who lifts the valve a little more. The ship is beginning to vibrate a little, she is alive. What a feeling this is!

With everything working satisfactory she would run for two or three hours, with the two men checking everything systematically, donkey pump, telegraph, whistle. The capstan would be given a run by one of Elliott and Garrood's fitters. By the end of the day everybody would be feeling well pleased.

Dry Dock

In the morning the fires, which had been banked up for the night, would be shaken up, cleaned, and given a little coal, not too much, just enough to take her down the harbour just before tide time. After that they will be allowed to die out.

As the time draws ever nearer, Jack, who will be taking her down, climbs into the wheelhouse, gives the order "let go", then rings down for "slow ahead". In a minute or so she is under way for Lowestoft and the dry dock.

What had been a collection of trees a few months ago is now moving under her own power, leaving her place of birth for ever.

As she arrives at the dock the caisson is being floated out. *Formidable*, together with three or four other vessels, enters to be lined up, to have shores dropped between them and from ship's side to dock wall. They will be set up tight with wedges when the ship sues, as we would say, or touches the blocks. As the dock is pumped out after the replacement of the caisson and she begins to settle on the blocks, a number of men working on rafts scrub the bottom, using brooms and water from the dock. Not that the bottom is very bad, bearing in mind that the vessel is new.

At the time of which I am writing neither the inner nor the outer harbour at Lowestoft was as polluted as they are today, nor were they so untidy, even though there was more hustle and bustle. The pollution is, of course, due to the times in which we live and the dereliction is due to a large extent to the depression of the thirties, when men were trying to eke out a living by cutting these vessels apart for a wage of six old pence an hour; they were desperate. The timber which they retrieved would be sold for fencing on

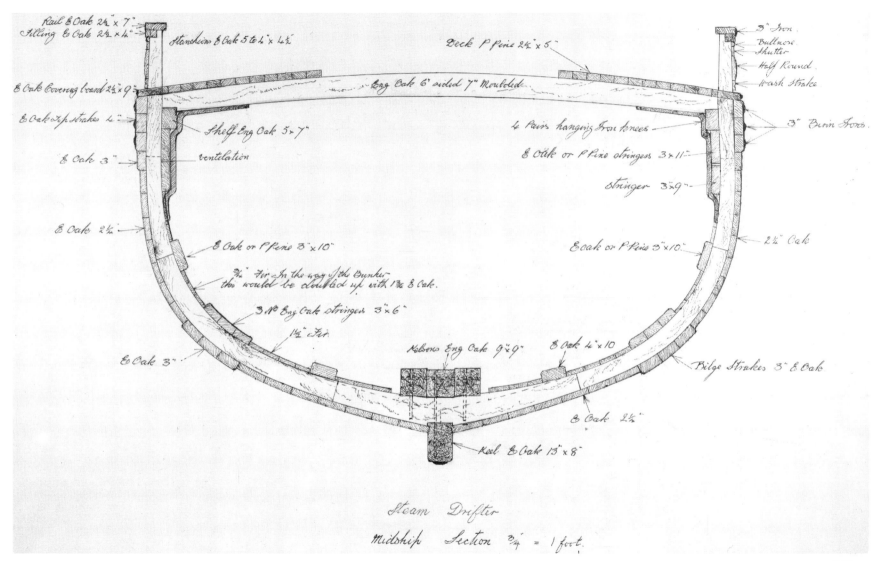

Rail E Oak 2½" x 7"
Filling E Oak 2½" x 4"
Stanchions E Oak 5 to 4" x 4½"
Deck P Pine 2½" x 5"
3" Iron
Bullnose
Shutter
Half Round
Wash Strake
E Oak Covering board 2½ x 9"
Eng Oak 6" sided 7" Moulded
E Oak Top strakes 4"
Shelf Eng Oak 5 x 7"
4 Pairs hanging Iron knees
3" Burin Irons
E Oak 3"
ventelation
E Oak or P Pine stringers 3 x 11"
stringer 3 x 9"
E Oak 2½"
E Oak or P Pine 3" x 10"
E Oak or P Pine 3" x 10"
2½" Oak
¾" Fir In the way of the Bunker
this would be doubled up with 1½ E Oak.
3 N° Eng Oak stringers 3" x 6"
1½" Fir
Kelsons Eng Oak 9" x 9"
E Oak 4" x 10
E Oak 3"
Bilge Strakes 3" E Oak
E Oak 2½"
Keel E Oak 13" x 8"

Steam Drifter
Midship Section ¾" = 1 foot.

169

170

farms and things of that sort; quite a large amount was sawn up small enough for home fires, for which it would be sold at prices lower than those charged for coal. When cut to that size timber was spoken of as "chumps". Nobody at that time had the means of pulling the heavier and more awkward parts of the vessel clear of the mud, hence the untidiness that remains.

Most of the vessels broken up were old. Smacks were the hardest to break up, every other bolt being a through bolt in them.

After the bottom of the vessel had been scrubbed it would be allowed to dry and then be given a final coat of anti-fouling composition; the propeller would be given a coat of white paint.

Once she was taken out of dock, steam could again be raised. Then, on the final day of days, she would go down "through bridge" to lay at the ice house pier.

Her burgee would be hoisted on the foremast, with the name *Formidable* proudly waving in the breeze, while at the mizzen masthead would be another flag, most probably that of the insurance company to which her owners belonged.

Gradually the people who were to go on the trial trip would begin to drift down to the vessel for the appointed sailing time. There would be the crew, of course, who would come down early, bringing their personal gear on board. Others would be the compass adjuster, representatives of the builders, the engine makers, the owners, relations of these various groups and of the crew, one shipwright, Pieter, and possibly one or two people from the "chamber", as the company's net store was known. If the weather was fine two or three beatsters, the ladies who mended the nets, might come along. On some ships quite a crowd would collect.

A few cases of beer would be brought on board and some mineral waters for those who preferred them. Bread, cheese, some cakes, plenty of dry tea, condensed milk and sugar; one can be sure that the kettle would be busy.

At the appointed time, the skipper in the wheelhouse would at last give the order "Let go!" With a blast on the whistle which would make everybody jump, the ship would begin to move towards the harbour mouth, and for the first time lift to the gentle swell.

On getting outside the compass adjuster would need to do his job. Some of the passengers would begin to feel unwell, as this meant turning about and often being broadside on to any swell which might be running. After this was done she would be headed away towards Yarmouth, with a good bit of black smoke coming from the funnel as she made her own breeze.

She would be timed as she passed the measured mile beacons on Lowestoft's North Denes. Then she would be turned, possibly off the harbour mouth at Gorleston, and timed again on the way south, when she would be opened up. After a little more manoeuvring she would return to harbour. The owners would listen to the comments of the skipper, the driver and the engine builder's representative; and no doubt shortly afterwards she would be accepted.

Experience would have made each vessel a little better than its predecessor. The *Formidable* was the culmination of years of experience in the building of wooden steam drifters.

Leaving Penzance for mackerel.

171

Glossary

Abaft the beam Aft of amidships.

Account, to take account of To measure up for some purpose and to record the measurements.

Adze, Shipwright's A curved single-edged cutting tool that has to be used vigorously with a chopping motion. The helve is curved to give a correct balance.

Adze helve A curved shaft, usually of ash, fitted through the eye of the adze. Care has to be taken when fitting this as the helve has to sit right in order to make the tool usable.

Aft Towards the stern.

Amidships The mid-point of the length of the vessel.

Apron A substantial piece of timber bolted to the after side of the stem and to which the hooding ends of the planks are fastened.

Back end The combustion chamber, where the heat and smoke leave the furnaces, to turn upwards into the boiler tubes and through them into the smoke box and funnel.

Back or mackerel boards Boards over which mackerel nets were hauled from the vessel's side to the hatch. The boards prevented the nets from sagging to the deck.

Baggywrinkle A chafing mat formed of rope yarn and fitted to a topping lift where chafing of a sail might occur.

Banker board A portable platform of wood on which to mix concrete.

Beams Wooden or metal members which connect the two sides of the vessel at sheer height and support the deck.

Beetle A large hooped mallet of wood with which to horse or harden up the garboard seam when caulking.

Belay Make fast.

Below Anywhere below the deck.

Bevel board A board on which are shown the bevels at the various sur marks on the frame. A separate bevel board for each frame is attached to the bandsaw table when cutting frames; the turning of the bevels when cutting has to be synchronised with the speed of the wood through the saw so that each sur mark is reached at the right time.

Bevel board, Shipwright's The board on which the shipwright would mark down the bevel found at each station when taking account of a plank.

Binn or bent iron A length of convex or half-round iron fastened round the vessel's hull to prevent chafing.

Bole The trunk of a tree.

Bollard A strong wooden or metal post to which a rope can be made fast.

Boring bar A revolving bar on to which cutters are secured, used to bore out the hole for the stern tube to its correct size.

Bowl or bowel A small cooper-made barrel of wood used to support and mark the nets of a sailing drifter.

Breasthook A crook used to connect the two sides of the vessel at sheer height for'ad which was fastened through knightheads, frames, stem and apron.

Buff A stitched canvas pear-shaped bladder, tarred inside and painted outside, used at every junction of a pair of drift nets to help support the fleet of nets and to mark its position.

Bunker ring A cast iron ring let into a hole in the deck through which the bunker was filled with coal; a lid was put on and made reasonably watertight when at sea.

Butt The meeting of two squared ends of plank. Also the base of the bole of a tree.

Butt board The board on which is marked the predetermined position of the butts, used by the shipwright who is lining out plank.

Buttock A vertical fore-and-aft section.

Cage A lignum vitae lined tube fitted into the stern tube as a bearing for the tail shaft, and in which the tail shaft revolved. It was lubricated with seawater.

Cant frames Single timber frames canted off the centre line and forming the elliptical shape of the stern. Set out in a fan shape, they were fastened to the stern timbers. Two others were fastened in the bow on each side of the stem knee.

Capstan The machine by means of which the nets were hauled and the catch discharged. The steam capstan with which most steam drifters were fitted was developed by the Beccles firm of Elliott and Garrood; in this the steam pipe passed up the hollow spindle to a small engine on top of the capstan.

Carbide Crystals of calcium carbide from which acetylene gas was generated by the addition of water for use in working lights.

Carvel built A vessel in which the planking, edge to edge, is fastened to a framework of timbers is said to be carvel built.

Caulking To insert and drive home oakum into a seam between two planks to render it watertight.

Cavil or cavel A strengthening timber fastened round the inside of the stanchions forming the stern, midway between deck and taffrail.

Chequer plates Non-slip steel plates used on the engine room floor and on deck over the boiler aperture beside the casing.

Chop When preparing timber for the frame saw the part that will be the underside when on the saw has to be chopped plumb so that the saws will cut vertically and run straight.

Cleat A piece of wood nailed on to a timber against which a wedge can be driven to set down a plank; a piece of wood temporarily nailed on to secure a batten; a wooden or metal fitting to which a rope can be belayed.

Clench or clink, To To expand the end of a driven fastening over a rove or washer by the use of a ball pein hammer after cutting it off. Hence clencher or clinker built.

Clinker built A vessel in which the planking is overlapping, with each plank fastened to its neighbour, is said to be clinker built (the nails which fasten the planks are clenched or clinked over roves). In this form of building the planking is completed before the frames, often of steamed ash, are inserted.

Coaming Timber placed on edge around an aperture such as a hatchway.

Compo A mixture of sand, cement and water used to fill over bolt heads.

Cork A small piece of cork cut in cylindrical form used in large numbers to help support drift nets and to keep them in a vertical position in the water.

Cork fender A fender made up of hitched coir and stuffed with granulated cork.

Crab winch A wooden mechanism with a vertical barrel used to wind a rope and so manoeuvre ships about on a shipyard. Built on a triangular base, it had three timber supports, two of them fitted on the main timber by means of a cut similar in shape to a crab's claw, hence the name. The winch was motivated by horsepower.

Cran A measure consisting of four quarter-cran baskets of herring, the total weight of which would be 28 stones.

Crease iron A purpose-made iron used in caulking which leaves the oakum in a seam as a trouser crease in shape, ready for paying up.

Cross spalls Boards cut to the moulded breadth of the vessel, one for each frame, with a precise centre mark cut in each. They were nailed on their respective frames at top height and held the two halves of the frames together during construction.

Dead man A large piece of timber with a chain secured to it or put around it, buried several feet deep but leaving the loose end of the chain exposed, to be used for hauling purposes.

Deadwood A substantial piece of timber, in the case of ships built by Chambers usually English elm, fitted on top of the keel and meeting the stern post. The foot frames were secured to it.

Dog A steel rod turned at a right angle at each end and sharpened at the two ends, used as a temporary measure for holding blocks, timber, ways, etc. They varied in length from about a foot to three feet.

Drift To move with the wind and/or tide. A vessel would move with the tide when lying at her nets, hence the term drifter for a fishing vessel using this particular type of net into which fish would swim, to be caught by their gills. Also a short tapered steel punch, used to pull together two bolt holes in steel plates.

Dump bolt A galvanised wrought iron bolt with upset head which would be sheered off according to the length required. The ends always had to be slightly rounded before driving.

Driver The engineer in a steam drifter.

Ease, To To take a little off a piece of timber when fitting it.

Fair, To To remove humps, bumps and hollows so that any given line runs in a regular curve; to plane the edge of a piece of timber so that the line is regular.

Fashion frame The first of the frames forming the stern, fitted on the stern post. This frame literally fashions the shape of the stern at that point.

Fireman or stoker The man working with the driver in the engine room of a steam drifter. His main function was to attend to the furnaces, keeping them clean, and using the coal to the best advantage.

Fishrings Small galvanised bunker rings with covers fitted in the fore deck to allow herrings to cascade through into the fish room.

Fleet along, To When launching by hollows and rounds, to move a length of hollow just released by the movement of the vessel into position to receive the vessel again as she is pulled down towards the water.

Floor The connecting timber lying across the top of the vessel's keel linking the two halves of a frame.

Foc's'le Living quarters in the fore part of the ship.

Foot frames The frames fitted to the deadwood.

Forelock A flattened steel pin made to pass through a slot in a bolt, such as the tizzard bolt, in order to prevent the bolt from slipping back.

Forestay The wire stay from the foremast head down to the stem head, used to support the mast and also to lower and raise it when necessary. The foremast was normally lowered when the vessel was lying to her nets.

Frames Transverse timbers cut to the shape of the vessel, to which the planks are fastened.

Freeboard The distance between water level and sheer height amidships.

Full A piece of timber that needs reducing in size to make it fit; a bulge in a batten or line.

Gaff   The spar to which the head of a sail is made fast.

Galvanised flat points   Steel nails with a small rose head and a tapered flat shank used usually in oak.

Gill   A horse-drawn frame on two wheels used for the conveyance of tree trunks, baulks of timber, etc.

Gorger   A large enamelled jug used in drifters to carry tea from the galley to wherever men are working.

Hawse box   The piece of timber in the bulwark which is fastened to the stem, knighthead and first stanchion, through which the hawse pipe is fitted. The vessel's name, scroll and streak are carved on this timber.

Hollow   A long piece of timber hollowed out to receive either the vessel's keel or a round. When used for launching, one is placed in readiness to receive the keel and another in readines to receive the round on to which the vessel's bilge will be lowered when listing her.

Hooding ends   The ends of the vessel's planks where they fit into a rabbet.

House down, To   To fit down a piece of timber.

Jump up, To   To expand a piece of heated iron in a certain place for a certain purpose by striking the material at each end.

Keel   The main longitudinal member running from stem to stern on which the vessel is built.

Keelson or kelson   An internal fore-and-aft member providing additional strength. In some steam drifters a centre one was laid on top of the floors and then flanked by two side kelsons; bolts were driven through the centre kelson and the floors into the keel and through the side kelsons into the floors, and also horizontally through all three kelsons. The combination formed a strong backbone for the ship.

Kel   A local term for the steam trunk in which planks were steamed in preparation for working; the Suffolk pronunciation of the word kiln.

Kid   The deck space between the main hatch coamings, the bulwark and the thwartship boards.

Knees, hanging   Iron brackets, eight in number, four on each side, through bolted to the beams and to the topsides.

Knees, rising or lodging   Pieces of timber cut from crooks, connecting the beams to the vessel's side.

Knightheads   Two substantial timbers placed in the eyes of the vessel which accommodate the hawse pipe.

Lagging   Asbestos material placed around the boiler and steam pipe to retain the heat.

Laying off   Putting down the vessel's lines at full size on the mould loft floor. The loftsman would do this from offsets and lines given to him by the draughtsman.

Leading light   A light hoisted at a lower level than the mizzen masthead light and at least ten feet further forward when the nets were shot. This indicated the direction in which the nets were lying. The lamp was usually hoisted on the Tommy Hunter.

Lining out plank   The operation of drawing lines on a plank with the aid of a batten. The shipwright doing the job would have chosen the plank carefully to ensure that it was entirely suitable for the purpose required.

Lip crow   A strong bar with a fulcrum-shaped end, over which a loose link was fitted; used to remove unwanted bolts. The shipwright would get the bolt between the tip of the bar and the loose link and lever it out.

Loftsman   The shipwright who had the job of developing the vessel's lines up to full size on the mould loft floor.

Long and short leg   When moulding out floors the shipwright would try to keep one side longer than the other, alternating the long and short legs between the frames.

Look on   To heave the vessel up to the nets to have a look at the first net or two, so as to get some idea of the catch.

Mould   The pattern of a frame, made up of P.A.R. deal.

Mould loft   The building containing the floor on which the lines of the vessel are laid off.

Moulded edge   The edge of the frame which was marked off the mould.

Oakum   Material such as stranded rope yarn, combined with hemp and impregnated with Stockholm tar, used for caulking.

Offset   A dimension taken from a set of lines.

Oil box   A small box, generally carved out of the solid wood, usually beech, containing a quantity of oakum saturated with engine oil, in which the shipwright would dip his iron occasionally while caulking to prevent the oakum from sticking to the iron.

P.A.R.   Planed all round.

Parbuckle, To   A means of hauling up or lowering a heavy object such as a tree trunk. When loading a tree one would place two strong bearers from the ground up to the timber drug, then put several turns of two wires round the bole roughly equidistant from the midpoint; the wires would be led to a traction engine or hitched to horses' traces, and when the wires were heaved upon the tree would roll up the bearers on to the drug.

Paying up   Over the side, to work hot pitch into a seam, filling in over the oakum, by means of a mop. On deck, to fill a seam over the oakum with hot pitch by means of a ladle.

Plumbing up   To bring the centre line cut in a cross spall on a frame in line with the plumbline hanging on the centre line in the vessel by means of temporary shores.

Up on Chambers' slip for bottom cleaning.

Podger spanner   A spanner with a long tapering shank which would be used to guide two plates together by means of the holes, as when hanging bunker plates.

Pole waggon   A four-wheeled frame on which tree trunks or baulks were carried, known locally as a timber drug. The rear wheels were adjustable on the centre pole to suit the length of the load being carried.

Quarters   The area of the vessel from the centre of the stern round to the vessel's side.

Rabbet   A groove formed on keel, stem and stern post to receive the edges and ends of planks.

Race knife   A knife used by the shipwright moulding out timber. This knife has a sharpened curled end to the blade which will leave a very small groove in the timber when pulled round a mould.

Rail   Timber capping on the stanchions.

Ribband   A length of timber used temporarily right round the vessel to space and secure the frames at their correct stations, which are marked on the ribband. One ribband was used at sheer height and one at the turn of the bilge.

Round nose chisel   A tool with a tapered and very slightly curved end, sharpened to a small horseshoe-shaped point and hardened. One would literally cut or dig a hole through a plate with this tool.

Scarph   A lapped joint between two pieces of timber which links them so as to form a continuous section.

Scoot   A deck fitting on which to stand a funnel.

Score   A slot such as that across a keel in which a floor would be seated.

Sea cock   A pipe with stop valve passing through the vessel's bottom forming an intake for the circulating pump.

Shadow frames   Frames between the fashion frames and the cant frames.

Sheer   The line of the upper edge of the vessel's side fore and aft, on fishing vessels usually forming a graceful curve.

Shelf   A substantial piece of timber along the whole length of the inside of the vessel's frames at just below sheer height on which the beams are laid.

Sided   Timber that has been thicknessed.

Slice   A long steel bar used in the furnace by the fireman to break up clinker or used to lever coal down into the bunker when coaling. Also a long wide chisel used by the shipwright for such work as cutting a score across a keel in order to fit a floor.

Snedded   A felled tree that has been cleared of all coarse growth and twigs during the preparation for loading is said to have been snedded.

Stations   The spacing measurements between frames set out on the keel, also on ribbands, to which the frames will be set in order to bring each to its correct position in the vessel's hull.

Stern tube   The tube passing through the stern post in which the tail shaft is carried.

Stopwater   A soft wood plug used to prevent water from entering the vessel at the junction of keel, stern post and deadwood, etc.

Stuffing box   The gland on the inner end of the stern tube.

Sur marks   Marks placed on pieces of frame when making the frame up to ensure correct fitting together of the pieces. The sur marks on each piece have to coincide with marks on adjacent pieces.

Tabernacle   A substantial structure of oak in which the foremast is accommodated. As the tabernacle was fastened to the kelson as well as to beams and carlins it stiffened the fore part of the ship considerably.

Through bolt   A galvanised iron bolt with a jumped up head and pilot point which when driven is cut off and clenched over a washer.

Thrust block   A shaft bearing designed to transmit the thrust of the propeller shaft to the hull through collars on the shaft and in the bearing.

Thundershakes   When shakes are found in a tree after felling this is generally due to shock either from felling or from being struck by lightning.

Tie irons   Shaped irons let in flush at the junction of keel and stem and at the junction of keel and stern post. They were through fastened.

Tizzard   A bass rope of some size used as a spring between the drifter and its nets and so to relieve the messenger rope or warp when the vessel is ranging about.

Tizzard bolt   A bolt through the stem and apron half way between deck and stem head, secured by a forelock. At its outer end is a loose link into which the tizzard is hooked.

Tommy Hunter   The mizzen mast head stay. This was fitted with a purchase and was used when necessary to get the small boat inboard.

Top height   A mark put on the top piece of frame when being moulded out to indicate the timber top.

Tub   Small barrel used as a toilet. See Bowl.

Wash port   A space left in the wash strake to relieve the deck of water.

Water levels   Horizontal planes used in the design of the vessel.

Whelps   Metal guards used on capstan chocks to prevent wear.

Wrongs   Bent or twisted boughs used for making frames, knees and similar items. The word wrong derives from the Old English *wrang*, *wrong*, meaning curved or crooked in form.

Daybreak.

Index